Logical Design of Switching Circuits

Second edition

Logical Design of Switching Circuits

Second edition

Douglas Lewin

Professor of Digital Processes
Brunel University

Nelson

Logical Design of Switching Circuits

Second edition

Douglas Lewin

Professor of Digital Processes
Brunel University

Nelson

THOMAS NELSON AND SONS LTD
Lincoln Way Windmill Road Sunbury-on-Thames Middlesex TW16 7HP

NELSON (AFRICA) LTD
PO Box 73146 Nairobi Kenya

THOMAS NELSON (AUSTRALIA) LTD
19–39 Jeffcott Street West Melbourne Victoria 3003

THOMAS NELSON AND SONS (CANADA) LTD
81 Curlew Drive Don Mills Ontario

THOMAS NELSON (NIGERIA) LTD
8 Ilupeju Bypass PMB 1303 Ikeja Lagos

First published in Great Britain by Thomas Nelson and Sons Ltd, 1968

Reprinted 1970

Second edition, 1974

Reprinted 1975, 1976

Copyright © Douglas Lewin 1968, 1974

Illustrations copyright © Thomas Nelson and Sons Ltd, 1974

ISBN 017 761039 5

Printed by The Whitefriars Press Ltd, London and Tonbridge

To my Mother and Father and dearest Terina

Contents

Contents

Preface

NOTE TO SECOND EDITION

The logical design of digital systems or switching circuits is the process of interconnecting commercially available logic modules, utilizing such physical devices as integrated circuits, fluidic elements, reed relays, etc., to perform a specific task. The intelligent application of switching theory (the mathematical basis of logical design) to these system problems enables a viable, economic, and reliable circuit to be engineered in the minimum of time. It also has the added advantage that engineers, inexperienced in logical circuits, can rapidly master the fairly simple design techniques and apply them to practical systems. Thus switching theory (or logical design) is concerned with establishing the optimal interconnection paths of logical gating elements, required to meet a particular functional input/output specification. It is basic to all digital systems design, including telephone switching, digital computers, automatic warehousing, etc.

It is the object of this book to describe, from an engineering viewpoint, those methods of designing logical circuits which have evolved as useful and practical techniques, from the vast amount of published work on switching theory. This has been done by adopting a general approach (that is, without having recourse to any particular physical device), while at the same time a serious attempt has been made to retain the basic mathematical ideas.

The book is primarily intended as a text for courses on logical design and switching theory for final year engineering students in Universities and Colleges of Technology, and as a preliminary introduction to the subject for post-graduate students. However, in order to assist the practising engineer (or student) working on his own, the book has been written in a tutorial style and the numerous problems with fully worked solutions allow maximum benefit to be derived from private study. Virtually no previous knowledge of the subject has been assumed for the reader (except for an appreciation of mathematical concepts), who after studying the book should be able to design logical circuits and to read and utilize current research papers in this field. For this last reason, an extensive bibliography appears at the end of each chapter, together with certain key references.

My thanks and appreciation are extended to Audrey without whose gentle encouragement and excellent typing this book would never have been finished. Finally the author would welcome constructive criticism or comment and the indication of any errors that may have occurred in the text.

DOUGLAS LEWIN

NOTE TO SECOND EDITION

The fundamental aspects of switching theory are still highly relevant to the logic designer; consequently it was decided to make little or no changes to the main text for the second edition. However, over the last two years major developments have taken place in integrated circuit technology which are rapidly changing the philosophy of digital systems design. In order to keep abreast of these techniques an entirely new chapter on designing with complex integrated circuits has been included in this edition. A further innovation is that the diagrams have been completely reset using MILSPEC symbols, thus conforming to what is now accepted practice in industry.

DOUGLAS LEWIN

LOGIC SYMBOLS
Based on MIL–STD–806B (U.S. Dept. of Defence)

1. AND gates

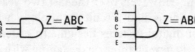

$$Z = ABC$$

$$Z = ABCDE$$

2. NAND gates

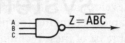

$$Z = \overline{ABC}$$

3. OR gates

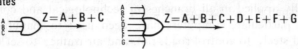

$$Z = A + B + C$$

$$Z = A + B + C + D + E + F + G$$

4. Exclusive OR gates

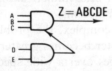

$$Z = \overline{A}B + A\overline{B}$$

5. NOR gates

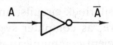

$$Z = \overline{A + B + C}$$

6. Expander input gates

$$Z = ABCDE$$

7. Invertor amplifiers

A ▷ $\overline{A}$

8. Bistable circuits

JK-bistable   DC latch or toggle   D-bistable

9. Delay units

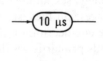

10 μs

10. Register stages

Parallel outputs

Serial input

Serial o/p

Clock

Parallel inputs

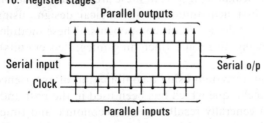

1 Introduction to digital systems

1–1 Introduction

Since the advent of electronic digital computers, digital methods in general are being rapidly applied in all branches of technological and commercial endeavour. In particular, computers have been used to manufacture ice cream, gas, and steel; to control road, rail, and air traffic; to set up newspaper type; and to supervise stock control and insurance records. As early as 1967 a survey[1] showed that there were some 1,600 process control computer installations throughout the world, not counting business and scientific systems. With the availability of the minicomputer this number must by now have increased phenomenally.

A parallel development to this has been the growing use of digital techniques in the engineering of smaller systems, not necessarily involving digital computers, for example, in the control of passenger lifts, numerical machine tools, safety interlock circuits, and communication systems.

Furthermore, as computer systems grow more complex, the problem of providing efficient communication with the computer becomes greater. The equipment required to input and output data ranges over a wide spectrum, from simple keyboard typewriters to sophisticated audio and visual input/output devices. The connection of this equipment to the computer requires, in some cases, almost a small digital system in its own right (known as the interface); in fact, small computers have been used for this purpose.

The engineering of all these systems, including the actual computer itself, depends primarily on the design of suitable switching circuits and their interconnections. This process of connecting together switching (or gating) circuits[2] in a logical or systematic way in order to satisfy the required system specification is called *logical design*. It is in these areas that the majority of engineers make their first acquaintance with logical design, using standard manufactured logic modules as circuit components. These modules can vary considerably, embracing electronic (including integrated circuits), hydraulic, and relay devices.

To attempt to engineer a digital system using a combination of experience and 'cut and try' methods (a technique which has been used in the past and, in certain cases, is still used!) generally results in an uneconomic and time-wasting design project. Furthermore, another major drawback of intuitive design is that a particular combination of inputs, or operating sequences within the machine, may be overlooked in the initial design phase. Due to the immensity of the task of exhaustively checking out large digital systems, the errors would not necessarily show up in any final equipment acceptance test, but the system could still fulfil its required performance specification. Thus we have the situation, very common in early computer systems, of logical design errors not appearing until some time after the equipment has been sold and delivered to the customer. With computer systems getting larger and more complex as the applications increase, this state of affairs is intolerable, particularly in a large military air defence network for instance.

The majority of these design problems can be obviated if *switching theory—* the mathematical basis of logical design—is used in the definition and synthesis of the digital system. The logical design process consists of two main activities:

(a) enumerating the problem and, in so doing, forming a set of input/output specifications for the digital system, and

(b) implementing these specifications in terms of appropriate hardware, taking into account such constraints as cost, reliability (directly related to the number of units), ease of maintenance, and type of switching circuit used.

The outcome of the design procedure should be an optimum (e.g. economic) interconnection diagram for the logic modules. The use of switching theory enables the problem to be completely understood and formally specified in mathematical terms. Moreover, by applying certain rules (algorithms), the specification may be reduced to a simpler or more convenient form which can then be directly implemented in terms of hardware. Thus switching theory enables a feasible design to be developed, in the sense that the input/output specifications are completely fulfilled. However, it does not automatically produce an optimum design for all cases, and it is when this happens that the designer has to rely once again on his own initiative.

Unfortunately then, with the present state of the art, switching theory is not the panacea it might seem, for two main reasons. First, the theory of large complex switching systems, or automata, is not yet fully understood. Second, for systems involving a large number of variables, the amount of computation required becomes impracticable if done by hand. However, a system may be decomposed into smaller sub-system blocks which then become amenable to theoretical design, and the necessary computation can in most cases be performed by suitably programming a digital computer.

Switching theory, then, is a powerful tool (and the only possible one) for the definition and design of large digital systems. Logical designers must be able to apply the theory, to appreciate its limitations, and in so doing arrive at an optimum system design. In the following chapters we try to explain the theory and techniques of logical design, but we must start at the very beginning with the coding of the basic information.

1–2 Number systems

In order to manipulate, display, or transmit numbers using electrical or mechanical devices it is necessary to represent each symbol (0–9 in the case of decimal numbers) by a discrete state or condition of the device. For example, consider a decimal number counter consisting of mechanical gear-wheels, of the type found in most car mileometers. The ten symbols are represented by ten cogs on the gearwheels, and each decade has its own individual gearwheel. Thus, to represent a five-digit decimal number, we require five gearwheels each with ten cogs. Each complete revolution of a gearwheel (count of 10, 10^2, 10^3, etc.) causes the next gearwheel, representing the next highest power of ten, to enmesh so producing the effect of a carry. To perform the same task electronically, we would need either a ten-state device such as a dekatron or digitron, or a specially constructed device using, in the simplest sense, ten on/off switches each connected to a lamp to represent one decade. As naturally occurring ten-state devices are very rare, and when specially made tend to be expensive in components, it would appear obvious to use a number system with fewer symbols. Furthermore, there are many examples of readily available two-state devices, such as switches (on/off), relay contacts (made/unmade), transistors and valves (conducting/cut-off), etc. Thus, if we could use a method of counting which involved only two symbols (the *binary system*), we could utilize these two-state devices to devise an economical hardware number representation.

This approach is perfectly feasible, since there is nothing unique about the decimal system with its ten symbols and place value system of representation, i.e. units, tens, hundreds columns. In fact, the only reason for this choice of *base* (or radix) seems to be the anatomical fact that we have ten fingers (and thumbs!). A number system based on a positive-integer radix may be defined mathematically in terms of the polynomial:

$$N = a_n q^n + a_{n-1} q^{n-1} + \cdots a_2 q^2 + a_1 q^1 + a_0 q^0 + a_{-1} q^{-1} + \cdots a_{-m} q^{-m}$$

where N is a positive real number, q the radix, and a represents the symbols. That this is a place value system is apparent from the polynomial, the *radix point* (decimal point for radix 10) occurring between terms with positive and negative radix indices. Movement of the radix point left or right produces division and multiplication respectively by the radix.

As an example of the use of this polynomial let us express the decimal number 148·5 using various number systems.

Decimal: $q = 10$, symbols 0, 1, 2, 3, 4, 5, 6, 7, 8, 9.

$$(148·5)_{10} = 1 \times 10^2 + 4 \times 10^1 + 8 \times 10^0 + 5 \times 10^{-1}$$

Duo-decimal: $q = 12$, symbols 0, 1, 2, 3, 4, 5, 6, 7, 8, 9, **T**, **E**. Note that

Table 1–1 Number systems

Decimal radix of 10

10^2	10^1	10^0	.	10^{-1}	10^{-2}	10^{-3}
100	10	1	.	$\frac{1}{10}$	$\frac{1}{100}$	$\frac{1}{1000}$
		0	.	1	2	5
		0	.	2	5	0
		0	.	5	0	0
		1	.	0	0	0
		2	.	0	0	0
		3	.	0	0	0
		4	.	0	0	0
		5	.	0	0	0
		6	.	0	0	0
		7	.	0	0	0
		8	.	0	0	0
		9	.	0	0	0
	1	0	.	0	0	0
	1	1	.	0	0	0
	1	2	.	0	0	0
1	0	0	.	0	0	0

Duo-decimal radix of 12

12^2	12^1	12^0	.	12^{-1}	12^{-2}
144	12	1	.	$\frac{1}{12}$	$\frac{1}{144}$
		0	.	1	6
		0	.	3	0
		0	.	6	0
		1	.	0	0
		2	.	0	0
		3	.	0	0
		4	.	0	0
		5	.	0	0
		6	.	0	0
		7	.	0	0
		8	.	0	0
		9	.	0	0
		T	.	0	0
		E	.	0	0
	1	0	.	0	0
	8	4	.	0	0

Binary radix of 2

2^6	2^5	2^4	2^3	2^2	2^1	2^0	.	2^{-1}	2^{-2}	2^{-3}
64	32	16	8	4	2	1	.	$\frac{1}{2}$	$\frac{1}{4}$	$\frac{1}{8}$
						0	.	0	0	1
						0	.	0	1	0
						0	.	1	0	0
						1	.	0	0	0
					1	0	.	0	0	0
					1	1	.	0	0	0
				1	0	0	.	0	0	0
				1	0	1	.	0	0	0
				1	1	0	.	0	0	0
				1	1	1	.	0	0	0
			1	0	0	0	.	0	0	0
			1	0	0	1	.	0	0	0
			1	0	1	0	.	0	0	0
			1	0	1	1	.	0	0	0
			1	1	0	0	.	0	0	0
1	1	0	0	1	0	0	.	0	0	0

new symbols need to be invented when the radix is greater than 10, i.e. $T = 10$ decimal, and $E = 11$ decimal.

$$(148 \cdot 5)_{10} = (104 \cdot 6)_{12} = 1 \times 12^2 + 0 \times 12^1 + 4 \times 12^0 + 6 \times 12^{-1}$$

Octal: $q = 8$, symbols 0, 1, 2, 3, 4, 5, 6, 7.

$$(148 \cdot 5)_{10} = (224 \cdot 4)_8 = 2 \times 8^2 + 2 \times 8^1 + 4 \times 8^0 + 4 \times 8^{-1}$$

Binary: $q = 2$, symbols 0, 1.

$$(148 \cdot 5)_{10} = (10010100 \cdot 1)_2$$
$$= 1 \times 2^7 + 0 \times 2^6 + 0 \times 2^5 + 1 \times 2^4 + 0 \times 2^3$$
$$+ 1 \times 2^2 + 0 \times 2^1 + 0 \times 2^0 + 1 \times 2^{-1}$$

Ternary: $q = 3$, symbols 0, 1, 2.

$$(148 \cdot 5)_{10} = (12111 \cdot 111 \cdots)_3$$
$$= 1 \times 3^4 + 2 \times 3^3 + 1 \times 3^2 + 1 \times 3^1 + 1 \times 3^0$$
$$+ 1 \times 3^{-1} + 1 \times 3^{-2} + 1 \times 3^{-3} \cdots$$

Table 1–1 shows a selection of number systems expressed in the more familiar concept of allocating columns to various powers of the radix. Each time we count up to the radix times the column power we add 1 to the next left-hand column, i.e. a carry over.

Several interesting points arise from considering these examples.

(a) The number length depends on the magnitude of the chosen radix. For example, binary numbers require many more symbols than their decimal equivalent.

(b) The factors of the radix determine the ease and accuracy of representing common fractions. In a decimal system, the fraction $\frac{1}{3}$ is $0 \cdot 333 \cdots$ (recurring), since 3 is not a factor of the base 10. However, in the duo-decimal system it becomes $0 \cdot 4$, and in ternary $0 \cdot 1$, since 3 is a factor of both 12 and 3.

(c) If a radix is chosen with more than ten symbols it is necessary to invent new ones. This can be confusing if well known symbols (as above) are used; the best solution would be to devise completely new graphical signs.

(d) The complexity of the multiplication tables tends to increase with the size of the radix. For example, compare the binary multiplication table with that for octal (Table 1–2).

Of these number representations the only ones that have found universal acceptance are the decimal and binary systems. Duodecimal was suggested by Aitken[3] as a possible alternative in the U.K. to the decimal system, since at that time (1961) 12 was used in such units as feet and inches, shillings and pence and dozens. As 12 is divisible by 2, 3, 4, and 6, and the gross (12 dozen) also has a wealth of functions, to adopt duodecimal (it was argued) would lead to greater accuracy and speed of calculation. However, the subsequent adoption of decimalization and metrication policies in order to achieve parity with other countries quickly made these ideas obsolete.

1–3 The binary system

Let us now discuss the binary system[1] in greater detail. It is apparent that with only two symbols it is easier to represent numbers more economically in terms of hardware by using two-state devices such as switches. However, the numbers so represented are much longer than their decimal counterparts. Thus, if we wish to represent the decimal number 10^n as a binary number, it follows that

$$2^b \geq 10^n$$

and

$$b = \left\lceil \frac{n}{\log_{10} 2} \right\rceil = \frac{n}{0 \cdot 301}$$

where b is the number of binary digits (bits) required in the representation; b must be either an integer or the next largest integer. To represent decimal

Table 1–2 Arithmetic tables

	0	1
0	0	0
1	0	1

Binary multiplication

	0	1
0	0	1
1	1	0 (carry 1)

Binary addition

	0	1	2	3	4	5	6	7
0	0	0	0	0	0	0	0	0
1	0	1	2	3	4	5	6	7
2	0	2	4	6	10	12	14	16
3	0	3	6	11	14	17	22	25
4	0	4	10	14	20	24	30	34
5	0	5	12	17	24	31	36	43
6	0	6	14	22	30	36	44	52
7	0	7	16	25	34	43	52	61

Octal multiplication

	0	1	2	3	4	5	6	7
0	0	1	2	3	4	5	6	7
1	1	2	3	4	5	6	7	10
2	2	3	4	5	6	7	10	11
3	3	4	5	6	7	10	11	12
4	4	5	6	7	10	11	12	13
5	5	6	7	10	11	12	13	14
6	6	7	10	11	12	13	14	15
7	7	10	11	12	13	14	15	16

Octal addition

numbers in binary thus requires approximately three times as many digits, e.g. to obtain an accuracy of 1 part in 10^3 requires a ten-bit binary number. This makes the manual transcription of large binary numbers a time-consuming process which often leads to errors.

One convenient way of overcoming this is to use the octal system. Conversion from binary to octal and vice versa is a very simple process. For example, take the binary number

$$110110111010011110110101$$

To find its octal equivalent, we split the binary number into groups of three, starting from the right-hand least significant digit, and then write down the octal equivalent of each three-bit group:

1	101	101	110	100	111	101	101	101
1	5	5	6	4	7	5	5	5

Conversion from octal to binary is the direct inverse of this operation. Octal numbers are frequently used in allocating codes for digital computer machine-code orders and addresses on account of this easy conversion to binary numbers, which is the internal system used by the majority of computers.

Arithmetic using binary numbers is a far simpler procedure than the corresponding decimal process, due to the very elementary rules of addition and multiplication (see Table 1–2). However, the long numbers can still be a handicap, especially in the case of protracted carries. Consider the addition sums below:

				↓↓ ↓		
(a)	Augend	101101	45	(b)	10101111	175
	Addend	10110	22		100101	37
	Sum	1000011	67		111101	61
					110010	50
					101000011	323

Note that in example (b), columns 3, 5 and 6, the sum obtained is effectively 4, i.e. binary 100, and the carryover is to the second column up. This would happen of course in decimal addition if a column of numbers summed to a value greater than 99, an unusual occurrence due to the short numbers involved.

Subtraction is carried out by following the normal method except that the borrow now becomes the next power of 2:

(a)	Minuend	101110	46	(b)	111100	60
	Subtrahend	10001	17		110111	55
	Difference	011101	29		000101	5

An alternative method of subtraction is to add a negative number to the minuend, i.e. $46 - 17 = 46 + (-17)$. To use this method we must have some means of representing negative numbers in the binary system. There are two ways of doing this:

1. to express the number as a magnitude with a minus sign attached, and
2. to use a complement notation.

Method 1 is familiar and easy to use except that, as well as doing the actual arithmetic, we have also to deduce the correct sign. This can lead to problems in machine implementation.

The most convenient method is that in which we use the 2's complement of the number; this is defined as $2^n - N$, where N is the binary number and 2^n is the *next* highest power of 2. In order to distinguish negative numbers from positive numbers, the range of N is restricted and the most significant digit (M.S.D.) is used to represent the sign (positive 0, negative 1) of the number. For example, let N be an eight-bit number, then the maximum number that can be represented is $N = 2^8 - 1 = 255$. If we now use the M.S.D. as a *sign-digit*, the number range is restricted to $-2^7 \leq N < 2^7$ with a maximum positive number of $2^7 - 1$. To find the 2's complement of N, say 17, we must subtract this from the next highest power of 2, i.e. 2^8:

$$
\begin{array}{c|ll}
1 & 00000000 & \\
  & 00010001 & 17 \\
\hline
1 & 11101111 & -17 \\
  & \text{sign digit} &
\end{array}
$$

Disregard overflow

Now we may perform the subtraction $46 - 17$ as

$$
\begin{array}{c|ll}
  & 00101110 & 46 \\
  & 11101111 & -17 \\
\hline
1 & 00011101 & 29 \\
\end{array}
$$

The 2's complement may be found easily by taking the 1's complement (that is, the inverse—replace 0's by 1's and vice versa) and adding $+1$ to the least significant digit. Note also that using this method the correct sign-digit appears automatically as a result of including it in the arithmetic operations. The idea of complements applies to any number system, and for this reason the binary 2's complement is also referred to as the radix complement.

Multiplication is performed in the usual way by multiplying and then shifting one place to the left, finally adding the partial products. Care must be exercised in the addition due to the frequent formation of protracted carries as in the following example. Note that since the multiplier can only be 0 or 1, the partial product is either zero or equal to the multiplicand.

	Multiplicand	1101101	109
	Multiplier	1011	11
		1101101	
		1101101	
		1101101	
	Product	10010101111	1199

Again, the process of division is very similar to standard decimal arithmetic, but simplified because it is only possible to divide once or not at all.

```
                  1101100        Quotient        108
Divisor  11011)101101101101      Dividend     27)2925
                  11011          Remainder      9
                 100101
                  11011
                 101001
                  11011
                   11101
                   11011
Remainder          1001
```

Integral binary numbers may be converted into decimal numbers either by directly adding the relevant power of two, or by successive division by binary ten and converting each remainder into a decimal number; in the last method, the equivalent decimal number appears with the least significant number first. Consider the binary number 101101101, this is equivalent to

$$1 \times 2^8 + 0 \times 2^7 + 1 \times 2^6 + 1 \times 2^5 + 0 \times 2^4$$
$$+ 1 \times 2^3 + 1 \times 2^2 + 0 \times 2^1 + 1 \times 2^0$$

which is equal to $256 + 64 + 32 + 8 + 4 + 1 = 365$. Using the alternative method we divide the binary number by binary ten:

```
(a)         100100        (b)          11         (c)      1010)11
     1010)101101101            1010)100100                 Remainder 11 = 3
          1010                     1010
          1011                    10000
          1010                     1010
Remainder 101 = 5          Remainder 110 = 6
```

Thus, decimal equivalent = 365

The reverse procedure (that is, decimal to binary) is accomplished by successive division by 2, noting the remainder at each stage; again the least significant digit appears first. Using the same example, we have:

$$
\begin{array}{r}
2)\overline{365} \\
2)\overline{182} \quad \text{Remainder} \quad 1 \quad \text{least significant digit} \\
91 \qquad\qquad 0 \\
45 \qquad\qquad 1 \\
22 \qquad\qquad 1 \\
11 \qquad\qquad 0 \\
5 \qquad\qquad 1 \\
2 \qquad\qquad 1 \\
1 \qquad\qquad 0 \\
1 \\
\end{array}
$$

The equivalent binary number is, then, 101101101.

Fractional numbers may be converted in a similar way. For example, to convert decimal fractions to binary, the fraction is multiplied successively by 2 and the integral (whole number) part of each product (either 0 or 1) is retained as the binary fraction. For instance, consider the decimal fraction 0·45678. Multiplying by 2 we have:

$$
\begin{array}{rl}
\text{Binary point} \quad \cdot & 0·45678 \\
0 & 0·91356 \\
1 & 1·82712 \\
1 & 1·65424 \\
1 & 1·30848 \\
0 & 0·61696, \text{etc.} \\
\end{array}
$$

Thus the binary equivalent of 0·45678 is 0·01110 · · · . To convert binary fractions to decimal, a similar procedure is followed; the binary fraction is repeatedly multiplied by binary ten, and after each operation the integral part is converted to its decimal equivalent.

1–4 Binary coded decimals

In the preceding section we have seen how numbers represented in the pure binary system may be manipulated arithmetically in much the same way as the more familiar decimal numbers. In fact there is no great difference in technique except for the change of radix. Though this is ideal for computing machines, the human operator still likes to think and communicate in the decimal system. Furthermore, there is a need to transmit and process data for basic communication purposes as well as for numerical computation. Thus there is a need to code numbers and alphabetical characters (often abbreviated to alpha-numerics) in terms of binary symbols or bits. In this way we can communicate in our normal language, the data being encoded into some form of binary code for the convenience of the hardware, or logic circuits, comprising the digital system.

In order to represent the ten decimal numbers 0 to 9 we need four bits, giving 2^4 or 16 possible combinations, of which only ten are used. Each code, then, has four bits and these bits can be arranged in any way to represent the decimal digits. They are, however, generally assigned values—*weights*—which when summed give the decimal number represented by the four-bit combination; the most frequently used set of weights is the 8-4-2-1 of pure binary. Such codes are called *arithmetic codes* (see Table 1–3). For example, to represent the decimal number 9873 in 8421 binary-coded decimal, we would code up as follows:

$$1001 \quad\quad 1000 \quad\quad 0111 \quad\quad 0011$$

Many different weighted codes are possible, but the weights must be chosen in such a way that their sums are not greater than 15 and not less than 9; moreover, one of the weights must be 1 and another must be either 1 or 2. Weights can also be either positive or negative. Examples of possible combinations are:

$$3321 \quad\quad 5321 \quad\quad 7421 \quad\quad 8421 \quad\quad 5421 \quad\quad 5211$$

Some binary-coded decimal codes have additional useful properties. The 7421 code, for example, has a minimum number of 1's in its representation and, if used in such a way that an electrical device must be in a power consuming state to indicate a 1, results in minimum power consumption. Arithmetic codes in which the sum of the weights is exactly 9 have the property that the 9's complement of the number (analogous to the 1's complement mentioned above, i.e. $9 - N$, where N is the number) can be obtained

Table 1–3 Binary codes

Decimal number	Pure binary $2^3\ 2^2\ 2^1\ 2^0$	Binary coded decimal 7421	5421	5211	Excess three code	Reflected or Gray code $g_4\ g_3\ g_2\ g_1$
0	0 0 0 0	0000	0000	0000	0011	0 0 0 0
1	0 0 0 1	0001	0001	0001	0100	0 0 0 1
2	0 0 1 0	0010	0010	0100	0101	0 0 1 1
3	0 0 1 1	0011	0011	0110	0110	0 0 1 0 ↑
4	0 1 0 0	0100	0100	0111↑	0111↑	0 1 1 0 ↓
5	0 1 0 1	0101	1000	1000↓	1000↓	0 1 1 1
6	0 1 1 0	0110	1001	1001	1001	0 1 0 1
7	0 1 1 1	1000	1010	1011	1010	0 1 0 0 ↑
8	1 0 0 0	1001	1011	1110	1011	1 1 0 0 ↓
9	1 0 0 1	1010	1100	1111	1100	1 1 0 1

by simply inverting the binary equivalent. For example, in the 5211 code shown in Table 1–3, decimal $4 \equiv 0111$, $9 - 4 = 5 \equiv 1000$. A further requirement is that the arithmetic code must be symmetrically organized about its centre, this is apparent by inspection of the code and the example above. Self-complementing codes such as these (and also the excess three code, which is obtained by adding 3 to each group of the pure binary code) are very useful when performing decimal or binary-coded decimal arithmetic.

The reflected binary or Gray code (also called a cyclic progressive code) is used chiefly in digital shaft position encoders and has the merit of incurring only one digit change when passing from any one combination to the next. A code is said to be reflecting when its mirror-image is reproduced (excluding the most significant digit) about the midpoint of a complete ascending tabulation of the code. For example, in the Gray code (Table 1–3) the first eight combinations form a three-bit Gray code of length eight (ignoring digit g_4). That this reflects can be seen by noting that digits $g_1 g_2$ are symmetrical about the midpoint, with the most significant digit g_3 inverted.

1–5 Error-detecting and -correcting codes

If codes are used which utilize all possible combinations, such as representing the decimal numbers 0–15 by pure binary equivalents, any error which may occur (such as picking up or dropping digits) will go undetected, since the incorrect combination will still represent a valid number. To overcome this problem, *redundancy* must be introduced by adding extra bits to the code. All of the codes described above, if used solely to represent the decimal digits 0–9, contain some redundancy in the sense that not all of the possible 2^4 code combinations are used. However, this is inadequate since there is still a chance of undetected errors occurring—for example, in the 5421 code the combination 1001 can, by picking up a digit, become 1101 or 1011. The

Table 1–4 Error-detecting codes

Decimal number	Odd parity check pure binary PB 2^3 2^2 2^1 2^0					2-out-of-5 code	Diamond code
0	1	0	0	0	0	01100	00010
1	0	0	0	0	1	10001	00101
2	0	0	0	1	0	10010	01000
3	1	0	0	1	1	00011	01011
4	0	0	1	0	0	10100	01110
5	1	0	1	0	1	00101	10001
6	1	0	1	1	0	00110	10100
7	0	0	1	1	1	11000	10111
8	0	1	0	0	0	01001	11010
9	1	1	0	0	1	01010	11101

first is obviously in error as no such number exists in the code, but the second would be treated as a valid combination.

The simplest way of adding redundancy is to insert an extra bit, called a *parity* bit, into each code combination. The value of this, 0 or 1, is such as to make the total number of 1's in each combination either even or odd according to the checking convention adopted. Should an error occur, the sum of the digits will no longer be odd (even), thus indicating the presence of an error in the code. Note, however, that only single errors, or errors resulting in an odd (even) number of 1's, will be detected. Odd parity is most frequently used (for example, in teleprinter codes for computer punched tape input/output), since there is no all-zero combination. Table 1–4 shows examples of typical codes. Another approach is to arrange that an error gives rise to a non-valid combination; an example is the 2-out-of-5 code shown in Table 1–4. It is possible to devise many codes like this (2-out-of-7, 3-out-of-8, or in general p-out-of-q).[5] Since if an error occurs the number of 1's will be wrong, all these methods will only detect single errors.

Blocks of information can be checked by arranging the data in the form of a matrix and then making parity checks on the rows and columns, including the extra row formed by the column parity check in the data sent (note that an extra bit is required to check this row). Consider the following example which uses odd parity,

$$
\begin{array}{ll}
9 & 11001 \\
8 & 01000 \\
7 & 00111 \\
3 & \underline{10011} \\
  & 011010 \quad \text{parity check on columns}
\end{array}
$$

The encoded data would be sent as

$$11001 \quad 01000 \quad 00111 \quad 10011 \quad 011010$$

To decode, individual parity checks are made on the rows and columns, and this will pinpoint the incorrect digit in the matrix. Since we are working in a two-valued system the correct digit can be obtained by inversion. This technique will detect multiple errors and also correct single errors, becoming more efficient if different checking methods are used for rows and columns.

Hamming[6] has described a single-error detecting and correcting code (which also detects multiple errors) which employs check digits distributed throughout the message group. These check digits provide even parity checks on particular message digit positions in such a way that, if the parity checks are made in order, successful checks being designated by 0 and failure by 1, the resulting binary number gives the position of the incorrect digit. For this to apply, the first parity digit must check those positions (see Table 1–5) which contain a 1 in the 2^0 column (that is, 1, 3, 5, 7, 9, 11, 13, etc.); similarly, the second digit checks those positions which contain a 1 in the 2^1 column (2,3 – 6,7 – 10,11 – 14,15 etc.); the third check digit checks the positions with a 1 in the 2^2 column (4,5,6,7 – 12,13,14,15, etc.), and so on. This process may be extended indefinitely for message groups of any length. The amount of redundancy required becomes appreciably less as the message length is increased; for example, a seven-bit message group requires three check bits, but only five check bits are required for a 30-bit group. As an example of its use, suppose the message group 1011 is to be transmitted; the check digits are placed in the 2^0, 2^1, 2^2, etc., positions with data digits taking up the remaining places. Thus the message group would be encoded as

Table 1–5 Hamming code

Digit position	Binary equivalent 2^2 2^1 2^0	Digit function	Weight for data bits
1	0 0 1	Check	
2	0 1 0	Check	
3	0 1 1	Data	8
4	1 0 0	Check	
5	1 0 1	Data	4
6	1 1 0	Data	2
7 (L.S.D.)	1 1 1	Data	1

0110011. Should an error occur in the fourth position from the right, giving 0111011, application of the checks would yield, 1st check 0, 2nd check 0, 3rd check 1; which, taking the first check digit to be the least significant, gives position 4 as incorrect. Unfortunately, the coding and encoding procedure has been found rather expensive to implement in terms of hardware, and simpler coding methods are generally employed in practical systems. However, if recourse is made to linear switching circuit theory,[7] and the Hamming code is treated as a cyclic or chain code, simple logic circuits can be evolved using shift registers as a basis; regrettably, this is beyond the scope of this book.

Diamond[8] has devised a checking code for multiple errors which uses the properties of all numbers which obey the formula $3n + 2$. This B.C.D. code complements on nine, and the sum of two numbers (in the Diamond code) can be obtained by normal binary addition and then subtracting binary two. The checking process is to subtract 2 from the received combination and reduce it to modulo 3 (the remainder after dividing by binary three). If there is no remainder after division, it is a valid number, with a low probability of error. The code may be extended to eight-bit numbers by using the formula $27n + 6$ in a similar way.

1–6 Logical switching circuits—definition and symbolism

So far we have concerned ourselves with the way in which data and numerical information can be represented and manipulated in a digital machine. Before we begin the serious study of switching circuits, however, it is profitable to define, in simple terms, the circuits and the symbols used in these circuits. The basic switching element is called a *gate*, and may perform either an OR/AND or NOR/NAND function; Fig. 1–1 shows these elements. Throughout this book the U.S. MILSPEC logic symbols (MIL–STD–806B) will be adhered to as far as possible.

The AND gate is a circuit that provides an output only when all the input signals are present simultaneously. In the relay circuit, normally open contacts A, B, and C need to be made before a signal can be transmitted, i.e. the appropriate relay coils require to be energized. If we allow the series relay contacts to be represented by a dot, we can express the action of the circuit as $T = A . B . C$. In the next chapter a more rigorous mathematical definition will be given to this symbol, and to those that follow. The OR circuit (known as the inclusive OR) requires at least one input to be present in order to provide an output. A signal will be transmitted through the relay circuit if A, or B, or C, or if all three, contacts are made. If, as before, we represent contacts in parallel by a plus sign we can say that $T = A + B + C$.

The NOT circuit shown in Fig. 1–1(c) produces an output when the input is absent. This is equivalent to a normally closed relay contact; that is, the presence of a signal energizes the relay coil and opens the contact. We shall denote a normally closed contact by using a bar sign, thus $\bar{A}$ is the opposite or inverse of A.

The NOR circuit produces an output provided all the inputs are absent, the equivalent relay circuit consists of normally closed contacts in series. A signal will be transmitted through the circuit if contacts $\bar{A}$, $\bar{B}$, and $\bar{C}$ remain closed, i.e. no inputs to the circuit. This circuit is also equivalent to inverting the output of an OR gate (OR/NOT function). The logical action of the circuit may be expressed as

$$T = \overline{A + B + C} = \bar{A} . \bar{B} . \bar{C}.$$

A similar circuit to the NOR is the NAND gate, which produces an output when at least one input is absent. The corresponding relay circuit consists of normally closed contacts in parallel; thus if one input is absent, the contact remains closed and a path is established through the circuit. From Fig. 1–1(e), we see that the circuit performs the function AND/NOT and may be represented as $T = \overline{A . B . C} = \bar{A} + \bar{B} + \bar{C}$.

A d.c. bistable element, used as a single-bit store or register, is shown symbolically together with its relay equivalent in Fig. 1–1(f). This particular

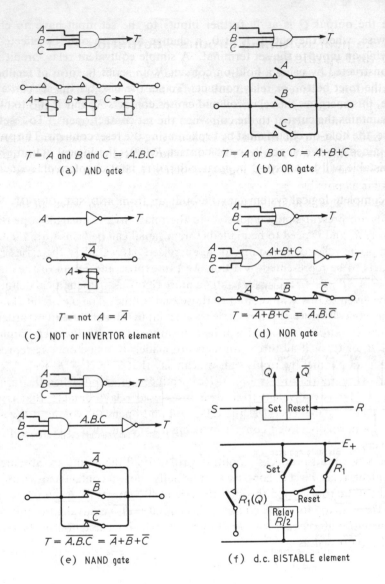

$T = A$ and B and $C = A.B.C$

(a) AND gate

$T = A$ or B or $C = A+B+C$

(b) OR gate

$T = $ not $A = \overline{A}$

(c) NOT or INVERTOR element

$T = \overline{A+B+C} = \overline{A}.\overline{B}.\overline{C}$

(d) NOR gate

$T = \overline{A.B.C} = \overline{A}+\overline{B}+\overline{C}$

(e) NAND gate

(f) d.c. BISTABLE element

Fig. 1–1 Basic logic switching circuits

type of bistable (variously known as a flip-flop or toggle) is of the set-reset (SR) variety. The operation is such that the output Q (the complement or inverse of the output appears at $\overline{Q}$) is set ON to, say, a positive voltage level representing a 1, when the set input receives a 1. The output is reset to OFF to a negative voltage level representing a 0, when the reset input receives a 1.

Once the output Q is at 1, further inputs to the set input have no effect. Likewise, when the output is at 0, a change to 1 can only be effected by applying an input to the set terminal. A simple equivalent relay circuit may be constructed by using a hold-on contact R_1 in series (a form of feedback) with the reset button or relay contact. To set the bistable the set contact is made, this energizes the relay coil and causes contacts R_1 and $R_1(Q)$ to close; R_1 maintains the current to the coil when the set contact opens. To reset the device, the hold-on circuit must be broken using the reset contact. The output is obtained via the normally open contact $R_1(Q)$; the logical action of the SR bistable will be analysed in greater detail in later chapters on sequential logic.

A complete logical system may be built up from AND/NOT, OR/NOT, NOR,

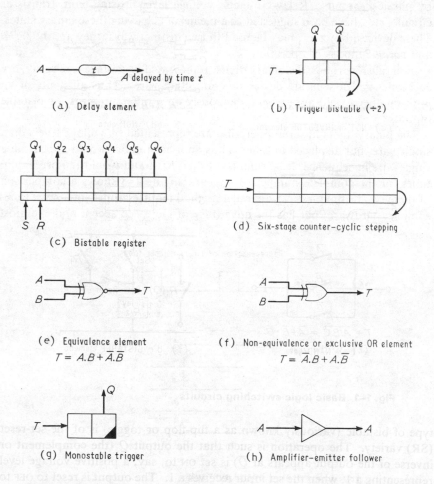

(a) Delay element

(b) Trigger bistable (÷2)

(c) Bistable register

(d) Six-stage counter–cyclic stepping

(e) Equivalence element
$T = A.B + \overline{A}.\overline{B}$

(f) Non-equivalence or exclusive OR element
$T = \overline{A}.B + A.\overline{B}$

(g) Monostable trigger

(h) Amplifier–emitter follower

Fig. 1–2 Ancillary logic circuits

or NAND units, and we shall justify this in Chapter 2. As well as these basic elements other units such as the delay, power amplifier, and monostable are useful in logic design, especially when dealing with synchronous (clocked) sequential systems. Furthermore, in some cases, it is convenient to have larger logic blocks, and logic subsystems such as counters and registers available, and to be able to represent these diagrammatically. Figure 1–2 shows a selection of these units with the appropriate logic symbol.

1–7 Parallel and serial representation

We have seen that the binary system is used to represent data because only two states are required (0 and 1), and these states may be readily represented by physical circuits. Relay contacts, voltage levels arising from transistor circuits, etc., have been suggested as a means of achieving these binary states. These devices, however, may be used in two distinct ways, they are the *serial* and *parallel* modes of operation.

In parallel working, the binary digits, represented by voltage levels, say, are each allocated a separate device or connecting wire. Thus all digits of an n-bit number would appear simultaneously on n different wires, or bistable outputs.

The binary digits in serial operation are represented by voltage levels on a single wire, but displaced in time. Thus an n-bit number would appear on a single wire in sequence, least significant digit first, and would require n digit times for the complete number to appear. Figure 1–3 shows a comparison of these two techniques. The parallel method requires approximately n times as much hardware, but has the advantage of increased speed, and is almost

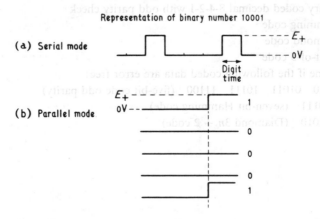

Representation of binary number 10001

Fig. 1–3 Parallel-serial systems

n times as fast. Serial systems are much slower but require considerably less hardware. These methods of operation will be considered in more detail when we deal with sequential logic in later chapters.

References and bibliography

(1) Process computer scorecard. *Control Engng*, 1967, **14**, 51–55.

(2) MILLMAN, J. and TAUB, H. *Pulse digital and switching waveforms*. McGraw-Hill, New York, 1965. Chaps 8 & 9.

(3) AITKEN, A. C. Decimal and duodecimal. *The Guardian*, May 16, 1961, p10.

(4) SCOTT, N. R. *Analog and digital computer technology*. 2nd edn. McGraw-Hill, New York, 1970.

(5) GILMOUR, W. D. P-out-of-Q codes. *Electron. Engng*, 1963, **35**, 41–43.

(6) HAMMING, R. W. Error-detecting and error-correcting codes. *Bell Syst. tech. J.*, 1950, **29**, 147–160.

(7) PETERSON, W. W. and WELDON, E. J. *Error correcting codes*. 2nd edn. Wiley, New York, 1972.

(8) DIAMOND, J. M. Checking codes for digital computers. *Proc. Inst. Radio Engrs*, 1955, **43**, 487–488.

(9) B.S. 530:1948 *Graphical symbols for telecommunications, Supplement No. 5* (1962). British Standards Institution, London.

Tutorial problems

1-1 Convert the following decimal numbers to their pure binary equivalent:

(a) 2397·55   (b) 0·79   (c) −90

1-2 Convert the following binary numbers to their decimal equivalent:

(a) 1011011·101   (b) 10111010111·0   (c) 0·111011

1-3 Express the number 149 in the following coded systems:

(a) Binary coded decimal 8-4-2-1 with odd parity check

(b) Hamming code

(c) Diamond code

(d) 2-out-of-5 code

1-4 Determine if the following coded data are error free:

(a) 11010   01011   10111   11100   (five-bit code odd parity)

(b) 0110111   (seven-bit Hamming code)

(c) 1101010   (Diamond 3*n* + 2 code)

2 Principles of switching algebra

2–1 Introduction

In order to describe, analyse, and design logical circuitry it is first necessary to become conversant with the underlying basic mathematics of the subject. The majority of books and research papers on switching theory are written in set-theoretic terminology which presents an immediate stumbling block to the uninitiated. It is the object of this chapter to review the relevant modern mathematical theory, including Boolean algebras, in such a way that any engineer may readily appreciate and apply it to the design of digital systems. For a more rigorous treatment of the subject the reader is referred to the bibliography at the end of this chapter.

2–2 Set theory

The concept of a set is already familiar to most people as a collection of objects. The items comprising the set may take any form, but must have at least one property in common, e.g. a set of vintage motor car prints, uniforms of the British army, families with more than three children, integers less than ten but greater than zero, inputs to a logical circuit. A set of sets is called a *class* and a set of classes is called a *family*.

Sets are normally specified by stating the actual members or elements of the set, the order is immaterial, and enclosing them in brackets:

$$N = \text{Set of integers less than 10 but greater than zero}$$
$$= \{1, 2, 3, 4, 5, 6, 7, 8, 9\}$$

or $\quad I = \text{Set of inputs to logical circuit} = \{x_1, x_2, x_3, x_5, x_4\}$

Note that capital letters are used to represent sets and small letters or numbers to represent the members. These sets in which all the members are known and can be described individually are called finite; we need a different notation to describe very large or infinite sets. A set may be defined in terms of some 'property' which all elements of the set are required to possess. Thus the set N above becomes:

$$N = \{x : 0 < x < 10 \text{ and is an integer}\}$$

This is read as 'the set of all x, *such that* x is greater than zero but less than 10 and is an integer'. Again the set I may be defined as:

$$I = \{x_i : i = 1, 2, 3, 4, 5,\} \text{ or sometimes just } \{x_i\}$$

It will be obvious that sets with an infinite number of members may be specified in this way, for example:

$$P = \{x : x \text{ is an even number}\}$$

Before we go further we must explain the symbology that is used. Membership of an element in a particular set is represented by the symbol $\in$. Thus $x_1 \in I$ means that x_1 is an element of the set I. Sets may contain single elements or no elements at all; these are called *unit* $\{1\}$ and *null* $\{\phi\}$ sets respectively.

In general, a set is a collection of objects chosen from some larger collection or *universal* set $\{I\}$. For example the set $N = \{1, 2, 3, 4, 5, 6, 7, 8, 9\}$ is contained in the set $X = \{x : x \text{ is a real number}\}$, this may be symbolized as $N \subseteq X$, where N is described as a subset of X. The expression $N \subseteq X$ however could mean that N contains all members of X, or just a few members; it is in fact a generic term (analogous to the mathematical symbol $\leq$, less than or equal to). To distinguish between these two cases we use the symbol $\subset$ when we mean a subset that does not contain all the members of the parent set, i.e. $N \subset X$, where N is called a *proper subset*. For two sets A and B to be equal $(A = B)$, every element of A must be in B and vice versa, that is, they contain identical elements. If $A = B$ it follows that $A \subseteq B$ and $B \subseteq A$. Consider the set $I = \{a, b, c\}$; the complete list of subsets is:

$$\{\phi\}; \ \{a\}; \ \{b\}; \ \{c\}; \ \{a, b\}; \ \{a, c\}; \ \{b, c\}$$

which are proper subsets, and $\{a, b, c\}$ which is a subset, i.e. the universal set.

2–3 Algebra of sets

Sets may be manipulated and combined algebraically using rather special operations which we now define.

(a) *Intersection*, represented by the symbol $\cap$ (cap). If $A = \{1, 5, 7, 8, 9\}$ and $B = \{4, 5, 6, 9, 12\}$ then $A \cap B = \{5, 9\}$. That is, the elements common to each set are used to form the new set.

(b) *Union*, represented by the symbol $\cup$ (cup). With the same sets as above, $A \cup B = \{1, 4, 5, 6, 7, 8, 9, 12\}$. In this case the elements in both sets are combined to form the new set; note that elements need occur once only in a set.

(c) *Complementation*, represented as a bar over a set, e.g. $\bar{A}$, is defined as the set of elements which do not belong to A.

Using these operations we are now in a position to define two important properties:

Covering—A class of sets A_1, A_2, $A_3 \cdots$, such that their union $A_1 \cup A_2 \cup A_3 \cdots$, is the set A, is said to *cover* A.

Partition—A partition of the set A is a covering of A such that the intersection of any pair of the sets in the covering has no members, i.e., is *disjoint*.

The sets forming the partition or covering are called *blocks*. Let $A = \{1, 2, 3, 4, 5, 6, 7, 8, 9\}$, then the class of sets is given by:

$$A_1 = \{1, 2, 3, 4\}, \quad A_2 = \{2, 4, 5, 6\}, \quad A_3 = \{4, 6, 7\}, \quad A_4 = \{1, 8, 9\}$$

To form a covering

$$C = (1, 2, 3, 4) \quad (2, 4, 5, 6) \quad (4, 6, 7) \quad (1, 8, 9)$$

This is not a partition since $A_1 \cap A_2 = \{2, 4\}$, $A_2 \cap A_3 = \{4, 6\}$, etc. The sets $A_1 = \{1, 2\}$, $A_2 = \{3, 4\}$, $A_3 = \{5, 6, 7\}$, $A_4 = \{8, 9\}$ are disjoint and hence form a partition $P = (1, 2) \quad (3, 4) \quad (5, 6, 7) \quad (8, 9)$.

The basic operations obey the following algebraic laws.

1. *Commutative law* $A \cap B = B \cap A; \quad A \cup B = B \cup A$
2. *Associative law* $A \cap (B \cap C) = (A \cap B) \cap C$
   $$A \cup (B \cup C) = (A \cup B) \cup C$$
3. *Distributive law* $A \cap (B \cup C) = (A \cap B) \cup (A \cap C)$
   $$A \cup (B \cap C) = (A \cup B) \cap (A \cup C)$$
4. *Absorption law* $A \cap (A \cup B) = A \cup (A \cap B) = A$
5. *Idempotent law* $A \cap A = A \cup A = A$
6. *Complement law* $A \cup \bar{A} = I \quad A \cap \bar{A} = \phi \quad \overline{(\bar{A})} = A$
   $$\overline{A \cap B} = \bar{A} \cup \bar{B}; \quad \overline{A \cup B} = \bar{A} \cap \bar{B}$$
   (De Morgan's Theorem)
7. *Universal and null law* $\phi \cap A = \phi, I \cap A = A$
   $$\phi \cup A = A, I \cup A = I$$

where A, B, and C are subsets of some universal set I, and ϕ is the null set.

These algebraic laws though similar to the laws of normal algebra (the associative and distributive laws are in fact identical) contain surprising differences, e.g. the absorption and idempotent laws which have no equivalent. Although the operation of subtraction as such has not been defined, for certain restricted cases where the sets are comparable, it is possible to say that $\bar{A} = I - A$; however the operation is best avoided.

As well as the union and intersection operations, there is a further operation which is often used in switching theory and hence worth including. This is set inclusion ($\subseteq$) which can be treated in the same way, but which obeys different basic laws, these are:

1. *Transitive Law*   If $A \subseteq B$ and $B \subseteq C$ then $A \subseteq C$. More strictly the relationship is called *implication*, and is denoted by the symbol $\Rightarrow$, i.e.
   $$A \subseteq B \text{ and } B \subseteq C \Rightarrow A \subseteq C$$
2. *Reflexive Law* $A \subseteq A$
3. *Anti-symmetric Law* $A \subseteq B$ and $B \subseteq A \Rightarrow A = B$

2–4 Venn diagrams

Though most of the laws can be proved intuitively or by logical induction using the basic postulates, we shall first use a method which will be of value later when considering switching problems. This is the *Venn diagram* approach. The Venn diagram is an aid to intuitive reasoning which represents sets as areas. In Fig. 2–1(a) the universal set, sometimes called the

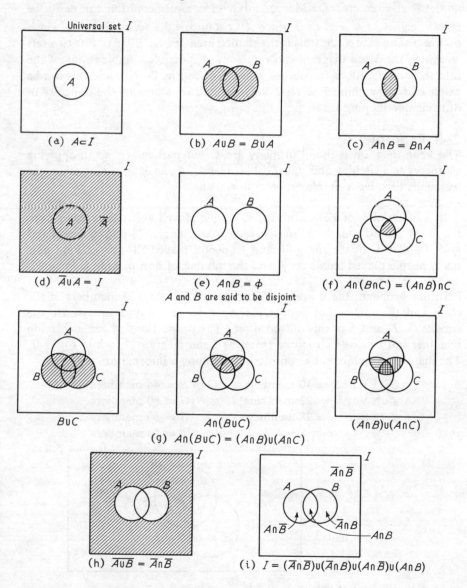

(a) $A \subset I$

(b) $A \cup B = B \cup A$

(c) $A \cap B = B \cap A$

(d) $\bar{A} \cup A = I$

(e) $A \cap B = \phi$
A and B are said to be disjoint

(f) $A \cap (B \cap C) = (A \cap B) \cap C$

$B \cup C$

$A \cap (B \cup C)$

$(A \cap B) \cup (A \cap C)$

(g) $A \cap (B \cup C) = (A \cap B) \cup (A \cap C)$

(h) $\overline{A \cup B} = \bar{A} \cap \bar{B}$

(i) $I = (\bar{A} \cap \bar{B}) \cup (\bar{A} \cap B) \cup (A \cap \bar{B}) \cup (A \cap B)$

Fig. 2–1 Venn diagram proofs

universe of discourse, is represented by the large rectangle, and the set A by a circle drawn inside it, thus representing $A \subset I$. Note that the shape of the areas is completely irrelevant. The shaded portion of Fig. 2–1(b) represents the union of the two sets A and B. Similarly, in Fig. 2–1(c) the shaded portion represents $A \cap B$.

Using these diagrams it is easy to appreciate the significance of $A \cup \bar{A} = I$ and $A \cap \bar{A} = \phi$, etc. De Morgan's law of complementation can easily be shown, e.g. $\overline{A \cup B} = \bar{A} \cap \bar{B}$, since $\overline{A \cup B}$ means the set of elements which do not belong in $A \cup B$; this is the shaded area in Fig. 2–1(h). For two sets A and B, the Venn diagram can represent all possible combinations of the intersection operations (subsets of A and B) [see Fig. 2–1(i)], and this can be extended to any number of sets, but is limited of course by the difficulty of drawing overlapping areas.

2–5 Example

The Venn diagram is useful in many areas, but particularly so in applying set theory to switching and statistical problems. As an example let us use the technique to solve a simple problem in statistics.

In a sports club of 120 members, 80 people played golf, 50 people played tennis, 60 played squash, 22 played squash and tennis, 28 played tennis and golf, 44 played squash and golf, and 10 people played all sports. Find how many people played tennis only, and the number of non-playing members?

In this problem, the universe of discourse $\{I\}$ is the 120 members of the club, and the number of people playing golf, tennis and squash are the subsets G, T, and S of this universal set. The proportions of games-playing members can be easily visualized from the Venn diagram shown in Fig. 2–2. The diagram is obtained by considering the known information:

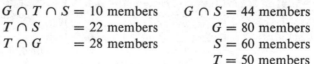

$$
\begin{aligned}
G \cap T \cap S &= 10 \text{ members} & G \cap S &= 44 \text{ members} \\
T \cap S &= 22 \text{ members} & G &= 80 \text{ members} \\
T \cap G &= 28 \text{ members} & S &= 60 \text{ members} \\
& & T &= 50 \text{ members}
\end{aligned}
$$

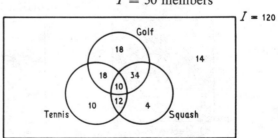

Fig. 2–2 Sports club problem

Then, by deduction, we have:

$$T \cap S \cap \bar{G} = 22 - 10 = 12 \text{ members}$$
$$T \cap G \cap \bar{S} = 28 - 10 = 18 \text{ members}$$
$$G \cap S \cap \bar{T} = 44 - 10 = 34 \text{ members}$$
$$G \cap \bar{S} \cap \bar{T} = 80 - (18 + 10 + 34) = 18 \text{ members}$$
$$T \cap \bar{S} \cap \bar{G} = 50 - (18 + 10 + 12) = 10 \text{ members}$$
$$S \cap \bar{T} \cap \bar{G} = 60 - (34 + 10 + 12) = 4 \text{ members}$$
$$\bar{S} \cap \bar{T} \cap \bar{G} = 120 - (18 + 18 + 10 + 34 + 10 + 12 + 4) = 14 \text{ members}$$

It is clear from the diagram that 10 people play tennis only and there are 14 non-playing members.

2–6 Boolean algebra

A Boolean algebra may be defined for a set $I = \{a, b, c, d \cdots\}$ by assuming the following postulates.

(a) For two binary operations (i.e. between two elements), say $(+)$ and $(.)$, the result must be a unique element in the set I; this is called the *closure property*.

(b) The operations must be commutative, i.e. $a + b = b + a$ and $a \cdot b = b \cdot a$.

(c) Both operations must be distributive, i.e. $a(b + c) = ab + ac$ and $a + bc = (a + b) \cdot (a + c)$.

(d) Identity elements must exist such that $0 + a = a$ and $1 \cdot a = a$ for all elements of I.

(e) For every element of I there must exist an inverse such that $a + \bar{a} = 1$ and $a \cdot \bar{a} = 0$.

Thus, by comparison, it is clear that under the operations of intersection, union, and complementation, the set of all subsets of a universal set I form a Boolean algebra, or as it is sometimes called an *algebra of classes*. Note that there is no restriction on the number of elements contained in the set I, which could be either finite or infinite. For example the set $S = \{a, b\}$ contains the subsets: $\{\phi\} = 0$; $\{a, b\} = 1$; $\{a\} = 2$; and $\{b\} = 3$. These four elements constitute a Boolean algebra with the laws of combination shown in Table 2–1.

Table 2–1 Laws of combination for four-element Boolean algebra

+	0	1	2	3		.	0	1	2	3		x	$\bar{x}$
0	0	1	2	3		0	0	0	0	0		0	1
1	1	1	1	1		1	0	1	2	3		1	0
2	2	1	2	1		2	0	2	2	0		2	3
3	3	1	1	3		3	0	3	0	3		3	2
	addition						multiplication					complementation	

Table 2–2 Laws of combination
for two-element Boolean algebra

+	0	1			0	1		x	$\bar{x}$
0	0	1		0	0	0		1	0
1	1	1		1	0	1		0	1

Suppose now that the set I contains just one set consisting of the two sub-sets or elements, say 0 and 1, which could represent the truth (1) or falsity (0) of a proposition or statement. The laws of combination for the operations (+) and (.) (also called inclusive OR and AND) are shown in Table 2 2. These operations, called logical connectives, are represented by ∨ (vee) and ∧ (wedge) respectively in this *propositional or logical algebra* first developed by Boole.[1] Thus for any given proposition it is also possible to form its complement which is called the denial, indicating that the proposition is false. Using this symbolic notation it is possible to reduce verbal statements (i.e. propositions) to an algebraic form. The algebra may then be used to evaluate the truth or falsity (called the truth-value) of a set of propositions either singly or joined together by the basic logical connectives. This may be done by applying the basic postulates of Boolean algebra algebraically or by means of a *truth-table*.

To explain this let us examine the conditions for employment at a certain company. Applicants must be:

1. male, married and under 35, or
2. male, unmarried and under 35, or
3. female, married and under 35, or
4. female, unmarried and over 35.

In order to apply logical algebra to the problem we must first represent each of the basic propositions by a symbol:

Male M	Unmarried S	Under 35 T	Applicants A
Female $\bar{M}$	Married $\bar{S}$	Over 35 $\bar{T}$	

We can now combine the basic propositions using the logical connectives AND (∧) and OR (∨):

$A = M$ and $\bar{S}$ and T, or M and S and T, or $\bar{M}$ and $\bar{S}$ and T, or $\bar{M}$ and S and $\bar{T}$

or $A = M \wedge \bar{S} \wedge T \vee M \wedge S \wedge T \vee \bar{M} \wedge \bar{S} \wedge T \vee \bar{M} \wedge S \wedge \bar{T}$

By applying the idempotent postulate $A \wedge A = A$, we can include an extra redundant term $M \wedge \bar{S} \wedge T$ in the equation, which then becomes

$A = M \wedge \bar{S} \wedge T \vee M \wedge S \wedge T \vee \bar{M} \wedge \bar{S} \wedge T \vee \bar{M} \wedge S \wedge \bar{T} \vee M \wedge \bar{S} \wedge T$

If we now apply the distributive law we have

$$A = M \wedge T(S \vee \bar{S}) \vee \bar{S} \wedge T(M \vee \bar{M}) \vee \bar{M} \wedge S \wedge \bar{T}$$

Since $A \vee \bar{A} = 1$ and $A \wedge 1 = A$ from the complement and universal laws respectively, the final and simpler expression becomes

$$A = M \wedge T \vee \bar{S} \wedge T \vee \bar{M} \wedge S \wedge \bar{T}$$

in other words applicants must be:

1. male and under 35, or
2. married and under 35, or
3. female, unmarried, and over 35.

Thus by representing the logical statements symbolically and applying the rules of logical algebra, we have arrived at a simpler statement of the original propositions.

To show that these two equations are equivalent (which does, of course, follow directly from the algebra) we can use the truth-table method. We have to prove that $A_1 = A_2$, where

$$A_1 = M \wedge T \vee \bar{S} \wedge T \vee \bar{M} \wedge S \wedge \bar{T}$$
$$A_2 = M \wedge \bar{S} \wedge T \vee M \wedge S \wedge T \vee \bar{M} \wedge \bar{S} \wedge T \vee \bar{M} \wedge S \wedge \bar{T}$$

The first step in the process is to form a table containing all possible combinations of the truth-values (either 0 or 1) of the basic propositions M, S, and T. It may be seen from Table 2–3 that these are the normal combinations formed by three two-valued binary variables. These values are then substituted into the equations for A_1 and A_2, and the resulting truth-value of the equations entered in the table. For example, consider the combination $MS\bar{T}$, i.e. 110, which is the symbolic representation of male, unmarried and over 35. If we substitute these values into the equations for A_1 and A_2, we have

$$A_1 = 1 \wedge 0 \vee 0 \wedge 0 \vee 0 \wedge 1 \wedge 1 = 0$$

$$A_2 = 1 \wedge 0 \wedge 0 \vee 1 \wedge 1 \wedge 0 \vee 0 \wedge 0 \wedge 0 \vee 0 \wedge 1 \wedge 1 = 0$$

Table 2–3 Truth-table for employment conditions

M	S	T	A_1	A_2
0	0	0	0	0
0	0	1	1	1
0	1	0	1	1
0	1	1	0	0
1	0	0	0	0
1	0	1	1	1
1	1	0	0	0
1	1	1	1	1

The results follow from the table of combinations shown in Table 2–2. If this procedure is repeated for all combinations, we eventually arrive at the full truth-table shown in Table 2–3. It will be seen that the results for the two equations are the same, thereby proving that they are identical expressions. This method of proving theorems or establishing equality is called *perfect induction*.

At this stage it might be rather difficult for the reader to fully understand or see the significance of set theory and Boolean algebras, and to appreciate their use in designing switching circuits. We shall now consider this particular application in more detail.

2–7 Switching algebra

Any switching circuit or network can be considered as a two-valued system, that is, at any given instant of time either an open or closed transmission path is established between its terminals. Furthermore, as we have seen, the binary method of counting with the use of only two symbols (0 and 1) is used extensively in digital systems to codify and manipulate data. Thus it is not surprising that the mathematical theory of switching circuits, first postulated by Shannon,[2] is based on a two-valued Boolean algebra closely related to the logical algebra described in the last section.

In switching algebra, the operations are called AND (.), OR (+) and NOT (−) (also known as inversion and complement). These operations are identical to those defined in Table 2–2, and also correspond to the basic switching circuit

Table 2–4 Theorems of switching algebra

1. $A + 0 = A$	10. $A + B = B + A$
2. $A \cdot 1 = A$	11. $A \cdot B = B \cdot A$
3. $A + 1 = 1$	12. $A + AB = A$
4. $A \cdot 0 = 0$	13. $A + \bar{A}B = A + B$
5. $A + A = A$	14. $AB + AC = A(B + C)$
6. $A \cdot A = A$	15. $(A + B)(A + C) = A + BC$
7. $(\bar{\bar{A}}) = A$	16. $A + B + C = (A + B) + C = A + (B + C)$
8. $A + \bar{A} = 1$	17. $\overline{A + B} = \bar{A} \cdot \bar{B}$
9. $A \cdot \bar{A} = 0$	18. $\overline{A \cdot B} = \bar{A} + \bar{B}$

functions discussed in Chapter 1. *Transmission* through a switching circuit is represented by the value 1, and corresponds to a short-circuit; the *hindrance*, corresponding to an open-circuit, is represented by the value 0. Each binary signal or variable is represented by a symbol, which can have a value of either 0 or 1, and these variables can be combined together under the AND/OR operations to form a term or function. In the same way, terms may be combined together to form a switching function. Variables may be in an uncomplemented or complemented form in these equations; when a variable appears, in either form, it is called a *literal*. Note that the algebraic definition is independent of the particular type of switching circuit under discussion—it could, for example, represent relay, electronic, or hydraulic logic.

Using the basic postulates discussed earlier for a two-valued Boolean algebra, numerous theorems may be deduced. These theorems apply equally well to the propositional logic but are stated here in switching terms; Table 2–4 shows a list of the most important theorems. The switching variables are represented by the symbols A, B, C, etc., and may assume a value of either 0 or 1. It follows from the definition of a two-state system, i.e. binary variable, that if $A = 0$, $\bar{A} = 1$, and if $A = 1$, $\bar{A} = 0$. It is interesting to note that a duality principle exists for the basic laws of combination (Table 2–2)— if the digits 0 and 1 and the operations (+) and (.) are interchanged, the alternative operation is obtained. This duality is expressed in general form by theorems 17 and 18 in Table 2–4, which we have met before in set theory, and is known as De Morgan's theorem. The theorem may be expressed in words: the complement of any function is obtained by replacing each variable by its complement and, at the same time, interchanging the symbol for the AND/OR operations.

The theorems may be proved algebraically or by using the truth-table method (sometimes called a conditions-function table in switching algebra). Before we proceed with this, however, let us try to interpret these theorems physically in terms of simple electrical contact circuits. Figure 2–3 shows the contact representation of the more important theorems; the contacts are

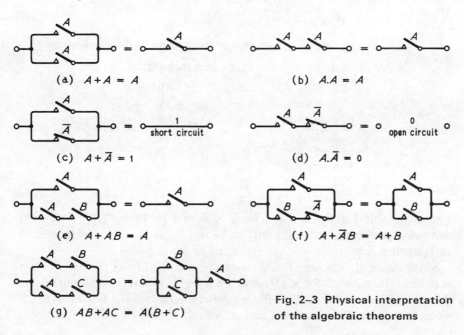

(a) $A + A = A$

(b) $A.A = A$

(c) $A + \bar{A} = 1$

(d) $A.\bar{A} = 0$

(e) $A + AB = A$

(f) $A + \bar{A}B = A + B$

(9) $AB + AC = A(B + C)$

Fig. 2–3 Physical interpretation of the algebraic theorems

assumed ideal in that common contacts open and close together, with no
bounce or delay. The AND operation represents contacts in series, each contact being a binary variable; similarly the OR operation represents contacts
in parallel. In these circuits, variables are represented by normally open
contacts (the presence of a signal closes the contact, e.g. current through a
relay coil), and complemented variables are represented by normally closed
contacts. This representation is also applicable to gating circuits using active
(as distinct from path-closing) devices such as transistors, etc. In this case
the binary variables are the two-state voltage levels (described as high or low,
up or down, positive or negative) representing the values 0 or 1, which are
applied to the input of the gates.

The technique of theorem-proving using algebra or truth-tables is identical
with that described above for propositional logic. Let us consider one more
example however. Suppose we have to prove the relationship

$$T = (A + C)(\bar{A} + B) = AB + \bar{A}C$$

Algebraically, we have

$$
\begin{aligned}
T &= A\bar{A} + AB + \bar{A}C + BC && \text{(Theorem 14)} \\
  &= AB + \bar{A}C + BC && \text{(Theorem 9)} \\
  &= AB + \bar{A}C + BC(A + \bar{A}) && \text{(Theorem 8)} \\
  &= AB + \bar{A}C + BCA + BC\bar{A} && \\
  &= AB(1 + C) + \bar{A}C(1 + B) && \text{(Theorem 12)}
\end{aligned}
$$

Hence $T = AB + \bar{A}C$

Table 2–5 Theorem proving using perfect induction

A	B	C	$(A + C)(\bar{A} + B)$	$(AB + \bar{A}C)$
0	0	0	0	0
0	0	1	1	1
0	1	0	0	0
0	1	1	1	1
1	0	0	0	0
1	0	1	0	0
1	1	0	1	1
1	1	1	1	1

The truth-table for the two functions is shown in Table 2–5. Again the
method of perfect induction is used, whereby all possible values of the binary
variables are substituted into the functions under comparison.

Many different switching functions can be obtained from the basic binary
variables. In general, for n variables we have 2^n possible combinations of
these variables and hence 2^{2^n} different switching functions. For example, if
we have two binary variables A and B, we can obtain 16 unique functions;

Table 2–6 Functions of two variables

A	B	F_0	F_1	F_2	F_3	F_4	F_5	F_6	F_7	F_8	F_9	F_{10}	F_{11}	F_{12}	F_{13}	F_{14}	F_{15}
			AND						OR	NOR						NAND	
0	0	0	0	0	0	0	0	0	0	1	1	1	1	1	1	1	1
0	1	0	0	0	0	1	1	1	1	0	0	0	0	1	1	1	1
1	0	0	0	1	1	0	0	1	1	0	0	1	1	0	0	1	1
1	1	0	1	0	1	0	1	0	1	0	1	0	1	0	1	0	1

these are shown in Table 2–6. Note that these include many functions we have already encountered: F_1 is the AND, F_7 the inclusive OR, F_8 the NOR, F_{14} the NAND, etc.

Any logical function can be expressed in terms of one of the basic operations (AND or OR) and the NOT operation. This follows from the duality of the basic postulates and can be seen by applying De Morgan's theorem. For example, the sum-of-products expression

$$T = \bar{a}bc + a\bar{b}\bar{c} + a\bar{d} + bcd$$

may be expressed in terms of AND/NOT, i.e. NAND, as

$$T = \overline{(\overline{\bar{a}bc})(\overline{a\bar{b}\bar{c}})(\overline{a\bar{d}})(\overline{bcd})}$$

and using OR/NOT, i.e. NOR, as

$$\bar{T} = \overline{(a + \bar{b} + \bar{c}) + (\bar{a} + b + c) + (\bar{a} + d) + (\bar{b} + \bar{c} + \bar{d})}$$

The implication of this is that the hardware for a switching system need only consist of either NAND/NOR logic, or basic AND/OR gates plus invertor amplifiers.

2–8 Derivation and classification of switching functions

Logical design problems are usually presented in the form of oral or written requirements that dictate the terminal behaviour of the required circuit. From this specification a mathematical statement for the switching circuit must be formulated. Consider the requirements for a hall lighting system that enables the hall light to be switched 'on' or 'off' from either one of two switches,

Table 2–7 Truth-table for exclusive OR

A	B	T
0	0	0
0	1	1
1	0	1
1	1	0

situated downstairs and upstairs. This is a system found in most houses in some form or other. The first step is to form a truth-table (Table 2–7) in which all possible input combinations of the two binary variables are examined. The variables A and B represent the two switches, which may be either on (A, B) or off $(\bar{A}, \bar{B})$. If the particular AB combination selected results in the hall light coming on, it is represented by a 1 in column T, otherwise by a 0. The truth-table may be expressed as a switching or transmission function by extracting from the table those combinations of AB that produce an output, i.e. cause the hall light to come on. Thus

$$T = A\bar{B} + \bar{A}B \tag{1}$$

This particular equation represents an important logical function in its own right (F_6 in Table 2–6), it is called the *exclusive* OR or *non-equivalence* circuit and is defined as a circuit that produces an output only when the two inputs are dissimilar. Furthermore, the equation also represents the result of adding two binary digits together (compare with the binary addition table given in the last chapter).

The form of equation we derived from the truth-table, equation (1), is called a *sum-of-products*. The *dual* equation may be obtained by extracting from the table those combinations that *do not* produce an output, i.e. the hindrance terms:

$$H = \bar{T} = \bar{A}\bar{B} + AB \tag{2}$$

Then by applying De Morgan's theorem we have

$$T = \overline{(\bar{A}\bar{B} + AB)} = (A + B)(\bar{A} + \bar{B})$$
$$= A\bar{A} + A\bar{B} + \bar{A}B + B\bar{B}$$
$$T = A\bar{B} + \bar{A}B$$

Therefore the equation

$$T = (A + B)(\bar{A} + \bar{B}) \tag{3}$$

is an equivalent and alternative form of equation (1) and is called the *product-of-sums* form. When implemented in terms of switching circuits (Fig. 2–4), the two forms of the function T given above have identical switching characteristics. Note however that the actual logic gates required to implement these functions are different, the sum-of-products requires two AND gates and one OR, while the product-of-sums needs two OR gates and one AND gate.

In these two alternative forms of switching function, all the binary variables or their complements (literals) appear once, and only once, in each term or factor. For this reason they are called the *canonical* (i.e. standard or normal) forms of the switching function. The sum-of-products is also called the normal *minterm* form, and the product-of-sums is called the normal *maxterm* form when referring to switching circuits. The minterms are all possible

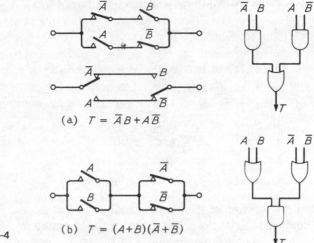

(a) $T = \bar{A}B + A\bar{B}$

(b) $T = (A+B)(\bar{A}+\bar{B})$

Fig. 2–4

combinations of the binary variables joined together by the AND operation; similarly the maxterms are expressed in the OR relationship. Table 2–8 shows all possible minterms and maxterms for the three binary variables A, B, and C.

The following theorems apply to minterm/maxterm relationships.

1. For n binary variables there are exactly 2^n minterms and 2^n maxterms.
2. The union (i.e. logical sum or OR) of all minterms of n binary variables is equal to 1. The converse is also true—the intersection (i.e. logical product or AND) of all maxterms of n binary variables is equal to 0. If we consider the binary input variables as three sets A, B, and C and let $T = \{A, B, C\}$, then the union of all minterms (i.e. subsets of T) forms a covering of T. This covering is also a partition since the intersection of any pair of minterms is disjoint (Section 2–3). The sets A, B, and C are referred to as the *generating sets* for the partition.
3. The complement of any minterm is a maxterm and vice versa.

Canonical expressions are useful in comparing and simplifying switching functions. For example, if we manipulate the functions to be examined to the same basic canonical form, they may then be compared term by term. Expansion formulae exist, due to Shannon, which may be used to expand non-canonical functions to the canonical form. These are:

Minterm form $f(A, B) = \bar{A}\bar{B} \cdot f(0, 0) + \bar{A}B \cdot f(0, 1) + A\bar{B} \cdot f(1, 0)$
$$+ AB \cdot f(1, 1)$$

Maxterm form $f(A, B) = [\bar{A} + \bar{B} + f(1, 1)][\bar{A} + B + f(1, 0)]$
$$[A + \bar{B} + f(0, 1)][A + B + f(0, 0)]$$

Table 2–8 Minterm and maxterm forms

A	B	C	Minterm		Maxterm	
0	0	0	M_0	$= \bar{A}\bar{B}\bar{C}$	M_0	$= \bar{A} + \bar{B} + \bar{C}$
0	0	1	M_1	$= \bar{A}\bar{B}C$	M_1	$= \bar{A} + \bar{B} + C$
0	1	0	M_2	$= \bar{A}B\bar{C}$	M_2	$= \bar{A} + B + \bar{C}$
0	1	1	M_3	$= \bar{A}BC$	M_3	$= \bar{A} + B + C$
1	0	0	M_4	$= A\bar{B}\bar{C}$	M_4	$= A + \bar{B} + \bar{C}$
1	0	1	M_5	$= A\bar{B}C$	M_5	$= A + \bar{B} + C$
1	1	0	M_6	$= AB\bar{C}$	M_6	$= A + B + \bar{C}$
1	1	1	M_7	$= ABC$	M_7	$= A + B + C$

where f is a Boolean function of the binary variables A and B; the formulae hold for any number of variables. The formula for the minterm expansion is applied by considering all possible values of the binary variables in turn, and then logically multiplying them by the truth-value of the actual function, for these values. For example, let us expand the function $T = AB + B\bar{C}$ into its canonical forms. There are three variables, so we have

$$T = AB + B\bar{C}$$
$$= \bar{A}\bar{B}\bar{C} \cdot 0 + \bar{A}\bar{B}C \cdot 0 + \bar{A}B\bar{C} \cdot 1 + \bar{A}BC \cdot 0 + A\bar{B}\bar{C} \cdot 0$$
$$+ A\bar{B}C \cdot 0 + AB\bar{C} \cdot 1 + ABC \cdot 1$$
$$T = \bar{A}B\bar{C} + AB\bar{C} + ABC$$

Again $T = [\bar{A} + \bar{B} + \bar{C} + 1][\bar{A} + \bar{B} + C + 1][\bar{A} + B + \bar{C} + 0]$
$$[\bar{A} + B + C + 0][A + \bar{B} + \bar{C} + 0][A + \bar{B} + C + 1]$$
$$[A + B + \bar{C} + 0][A + B + C + 0]$$
$$T = (\bar{A} + B + \bar{C})(\bar{A} + B + C)(A + \bar{B} + \bar{C})(A + B + \bar{C})$$
$$(A + B + C)$$

An alternative and perhaps easier algebraic method of expansion for minterms is to multiply logically each term by the absent variables expressed in the form $A + \bar{A}$. For example

$$T = AC + B$$
$$= AC(B + \bar{B}) + B(A + \bar{A})(C + \bar{C})$$
$$= ACB + AC\bar{B} + ABC + AB\bar{C} + \bar{A}BC + \bar{A}B\bar{C}$$
$$T = ABC + A\bar{B}C + AB\bar{C} + \bar{A}BC + \bar{A}B\bar{C}$$

This procedure is very easy to apply using a truth-table or the Karnaugh Map technique which will be described in the next chapter.

Another useful way of representing switching functions expressed as a sum-of-products is to replace each combination of binary variables by its direct decimal equivalent, the operation of logical addition being symbolized by a summation sign. Thus,

$$T = \bar{A}\bar{B}C + ABC + A\bar{B}\bar{C} + A\bar{B}C$$

becomes $T = \sum (1, 7, 4, 5)$

The use of switching algebra, then, allows switching circuits to be described symbolically, thereby providing a formal statement of the problem. Moreover in constructing the truth-table for the circuit, the designer is forced to consider all possible inputs, thereby eliminating any errors due to certain input conditions being overlooked. Furthermore, by using the postulates and theorems deduced above it is possible to analyse and synthesize this class of circuit. The resulting switching equations may then be simplified, or clarified, before being translated directly into equivalent hardware devices.

References and bibliography

(1) BOOLE, G. *An investigation of the laws of thought*. Dover Publications, New York, 1954. (Reprint of original publication in 1854.)

(2) SHANNON, C. E. A symbolic analysis of relay and switching circuits. *Trans. Am. Inst. elect. Engrs*, 1938, **57**, 713–723.

(3) BIRKHOFF, G. and MACLANE, S. *A survey of modern algebra*. 3rd edn. Macmillan Company, New York, 1965.

(4) WHITESITT, J. E. *Boolean algebra and its application*. Addison-Wesley, Reading, Mass., 1961.

(5) ADLER, IRVING. *Thinking machines*. Signet Science Library, New American Library, New York, 1962.

(6) PFEIFFER, P. E. *Sets, events and switching*. McGraw-Hill, New York, 1964.

Tutorial problems

2-1 Prove the following identities algebraically and then by perfect induction using a truth-table.

(a) $B + \bar{A}C = (A + B + C)(\bar{A} + B + C)(\bar{A} + B + \bar{C})$

(b) $\bar{A}D + \bar{C}D + A\bar{B} = \bar{A}\bar{C}D + A\bar{C}D + A\bar{B}\bar{C} + A\bar{B}C + \bar{A}CD$

(c) $D(\bar{A} + B + C + \bar{D})(A + B + \bar{C} + \bar{D})$

$$= (D + A\bar{C} + \bar{A}C)(\bar{A}\bar{C} + BD + AC)$$

2-2 Reduce the following functions by taking complements.

(a) $T = \overline{[\overline{(ab)} . a] . [\overline{(ab)} . b]}$

(b) $T = \overline{(a + b + \bar{c})(\overline{ab} + \overline{cd}) + (\overline{bcd})}$

(c) $T = \overline{(abc + b\bar{c}d) + (\overline{acd + b\bar{c}\bar{d} + bc\bar{d}})}$

2-3 Write down the switching function representing the circuits shown in Fig. 2–5. Then, for each circuit:

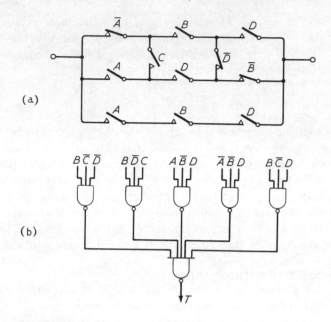

(a)

(b)

Fig. 2–5

(a) expand the function into the canonical sum-of-products and product-of-sums forms;

(b) simplify the original function algebraically and draw the resulting circuit.

2-4 Write down all the subsets of the set $A = \{x_1, x_2, x_3, x_4\}$. Draw a Venn diagram showing these subsets. Consider if this representation could be used to aid the simplification of Boolean functions.

2-5 It is required to design a lighting circuit for a warehouse such that the lights may be switched on or off from any one of three switch points. Set up the truth-table for the problem and derive the corresponding switching equation. Simplify this equation if possible and draw the resulting contact and logic gate circuit.

2-6 Four people, members of a television panel game, each have an on/off button that is used to record their opinion of a certain pop record. Instead of recording individual scores, some data processing is required such that the scoreboard shows a 'hit' when the majority vote is in favour and a 'miss' when against. Provision must also be made to indicate a 'tie'. From the verbal statement:

(a) derive a truth-table for the problem;

(b) extract the sum-of-products and product-of-sums equations;

(c) simplify the equations and suggest a suitable circuit.

2-7 Consider the following logical statements.

(a) Hubert never drinks.

(b) Joe drinks if, and only if, Hubert and Donald are present.

(c) Sidney drinks under all conditions—even by himself!

(d) Donald drinks if, and only if, Hubert is not present.

If A represents Hubert's presence in the bar, B Joe's presence, C Sidney's and D Donald's, determine the function representing a state of no drinking taking place in the bar. Express this function as a word statement.

3 Design of combinational switching circuits I

3–1 Combinational switching circuits

This class of switching circuit is perhaps the most important of all, as a thorough understanding of the principles of combinational design is an essential prerequisite to the study of more complex systems. A *combinational* logic circuit is one in which the output (or outputs) obtained from the circuit is solely dependent on the present state of the inputs. The main objective of combinational design is to produce a circuit having the required switching characteristics but utilizing the minimum number of components; either in terms of relay contacts, basic gating elements, or gate inputs.

Switching problems are usually presented to the designer in the form of an oral or written requirement specifying the logical behaviour of the circuit. From this specification a mathematical statement of the problem can be formulated by the construction of a truth-table, or conditions-function table. An algebraic representation, in the sum-of-products (or product-of-sums) form can then be derived from the table and simplified where possible. These simplified equations may then be directly related to a hardware diagram, in terms of actual circuits such as relay contacts, NAND/NOR gates, etc. Let us now consolidate these ideas by considering a design example in more detail.

3–2 Design example—binary full-adder circuit

Suppose it is required to design a switching circuit that will add two binary digits plus a carry digit. In other words, the circuit has three inputs x, y, and c, and two outputs, the sum S and the next carry C_+. This is the operation required in adding together two binary numbers; if parallel representation is used, one such full-adder stage per bit will be required. We begin the problem by constructing a truth-table which shows all the possible input conditions and the resulting outputs. This is done with reference to the binary addition rules; the complete table is shown in Table 3–1. Note that exactly the same procedure is followed as described in the previous chapter; with three inputs we have 2^3 possible input conditions and all these must be enumerated in the table. Writing down those input conditions which produce an output, we obtain the normal sum-of-products expressions for the sum and next carry:

$$S = \bar{x}\bar{y}c + \bar{x}y\bar{c} + x\bar{y}\bar{c} + xyc$$
$$C_+ = \bar{x}yc + x\bar{y}c + xy\bar{c} + xyc$$

Table 3–1 Truth-table for binary full-adder

x	y	c	S	C_+
0	0	0	0	0
0	0	1	1	0
0	1	0	1	0
0	1	1	0	1
1	0	0	1	0
1	0	1	0	1
1	1	0	0	1
1	1	1	1	1

The next stage in the process is to reduce and simplify the equations if possible; S will not reduce further, but C_+ can be expressed as

$$C_+ = \bar{x}yc + xyc + x\bar{y}c + xyc + xy\bar{c} + xyc$$
$$= yc(\bar{x} + x) + xc(\bar{y} + y) + xy(\bar{c} + c)$$
$$= yc + xc + xy$$

Note that the term xyc has been included three times in the equation, in other words we have added redundant terms, to effect the reduction. That this is possible and does not affect the equations follows from the Boolean algebra relationship $A + A = A$. The equations for S and C_+ may now be implemented in hardware to give the required switching circuit.

It is, however, possible to manipulate the equations in a different way by factorizing the canonical expressions:

$$S = c(\bar{x}\bar{y} + xy) + \bar{c}(\bar{x}y + x\bar{y})$$

Let $z = \bar{x}y + x\bar{y}$, then we have

$$S = c\bar{z} + \bar{c}z$$

since

$$\overline{(\bar{x}\bar{y} + xy)} = \bar{x}y + x\bar{y}$$

This is the exclusive OR function described in the last chapter, and often referred to as a *Modulo 2 adder* circuit, i.e. it gives no carry output. Again, for the carry equation, we can say

$$C_+ = c(\bar{x}y + x\bar{y}) + xy(\bar{c} + c)$$
$$C_+ = cz + xy$$

These equations may now be implemented using the exclusive OR gate, which is frequently obtained as a basic logic module. Figure 3–1 shows both forms of the required switching circuit. It is interesting to note that though circuit (b) uses one more element than circuit (a), only two-input gates are required in (b). Clearly then, the appropriate simplification of canonical switching

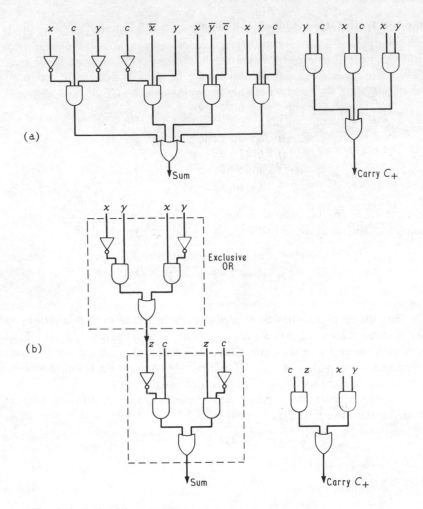

Fig. 3–1 Full-adder circuits

equations depends on hardware constraints, such as the type of logic module available, and the number of inputs to a gate (fan-in factor).

3–3 Minimization of switching equations

We have seen that the formal statement of a combinational problem leads to a Boolean canonical function which must, in the majority of cases, be simplified in some way to provide an economical hardware solution. Though it is possible to simplify algebraically, if the laws of switching algebra are applied haphazardly to, say, a function with more than five variables, the problem becomes prohibitively difficult. We now consider procedures which have been evolved to facilitate the reduction of switching equations to some minimal form (in the sense that there is no unique minimum). These methods, both graphical and algorithmic, do not represent a departure from algebraic principles since they are still based on the fundamental Boolean laws.

There are three main criteria which may be used to determine a minimal sum-of-products (or product-of-sums) expression:

1. The expression with the fewest literals; a literal is defined as either a complemented or uncomplemented binary variable.
2. The expression with the fewest terms.
3. The expression which requires the least number of logical units in its circuit implementation.

The last criterion is the one which must be met in practice, since this will affect the economics of the project. This means that the characteristics of the logic modules, such as type of logic function, number of inputs, speed of operation, etc., must be taken into account and used as constraints upon the design procedure. Most of the techniques we will discuss lead to a minimal result in terms of the fewest number of literals, and the least number of terms. However, this is a very good starting point since the simplification process yields the essential terms of the switching function and allows the implementation to proceed in an optimum manner.

As an illustration of the type of problem involved, consider the minimal switching equation

$$Z = \bar{a}\bar{b}\bar{c}d\bar{e} + \bar{a}\bar{b}\bar{c}d + ab\bar{c}d + a\bar{b}cde$$

Direct implementation would require five-input AND gates and a four-input OR gate, with an overall total of five basic modules, assuming that the complemented variables are already available. But suppose the logic modules to

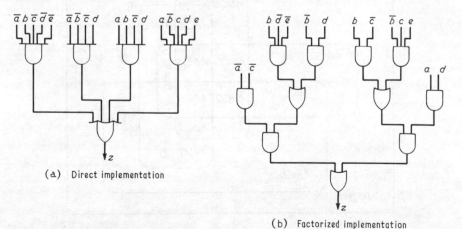

(a) Direct implementation

(b) Factorized implementation

Fig. 3–2 Circuit implementation

be used are three-input AND/OR gates, then the equation must be factorized accordingly:

$$Z = \bar{a}\bar{c}(bd\bar{e} + \bar{b}d) + ad(b\bar{c} + \bar{b}ce)$$

Note, however, that this now uses a total of nine basic modules and involves many more interconnections. Furthermore, as can be seen from Fig. 3–2(b), the factorized version has more stages and hence the switching delays through the circuit (propagation delays) will be greater, which could adversely affect the speed of operation. In high-speed logic systems, particularly those using fast integrated circuits, the minimization of interconnection paths could easily become the major design problem.

Thus the reduction of a switching equation to a form containing the least number of literals and (or) terms is not the complete answer to logical circuit design and the equations must be manipulated further to realize an optimum design in terms of actual hardware. These problems will be discussed in more detail in later chapters, but first we must consider the techniques of minimization.

3–4 Karnaugh map method

This graphical technique is based on the Venn diagram and was originally proposed by Veitch[1] but later improved by Karnaugh.[2] The starting point is really the Venn diagram which we have seen can be used to represent all the possible combinations of n switching variables as areas on a plane; Fig. 3–3 shows the Venn diagram for four variables. The diagram shows that in moving from one sub-area to another in a horizontal or vertical

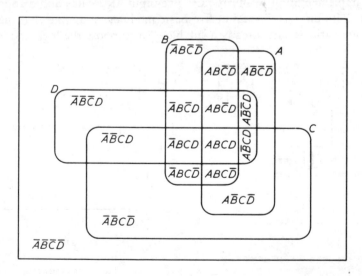

Fig. 3–3 Four-variable Venn diagram

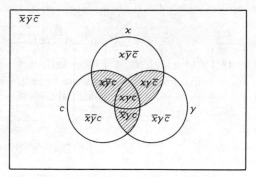

Fig. 3–4 Full-adder carry equations

direction a change in one variable only is involved, e.g. $\bar{A}\bar{B}\bar{C}\bar{D} - \bar{A}B\bar{C}\bar{D} - AB\bar{C}\bar{D} - A\bar{B}\bar{C}\bar{D}$. Thus all *adjacent states* (that is, combinations which differ in only one variable and which can be related according to the Boolean law $(BA + B\bar{A} = B)$ are depicted on the Venn diagram.

The technique is applied by plotting on the Venn diagram those variable combinations which occur in the basic canonical switching equation. For example, consider the equations obtained in the full-adder circuit

$$C_+ = \bar{x}yc + x\bar{y}c + xy\bar{c} + xyc$$

This is shown in Fig. 3–4 with the appropriate terms shaded. Clearly, the terms can be combined to give the reduced form obtained previously, i.e. $C_+ = xy + xc + yc$. However, it is very difficult to draw the Venn diagram for more than four variables, and furthermore it is not organized for convenient plotting and extraction of the switching terms.

In the Karnaugh map or matrix method, every possible combination of the binary input variables is represented on the map by a square (or cell); thus, for n variables we have 2^n squares. The squares in the matrix are generally coded using the reflected binary notation for columns and rows, which ensures that there is a change in one variable only between adjacent vertical or horizontal squares. In this way it becomes immediately obvious by inspection which terms can be combined and simplified using the relationship $BA + B\bar{A} = B$. Karnaugh maps for two, three, and four variables are shown in Table 3–2. Note that cells in adjacent rows differ by one variable, as do cells in adjacent columns. Moreover, there is a correspondence between top and bottom rows, and between extreme left- and right-hand columns.

To plot a canonical sum-of-products function on the Karnaugh map, we enter a 1 in each square of the map corresponding to a term in the function, thus the map completely defines the switching function. To save time, the Karnaugh map may be plotted directly from the truth-table without extracting the canonical equations. For example, consider the function

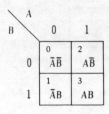

(a) Two-variable map

Three-variable map (b):

AB \\ C	$\bar{A}$ 00	01	A 11	10
$\bar{C}$ 0	$\bar{A}\bar{B}\bar{C}$ (0)	$\bar{A}B\bar{C}$ (2)	$AB\bar{C}$ (6)	$A\bar{B}\bar{C}$ (4)
C 1	$\bar{A}\bar{B}C$ (1)	$\bar{A}BC$ (3)	ABC (7)	$A\bar{B}C$ (5)

$\bar{B}$ | B | $\bar{B}$

(b) Three-variable map

Four-variable map (c):

AB \\ CD	$\bar{A}$ 00	01	A 11	10	
$\bar{C}$ 00	$\bar{A}\bar{B}\bar{C}\bar{D}$ (0)	$\bar{A}B\bar{C}\bar{D}$ (4)	$AB\bar{C}\bar{D}$ (12)	$A\bar{B}\bar{C}\bar{D}$ (8)	$\bar{D}$
01	$\bar{A}\bar{B}\bar{C}D$ (1)	$\bar{A}B\bar{C}D$ (5)	$AB\bar{C}D$ (13)	$A\bar{B}\bar{C}D$ (9)	D
C 11	$\bar{A}\bar{B}CD$ (3)	$\bar{A}BCD$ (7)	$ABCD$ (15)	$A\bar{B}CD$ (11)	D
10	$\bar{A}\bar{B}C\bar{D}$ (2)	$\bar{A}BC\bar{D}$ (6)	$ABC\bar{D}$ (14)	$A\bar{B}C\bar{D}$ (10)	$\bar{D}$

$\bar{B}$ | B | $\bar{B}$

(c) Four-variable map

Table 3–2 Karnaugh maps

$$T = \bar{A}\bar{B}\bar{C}\bar{D} + \bar{A}\bar{B}C\bar{D} + \bar{A}\bar{B}CD + \bar{A}BCD$$
$$+ A\bar{B}\bar{C}\bar{D} + A\bar{B}C\bar{D} + A\bar{B}CD + ABCD$$

or the numerical representation of it

$$T = \sum (0, 2, 3, 7, 8, 10, 11, 15)$$

If the numerical notation is used, it is an easy matter to plot the function—simply place a 1 in each square of the map corresponding to a number in the function (Table 3–3).

The inverse product of sums form is, of course, given by the remaining squares, and these may be indicated by a 0:

$$T = (A + \bar{B} + C + D)(\bar{A} + \bar{B} + C + D)(A + B + C + \bar{D})$$
$$(A + \bar{B} + C + \bar{D})(\bar{A} + \bar{B} + C + \bar{D})(\bar{A} + B + C + \bar{D})$$
$$(A + \bar{B} + \bar{C} + D)(\bar{A} + \bar{B} + \bar{C} + D)$$

Note that in this case, the inverses of the terms must be used to plot the function on the map. For example, $(A + \bar{B} + C + \bar{D})$ would be mentally inverted to $\bar{A}B\bar{C}D$ and plotted by placing a 0 in the appropriate cell.

It will be seen from Table 3–3 that sets of adjacent 1's have been enclosed; these correspond to terms in the function that can be combined (and reduced) using the expression $AB + \bar{A}B = B$. Thus, in moving from one square to another adjacent square, a variable will pass through both its possible values, i.e. 0 and 1; this variable must then be redundant. In Table 3–3 we have enclosed the terms $\bar{A}\bar{B}CD$, $\bar{A}BCD$, $ABCD$, and $A\bar{B}CD$; these combine to

Table 3–3 Function plotting with Karnaugh maps

$$T = \bar{B}\bar{D} + CD = (\bar{B} + D)(C + \bar{D})$$

form $BCD(A + \bar{A})$ and $\bar{B}CD(A + \bar{A})$, the results of which may then be combined to give $CD(B + \bar{B}) = CD$. Note that the loop formed by the enclosed 1's extends over both states of the two variables A and B. The final result is identical to that obtained by algebraic manipulation, i.e.

$$T = \bar{A}\bar{B}\bar{C}\bar{D} + \bar{A}\bar{B}CD + \bar{A}BCD + \bar{A}BCD + A\bar{B}\bar{C}\bar{D} + A\bar{B}C\bar{D}$$
$$+ A\bar{B}CD + ABCD$$
$$= \bar{A}\bar{B}\bar{D}(\bar{C} + C) + \bar{A}CD(\bar{B} + B) + A\bar{B}\bar{D}(\bar{C} + C) + ACD(\bar{B} + B)$$
$$= \bar{B}\bar{D}(\bar{A} + A) + CD(\bar{A} + A)$$
$$T = \bar{B}\bar{D} + CD$$

The cells containing 0's may be combined in the same way, except that in reading the result, the inverses of the variables must be used (this again can be done mentally) and combined in the product-of-sums form:

$$T = (\bar{B} + D)(C + \bar{D})$$

It is apparent, then, that the map is best suited to sum-of-products working, and for this reason it is often referred to as a *minterm* map.

Note that if the switching function is not in the canonical form it must first be expanded. This can be done by using the techniques described in Chapter 2, or it can be performed mentally during the plotting procedure. The latter approach is easier than it sounds because of the matrix organization of the map. For example, suppose we wished to plot the function

$$T = \bar{B}\bar{D} + CD$$

Referring to Table 3–3, we insert 1's in those squares where the $\bar{B}$ and $\bar{D}$ areas intersect; likewise we put 1's in the C and D intersecting areas; in this way the expansion is obtained automatically.

Table 3–4 Prime implicants

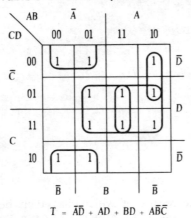

$$T = \bar{A}\bar{D} + AD + BD + A\bar{B}\bar{C}$$

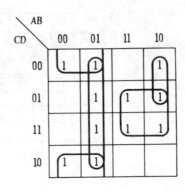

$$T = \bar{A}\bar{D} + AD + \bar{A}B + A\bar{B}\bar{C}$$

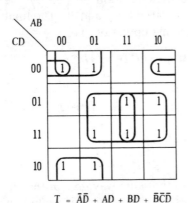

$$T = \bar{A}\bar{D} + AD + BD + \bar{B}\bar{C}\bar{D}$$

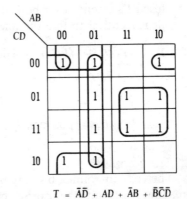

$$T = \bar{A}\bar{D} + AD + \bar{A}B + \bar{B}\bar{C}\bar{D}$$

Prime implicant set: $\bar{A}\bar{D}$, BD, AD, $A\bar{B}\bar{C}$, $\bar{A}B$, $\bar{B}\bar{C}\bar{D}$

Essential prime implicants: $\bar{A}\bar{D}$, AD

The looped terms which appear on the map and in the final expression are called *prime implicants* (they are called prime *implicates* in the case of product-of-sums). In this particular example, since each prime implicant contains original switching terms (represented by the cells containing 1) which are not involved in any other, they are called *essential prime implicants*. More precisely, an essential prime implicant is one which contains a 1 in a cell which cannot be included in any other prime implicant. That is, they must be included in the final minimal expression, and in this case the result obtained is a unique minimal function. In general, however, the method does not result in a unique solution since there are many possible ways of combining the cells, nevertheless all reduced expressions are valid solutions of the original switching problem. Table 3–4 shows all possible groupings for a particular switching problem; the minimal solutions are

$$T = \bar{A}\bar{D} + AD + BD + A\bar{B}\bar{C}$$

$$T = \bar{A}\bar{D} + AD + \bar{A}B + A\bar{B}\bar{C}$$

$$T = \bar{A}\bar{D} + AD + BD + \bar{B}\bar{C}\bar{D}$$

$$T = \bar{A}\bar{D} + AD + \bar{A}B + \bar{B}\bar{C}\bar{D}$$

Note that the essential prime implicants are $\bar{A}\bar{D}$ and AD, and the minimal solution is obtained by selecting a minimal subset from the complete set of prime implicants.

It will be clear that, unless some systematic procedure is followed, haphazard grouping of the cells will result in an expression which is not necessarily in the minimal form. In combining squares, the following general rules should be obeyed.

(a) Every cell containing a 1 must be included at least once.
(b) The largest possible group of squares (powers of 2 only) must be formed, these are the prime implicants. This ensures that the maximum number of variables is eliminated, i.e. groups formed of 2^n cells eliminate n variables.
(c) The 1's must be contained in the minimum number of groups to avoid duplication.

To obtain a minimal result we first select the essential prime implicants, and then those additional prime implicants necessary to completely cover the original function.

The Karnaugh map method may be extended to the solution of five- and six-variable problems, but above this number the method becomes ungainly and the adjacencies become difficult to recognize. The four-variable map is symmetrical in shape, having top-to-bottom and side-to-side adjacencies, as well as row-to-row and column-to-column adjacencies. In fact, the four-variable map can be likened to a motor car tyre inner-tube, or, in topological

Table 3–5 Five- and six-variable Karnaugh maps

(a) Five-variable map

(b) Six-variable map

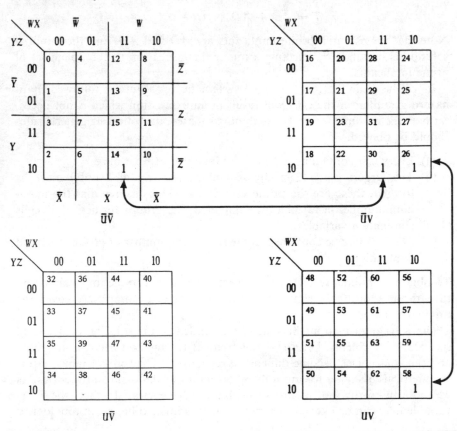

terms, a torus. For this reason it is used as the basis of five- and six-variable maps, as shown in Table 3–5. The five-variable map for $VWXYZ$ consists of two four-variable maps, each representing all possible combinations of the variables $WXYZ$, for the conditions $V = 0$ and $V = 1$. Thus, the maps are effectively grouped to correspond to the binary powers. The normal adjacencies apply to the four-variable maps, with a one-to-one correspondence between them, rather as if the two four-variable maps were superimposed. To use the maps, we first have to recognize and group the terms on the four-variable maps, and then search for correspondence between individual maps. An alternative method of drawing high order Karnaugh maps is to label the columns and rows according to the reflected Gray code. This ensures that there is a change of only one variable between each row and column, but there are also other column and row adjacencies which are spread throughout the map, thus making it difficult to recognize the adjacent groups.

An additional advantage of the mapping technique is that it enables the best use to be put to 'don't care' or 'can't happen' conditions. In some switching problems it is not possible, or even desirable, to specify all the outputs resulting from changing input conditions; these are called *incompletely specified functions*. For example, if we were designing a combinational logic circuit to encode a four-bit binary coded decimal to Gray code, six out of the possible 16 four-bit combinations would not be used since only the decimal numbers 0–9 have to be represented (Table 3–6). Thus, since these

Table 3–6 B.C.D. to Gray code 'don't care' conditions

	B_8	B_4	B_2	B_1	G_4	G_3	G_2	G_1
0	0	0	0	0	0	0	0	0
1	0	0	0	1	0	0	0	1
2	0	0	1	0	0	0	1	1
3	0	0	1	1	0	0	1	0
4	0	1	0	0	0	1	1	0
5	0	1	0	1	0	1	1	1
6	0	1	1	0	0	1	0	1
7	0	1	1	1	0	1	0	0
8	1	0	0	0	1	1	0	0
9	1	0	0	1	1	1	0	1
'Don't care' conditions	1	0	1	0	X	X	X	X
	1	0	1	1	X	X	X	X
	1	1	0	0	X	X	X	X
	1	1	0	1	X	X	X	X
	1	1	1	0	X	X	X	X
	1	1	1	1	X	X	X	X

Table 3–7 Karnaugh map B.C.D. to Gray code with 'don't care' conditions

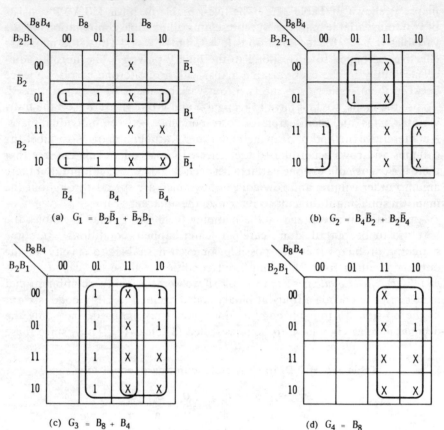

(a) $G_1 = B_2\bar{B}_1 + \bar{B}_2B_1$

(b) $G_2 = B_4\bar{B}_2 + B_2\bar{B}_4$

(c) $G_3 = B_8 + B_4$

(d) $G_4 = B_8$

combinations cannot occur, the outputs required for these input conditions are immaterial and can be assigned either 0 or 1 at will. It is often possible to use these combinations, which are normally represented in the truth-table and on the map by **X**, to effect further minimization. Table 3–7 shows the Karnaugh maps for this coding problem, and it is immediately obvious which is the best way to include the 'don't care' conditions, which take the value 1 within the loops, and 0 elsewhere. Note that in all cases the 'don't care' conditions have been included in such a way as to complete a maximum sized group.

3–5 Design example—nine's complement converter for 2-out-of-5 B.C.D.

Let us consider another design example to illustrate the treatment of 'don't care' conditions. Suppose a switching circuit is required to convert binary coded decimals in the 2-out-of-5 code to their corresponding nine's complement, as used to represent negative numbers. Thus when, for example, the number 5, coded as 00101, appears as an input to the circuit, the output must go to $9 - 5 = 4$, coded as 10100. The truth-table is shown in Table 3–8; since we are only concerned with the decimal numbers 0–9, the 'don't care' conditions are

$$D = (0, 1, 2, 4, 7, 8, 11, 13, 14, 15, 16, 19, 21, 22,$$
$$23, 25, 26, 27, 28, 29, 30, 31)$$

If we insert these 'don't care' conditions in the five-variable Karnaugh maps, together with the actual $VWXYZ$ terms required to give an output for $ABCDE$, we obtain the set of maps shown in Table 3–9. The first step in minimization is to form the largest groups, including the 'don't care' conditions, on the four-variable maps, noting at the same time if a corresponding group occurs in the other map. For example, in Table 3–9(a) the group ZX appears on both V and $\bar{V}$ maps, thus the variable V may be eliminated; the same applies to the group WZ. Proceeding in this way we eventually obtain the output equations

$$A - VW + VY \mid XZ + WZ$$
$$B = WX + WY + VZ + VY$$
$$C = ZX + YZ + VX + WY$$
$$D = YZ + WV + YX + WX$$
$$E = XY + WZ + VX + VZ$$

These equations are shown implemented in AND/OR logic in Fig. 3–5. This problem is really an example of a multi-terminal circuit (to be dealt with in

Table 3–8 Truth-table: nine's complement for 2-out-of-5 B.C.D.

Decimal	V	W	X	Y	Z	A	B	C	D	E	Decimal equivalent of 2-out-of-5 code combination
0	0	1	1	0	0	0	1	0	1	0	12
1	1	0	0	0	1	0	1	0	0	1	17
2	1	0	0	1	0	1	1	0	0	0	18
3	0	0	0	1	1	0	0	1	1	0	3
4	1	0	1	0	0	0	0	1	0	1	20
5	0	0	1	0	1	1	0	1	0	0	5
6	0	0	1	1	0	0	0	0	1	1	6
7	1	1	0	0	0	1	0	0	1	0	24
8	0	1	0	0	1	1	0	0	0	1	9
9	0	1	0	1	0	0	1	1	0	0	10

Remaining combinations
are 'don't-care'

the next chapter) since it has more than one output. In this type of circuit a greater degree of minimization may be achieved if prime implicants are selected which are common to more than one output function. In the equations above, all five output functions can be formed using the prime implicants VW, VY, XZ, WZ, WX, WY, XY, VZ, VX, and YZ. Consequently, only one gate is necessary to form each prime implicant, with the output being distributed to the appropriate output gates. This means that, for multiterminal circuits, forming the largest group for individual output maps does not necessarily lead to the minimal result.

Table 3–9 Karnaugh maps: nine's complement for 2-out-of-5 B.C.D.

Left map:

YZ \ WX	$\overline{W}$ 00	$\overline{W}$ 01	W 11	W 10	
$\overline{Y}$ 00	X (0)	X (4)	(12)	X (8)	$\overline{Z}$
01	X (1)	1 (5)	X (13)	1 (9)	Z
Y 11	(3)	X (7)	X (15)	X (11)	
10	X (2)	(6)	X (14)	(10)	$\overline{Z}$
	$\overline{X}$	X	$\overline{X}$		
		$\overline{V}$			

Right map:

YZ \ WX	00	01	11	10
00	X (16)	(20)	X (28)	1 (24)
01	(17)	X (21)	X (29)	X (25)
11	X (19)	X (23)	X (31)	X (27)
10	1 (18)	X (22)	X (30)	X (26)

V

(a) $A = VW + VY + XZ + WZ$

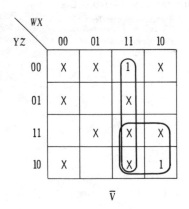
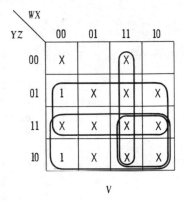

(b) $B = WX + WY + VZ + VY$

Table 3–9 continued

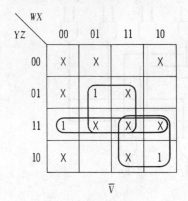

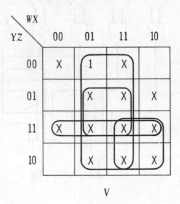

(c) $C = ZX + YZ + VX + WY$

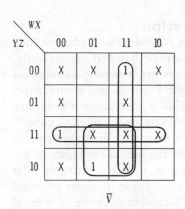

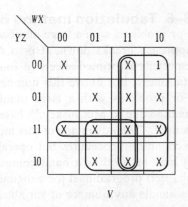

(d) $D = YZ + WV + YX + WX$

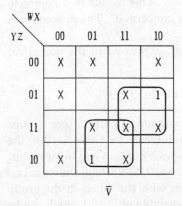

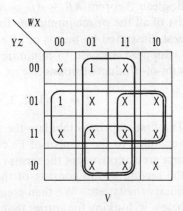

(e) $E = XY + WZ + VX + VZ$

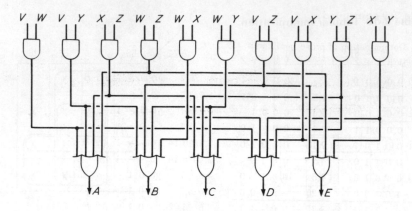

Fig. 3–5 Nine's complement of 2-out-of-5 B.C.D.

3–6 Tabulation method of minimization

For problems with a large number of switching variables the Karnaugh map approach breaks down. Up to six variables can be handled conveniently, especially if printed sheets of four-variable maps are available as standard stationery, but above this number the technique becomes too complicated. For problems with a large number of variables a tabular or algorithmic method due to McCluskey,[3] based on an original technique due to Quine,[4] is used. The advantage of this method is that it does not depend on pattern recognition procedures but operates directly on the actual switching terms. It may be used as a hand computation technique, or better still (see later chapter) programmed for a digital computer; in addition it can be extended to handle any number of variables. The basic idea is to examine each term, and its reduced derivatives, exhaustively and systematically to see if the Boolean theorem $AB + A\bar{B} = \dot{A}$ can be applied. This results in a complete list of all the prime implicants for the function concerned. The procedure is best illustrated by means of an example.

Suppose we wish to minimize the expression, expressed in the numerical sum-of-products form as

$$T = \sum (1, 2, 3, 4, 5, 6, 7, 10, 14, 20, 22, 28)$$

The first step is to tabulate the terms of the switching function into groups according to the number of 1's contained in each term. In Table 3–10(a) the first group consists of the terms (1, 2, 4) all of which contain one binary digit, the second group consists of the terms (3, 5, 6, 10, 20) which contain two binary digits, etc. We then compare each term with the terms in the group below it, looking for entries that differ by one variable only and which can be combined according to the theorem $AB + A\bar{B} = A$. For example, 00001 is

Table 3–10 Tabular minimization

(a) Determination of prime implicants

	V W X Y Z			V W X Y Z			V W X Y Z	
1	0 0 0 0 1 ✓	1,3	0 0 0 – 1 ✓		1,3/5,7	0 0 – – 1	B
2	0 0 0 1 0 ✓	1,5	0 0 – 0 1 ✓		1,5/3,7	0 0 – – 1	
4	0 0 1 0 0 ✓	2,3	0 0 0 1 – ✓		2,3/6,7	0 0 – 1 –	C
3	0 0 0 1 1 ✓	2,6	0 0 – 1 0 ✓		2,6/3,7	0 0 – 1 –	
5	0 0 1 0 1 ✓	2,10	0 – 0 1 0 ✓		2,6/10,14	0 – – 1 0	D
6	0 0 1 1 0 ✓	4,5	0 0 1 0 – ✓		2,10/6,14	0 – – 1 0	
10	0 1 0 1 0 ✓	4,6	0 0 1 – 0 ✓		4,5/6,7	0 0 1 – –	E
20	1 0 1 0 0 ✓	4,20	– 0 1 0 0 ✓		4,6/6,7	0 0 1 – –	
7	0 0 1 1 1 ✓	3,7	0 0 – 1 1 ✓		4,6/20,22	– 0 1 – 0	F
14	0 1 1 1 0 ✓	5,7	0 0 1 – 1 ✓		4,20/6,22	– 0 1 – 0	
22	1 0 1 1 0 ✓	6,7	0 0 1 1 – ✓			List 3	
28	1 1 1 0 0 ✓	6,14	0 – 1 1 0 ✓				
	List 1	6,22	– 0 1 1 0 ✓				
		10,14	0 1 – 1 0 ✓				
		20,22	1 0 1 – 0 ✓				
		20,28	1 – 1 0 0 A				
			List 2				

(b) Karnaugh maps.

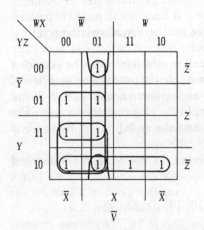

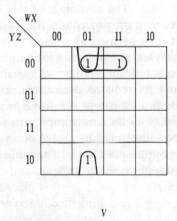

compared with 00011 and found to differ by one variable; the term 000–1 (the dash represents the eliminated variable) is used to start a new group in the next listing, List 2. Both combining terms are ticked off on the original list and the comparison continued until no more combinations can be formed. The comparison is exhaustive and it would compare, in the case of the example, terms (1, 3)(1, 5)(1, 6)(1, 10)(1, 20)(2, 3)(2, 5)(2, 6)(2, 10)(2, 20)

(4, 3)(4, 5)(4, 6)(4, 10)(4, 20), then (3, 7)(3, 14)(3, 22)(3, 28)(5, 7)(5, 14) $\cdots$ (20, 28). Terms need only be compared with those in the group immediately below (and numerically greater), as these are the only ones that can differ by one variable. The process is continued by comparing terms in the derived lists, Lists 2 and 3, in the same way, except that this time the 'dashed' variables must also correspond. It is also necessary to keep a check of the actual combining terms as they will be required later; this is done by noting at the side of each list entry the actual terms of the original switching function included in the reduced expression. The unticked entries (terms that cannot be combined further) are the prime implicants of the switching function. From Table 3–10 these are

$$\text{Prime Implicants P.I.} = (VX\bar{Y}\bar{Z},\ \bar{V}\bar{W}Z,\ \bar{V}\bar{W}Y,\ \bar{V}Y\bar{Z},\ \bar{V}\bar{W}X,\ \bar{W}X\bar{Z})$$

That these are, in fact, the complete set can easily be ascertained from the Karnaugh map in Table 3–10(b).

During the comparison process it is possible that the same reduced term may be formed in more than one way, for example in List 3 of Table 3–10(a), prime implicant B may be formed by combining 1, 3/5, 7 and 1, 5/3, 7. The repeated terms are best ignored and not repeated in succeeding new lists, though they are retained in the examples that follow to ensure a better appreciation of the technique.

3–7 Selecting a minimal P.I. subset—prime implicant tables

Having ascertained the complete P.I. set, it is now necessary to choose a minimal subset that will include, or cover, all the terms in the original switching expression. Each product term of the function must be included in at least one of the prime implicant terms in the minimal expression. The relationship between the prime implicants and the switching terms can best be seen by means of a *prime implicant table*, this is shown in Table 3–11 for the example above. The table takes the form of a matrix with the original product terms as columns and the prime implicants as rows. For each prime implicant row, a cross is placed in those columns that contain a term of the original switching function; for example, prime implicant row A, comprising terms 20, 28, would have crosses in columns 20 and 28. To choose an optimum set of prime implicants we first examine the table for any columns with only one cross. The corresponding rows are called *basis rows* and represent, of course, the essential prime implicants; these are marked in Table 3–11 by an asterisk, with the included column terms ticked off.

When this is done, a check is made to see if any column terms are uncovered by these basis rows, i.e. check for any terms of the original switching function not included in the essential prime implicants. In this example, the

Table 3–11 Extraction of minimal P.I. subset

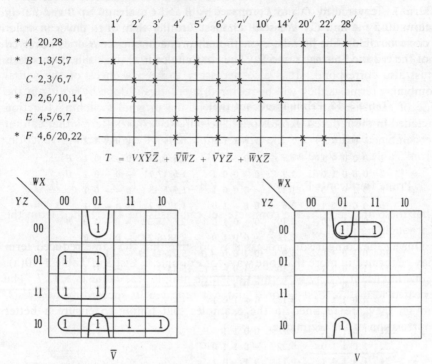

$$T = VX\overline{Y}\overline{Z} + \overline{V}\overline{W}Z + \overline{V}Y\overline{Z} + \overline{W}X\overline{Z}$$

basis rows (essential prime implicants) include all the switching terms, so that no other rows (prime implicants) are required. The minimal switching equation is given by the logical sum of the prime implicants, i.e.

$$T = A + B + D + F$$
$$= VX\overline{Y}\overline{Z} + \overline{V}\overline{W}Z + \overline{V}Y\overline{Z} + \overline{W}X\overline{Z}$$

If this had not been the case, however, it would have been necessary to select other rows to complete the covering. Thus, after selecting the basis rows, one would proceed by inspecting the table for those rows which can cover the remaining column terms. If more than one row exists, a selection is made in favour of the row which can cover the maximum number of remaining terms, or which contains the most crosses (and hence the fewest literals) in the prime implicant term. If two rows can cover the same terms, the row with the fewest literals is chosen. The process is repeated until all the rows are covered.

Consider the example shown in Table 3–12. The basis rows are G, H, and I, and these cover the column terms 1, 2, 5, 6, 13, 17, 18, 21, 22, 29. Now we examine the table for rows which can cover the remaining terms 7, 8, 9, 10.

Each of the remaining terms can be covered by two possible rows, that is, term 7 is covered by D and E; term 8 by B and C; term 9 by B and F; and term 10 by A and C. We shall choose F rather than B to cover 9 since it contains the fewest literals, even though prime implicant B does cover two of the required terms, 8 and 9. The next choice is C since this covers terms

Table 3–12 Prime implicant table

Function $T = \Sigma\,(1, 2, 5, 6, 7, 8, 9, 10, 13, 17, 18, 21, 22, 29)$

	V W X Y Z			V W X Y Z			V W X Y Z	
1	0 0 0 0 1 ✓	1,5	0 0 – 0 1 ✓	1,5/9,13	0 – – 0 1	F
2	0 0 0 1 0 ✓	1,9	0 – 0 0 1 ✓	1,5/17,21	– 0 – 0 1	G
8	0 1 0 0 0 ✓	1,17	– 0 0 0 1 ✓	1,9/5,13	0 – – 0 1	
5	0 0 1 0 1 ✓	2,6	0 0 – 1 0 ✓	1,17/5,21	– 0 – 0 1	
6	0 0 1 1 0 ✓	2,10	0 – 0 1 0 A	2,6/18,22	– 0 – 1 0	H
9	0 1 0 0 1 ✓	2,18	– 0 0 1 0 ✓	2,18/6,22	– 0 – 1 0	
10	0 1 0 1 0 ✓	8,9	0 1 0 0 – B	5,21/13,29	– – 1 0 1	I
17	1 0 0 0 1 ✓	8,10	0 1 0 – 0 C	5,13/21,29	– – 1 0 1	
18	1 0 0 1 0 ✓	5,7	0 0 1 – 1 D			
7	0 0 1 1 1 ✓	5,13	0 – 1 0 1 ✓			
13	0 1 1 0 1 ✓	5,21	– 0 1 0 1 ✓			
21	1 0 1 0 1 ✓	6,7	0 0 1 1 – E			
22	1 0 1 1 0 ✓	6,22	– 0 1 1 0 ✓			
29	1 1 1 0 1 ✓	9,13	0 1 – 0 1 ✓			
		17,21	1 0 – 0 1 ✓			
		18,22	1 0 – 1 0 ✓			
		13,29	– 1 1 0 1 ✓			
		21,29	1 – 1 0 1 ✓			

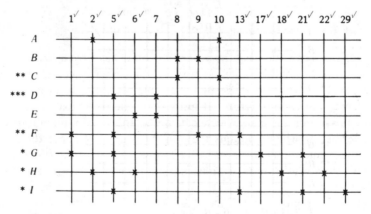

$$T = G + H + I + F + C + D \text{ (or } E)$$
$$= \overline{W}\overline{Y}Z + \overline{W}Y\overline{Z} + X\overline{Y}Z + \overline{V}\overline{Y}Z + \overline{V}W\overline{X}\overline{Z} + \overline{V}\overline{W}XZ \text{ (or } \overline{V}\overline{W}XY)$$

8 and 10, then we take either D or E as there is nothing to choose between them. The minimal solution, then, is

$$T = G + H + I + F + C + D \text{ (or } E)$$
$$= \overline{W}\overline{Y}Z + \overline{W}Y\overline{Z} + X\overline{Y}Z + \overline{V}\overline{Y}Z + \overline{V}W\overline{X}\overline{Z} + \overline{V}WXZ \text{ (or } \overline{V}\overline{W}XY)$$

This result is just one of many possible solutions, giving the minimum number of terms, though this particular one is truly minimal in the sense of both literals and terms.

For some functions it may happen that, after the basis rows have been selected, the remainder of the chart is such that there is no obvious way to choose the next rows; this structure is said to be *cyclic*. In other words, there are no unique rows which can be chosen so that other rows may be covered. Table 3–13 shows an example of a cyclic prime implicant table. After the basis row A has been chosen, there are several alternative ways of selecting rows to cover the remaining column terms. Since all terms contain

Table 3–13 Cyclic prime implicant table

Function $T = \Sigma\,(1, 3, 4, 5, 6, 8, 9, 10, 14)$

	W	X	Y	Z			W	X	Y	Z	
1	0	0	0	1✓		1,3	0	0	–	1	A
4	0	1	0	0✓		1,5	0	–	0	1	B
8	1	0	0	0✓		1,9	–	0	0	1	C
3	0	0	1	1✓		4,5	0	1	0	–	D
5	0	1	0	1✓		4,6	0	1	–	0	E
6	0	1	1	0✓		8,9	1	0	0	–	F
9	1	0	0	1✓		8,10	1	0	–	0	G
10	1	0	1	0✓		6,14	–	1	1	0	H
14	1	1	1	0✓		10,14	1	–	1	0	I

$$T = A + D + F + G + H$$
$$= \overline{W}\overline{X}Z + \overline{W}X\overline{Y} + W\overline{X}\overline{Y} + W\overline{X}\overline{Z} + X Y \overline{Z}$$

the same number of literals and cover the same number of column terms there is no obvious starting point. We must proceed, therefore, by selecting an arbitrary row, say D, and continuing until all column terms are covered. In this case a possible minimal selection is

$$T = A + D + F + G + H$$
$$= \overline{W}\overline{X}Z + \overline{W}X\overline{Y} + W\overline{X}\overline{Y} + W\overline{X}\overline{Z} + WY\overline{Z}$$

To ascertain if this is a unique minimal result, all possible alternative prime implicant sets must be obtained and examined in detail. This is essentially a trial and error process, the complexity of which rapidly increases with problem size.

3–8 Algebraic solution of prime implicant tables

Prime implicant tables, including cyclic ones, can be 'solved' by using an algebraic approach, due to Petrick[5] and later modified by Pyne and McCluskey,[6] which produces all the irredundant sums, that is, solutions from which no prime implicant may be removed if all the terms are to be accounted for. The minimal result can be obtained by direct examination and comparison of the alternative irredundant sum-of-products expressions. In this method, each row of the prime implicant table is considered as a binary variable, and a product-of-sums expression is derived for the complete table. This function is called a prime implicant function (P), and each variable corresponds to a prime implicant of the original switching function. From Table 3–13 we can see that, to account for all the terms in the table, the P function must contain A or B or C from column 1, A from column 3, and D or E from column 4, etc.

Combining these statements we have $(A + B + C)(A)(D + E)$, etc., and continuing in this way for the entire table we have

$$P = (A + B + C)(A)(D + E)(B + D)(E + H)$$
$$(F + G)(C + F)(G + I)(H + I)$$

Since this is a Boolean expression, we may reduce it in the normal way:

$$P = (A)(D + BE)(E + H)(F + GC)(I + GH)$$
$$= (A)(FD + BEF + DGC + BEGC)(EI + HG + HI)$$
$$= AFDEI + AFDHG + AFDHI + ABEFI + ABEFHG$$
$$+ ABEFHI + ADGCEI + ADGCH + ADGCHI$$
$$+ ABEGCI + ABEGCH + ABEGCHI$$

Thus, $\quad P = AFDEI + AFDHG + AFDHI + ABEFI + ABEFHG$
$$+ ADGCEI + ADGCH + ABEGCI + ABEGCH$$

There are, then, five minimal solutions each containing five prime implicant terms.

Again, let us consider the prime implicant table shown in Table 3–12; this may be expressed in the product-of-sums form

$$P = (F + G)(A + H)(D + F + G + I)(E + H)(D + E)(B + C)$$
$$(B + F)(A + C)(F + I)(G)(H)(G + I)(H)(I)$$
$$= (G)(H)(I)(D + E)(B + C)(B + F)(A + C)$$
$$= (G)(H)(I)(C + AB)(B + F)(D + E)$$
$$= (GHI)(BC + AB + FC + FAB)(D + E)$$
$$= (GHI)(BCD + ABD + FCD + FABD + BCE$$
$$+ ABE + FCE + FABE)$$

Thus, $P = GHIBCD + GHIABD + GHIFCD + GHIBCE$
$$+ GHIABE + GHIFCE$$

Now since $FGHI$ are the prime implicant terms with the fewest literals, there are two minimal solutions:

$$T = G + H + I + F + C + D$$
and $$T = G + H + I + F + C + E$$

which is the same result that we obtained using the prime implicant chart. This technique is the only way to manipulate complex tables, and moreover it is a very convenient algorithm for machine computation.

3–9 'Don't care' conditions

So far in our discussions of the tabulation method we have not mentioned how incompletely specified functions are treated. In fact the procedure is very nearly identical. The switching terms, including 'don't cares', are tabulated and examined as before to produce the complete set of prime implicants. The prime implicant table is then constructed in the usual way, but the 'don't care' conditions are ignored. This is feasible since the inclusion, or exclusion, of 'don't care' terms in the final expression is immaterial. Suppose, for example, we wish to minimize the function

$$T = \sum (5, 15, 20, 29, 41, 42, 45, 47, 53, 58, 61, 63)$$

with the 'don't care' conditions

$$D = (7, 9, 11, 13, 21, 25, 27, 31, 37, 39, 40, 43, 56, 57, 59)$$

The complete set of terms, including 'don't cares', are shown in Table 3–14.

Proceeding with the minimization routine, we establish a set of prime implicants:

$$\text{P.I.} = (A, B, C, D, E) = (\bar{U}V\bar{W}X\bar{Y}, \bar{V}XZ, X\bar{Y}Z, UW\bar{X}, WZ)$$

If these are now plotted on to a prime implicant chart (Table 3–15) containing the original transmission terms only, we find that A, C, D, and E are essential prime implicants which give a unique minimal function:

$$T = A + C + D + E$$
$$= \bar{U}V\bar{W}X\bar{Y} + XYZ + UW\bar{X} + WZ$$

Table 3–14 Minimization with 'don't care' condition

	U	V	W	X	Y	Z	
5	0	0	0	1	0	1	√
9	0	0	1	0	0	1	√
20	0	1	0	1	0	0	√
40	1	0	1	0	0	0	√
7	0	0	0	1	1	1	√
11	0	0	1	0	1	1	√
13	0	0	1	1	0	1	√
21	0	1	0	1	0	1	√
25	0	1	1	0	0	1	√
37	1	0	0	1	0	1	√
41	1	0	1	0	0	1	√
42	1	0	1	0	1	0	√
56	1	1	1	0	0	0	√
15	0	0	1	1	1	1	√
27	0	1	1	0	1	1	√
29	0	1	1	1	0	1	√
39	1	0	0	1	1	1	√
43	1	0	1	0	1	1	√
45	1	0	1	1	0	1	√
53	1	1	0	1	0	1	√
57	1	1	1	0	0	1	√
58	1	1	1	0	1	0	√
31	0	1	1	1	1	1	√
47	1	0	1	1	1	1	√
59	1	1	1	0	1	1	√
61	1	1	1	1	0	1	√
63	1	1	1	1	1	1	√

List 1

	U	V	W	X	Y	Z	
5,7	0	0	0	1	–	1	√
5,13	0	0	–	1	0	1	√
5,21	0	–	0	1	0	1	√
5,37	–	0	0	1	0	1	√
9,11	0	0	1	0	–	1	√
9,13	0	0	1	–	0	1	√
9,25	0	–	1	0	0	1	√
9,41	–	0	1	0	0	1	√
20,21	0	1	0	1	0	–	A
40,41	1	0	1	0	0	–	√
40,42	1	0	1	0	–	0	√
40,56	1	–	1	0	0	0	√
7,15	0	0	–	1	1	1	√
7,39	–	0	0	1	1	1	√
11,15	0	0	1	–	1	1	√
11,27	0	–	1	0	1	1	√
11,43	–	0	1	0	1	1	√
13,15	0	0	1	1	–	1	√
13,29	0	–	1	1	0	1	√
13,45	–	0	1	1	0	1	√
21,29	0	1	–	1	0	1	√
21,53	–	1	0	1	0	1	√
25,27	0	1	1	0	–	1	√
25,29	0	1	1	–	0	1	√
25,57	–	1	1	0	0	1	√
37,39	1	0	0	1	–	1	√
37,45	1	0	–	1	0	1	√
37,53	1	–	0	1	0	1	√
41,43	1	0	1	0	–	1	√

	U	V	W	X	Y	Z	
41,45	1	0	1	–	0	1	√
41,57	1	–	1	0	0	1	√
42,43	1	0	1	0	1	–	√
42,58	1	–	1	0	1	0	√
56,57	1	1	1	0	0	–	√
56,58	1	1	1	0	–	0	√
15,31	0	–	1	1	1	1	√
15,47	–	0	1	1	1	1	√
27,31	0	1	1	–	1	1	√
27,59	–	1	1	0	1	1	√
29,31	0	1	1	1	–	1	√
29,61	–	1	1	1	0	1	√
39,47	1	0	–	1	1	1	√
43,47	1	0	1	–	1	1	√
43,59	1	–	1	0	1	1	√
45,47	1	0	1	1	–	1	√
45,61	1	–	1	1	0	1	√
53,61	1	1	–	1	0	1	√
57,59	1	1	1	0	–	1	√
57,61	1	1	1	–	0	1	√
58,59	1	1	1	0	1	–	√
31,63	–	1	1	1	1	1	√
47,63	1	–	1	1	1	1	√
59,63	1	1	1	–	1	1	√
61,63	1	1	1	1	–	1	√

List 2

Table 3–14 continued

	U	V	W	X	Y	Z	
5,7/13,15	0	0	–	1	–	1	√
5,7/37,39	–	0	0	1	–	1	√
5,13/7,15	0	0	–	1	–	1	√
5,13/21,29	0	–	–	1	0	1	√
5,13/37,45	–	0	–	1	0	1	√
5,21/13,29	0	–	–	1	0	1	√
5,21/37,53	–	–	0	1	0	1	√
5,37/7,39	–	0	0	1	–	1	√
5,37/13,45	–	0	–	1	0	1	√
5,37/21,51	–	–	0	1	0	1	√
9,11/13,15	0	0	1	–	–	1	√
9,11/25,27	0	–	1	0	–	1	√
9,13/11,15	0	0	1	–	–	1	√
9,13/25,29	0	–	1	–	0	1	√
9,13/41,45	–	0	1	–	0	1	√
9,25/11,27	0	–	1	0	–	1	√
9,25/13,29	0	–	1	–	0	1	√
9,25/41,57	–	–	1	0	0	1	√
9,41/11,43	–	0	1	0	–	1	√
9,41/13,45	–	0	1	–	0	1	√
9,41/25,27	–	–	1	0	0	1	√
40,41/42,43	1	0	1	0	–	–	√
40,41/56,57	1	–	1	0	0	–	√
40,42/41,43	1	0	1	0	–	–	√
40,56/41,57	1	–	1	0	0	–	√
7,15/39,47	–	0	–	1	1	1	√
7,39/15,47	–	0	–	1	1	1	√
11,15/27,31	0	–	1	–	1	1	√
11,15/43,47	–	0	1	–	1	1	√
11,27/15,31	0	–	1	–	1	1	√
11,43/15,47	–	0	1	–	1	1	√
11,43/27,59	–	–	1	0	1	1	√
13,15/29,31	0	–	1	1	–	1	√
13,15/45,47	–	0	1	1	–	1	√
13,29/15,31	0	–	1	1	–	1	√
13,29/45,61	–	–	1	1	0	1	√
13,45/15,47	–	0	1	1	–	1	√
13,45/29,61	–	–	1	1	0	1	√
21,53/29,61	–	1	–	1	0	1	√
25,29/27,31	0	1	1	–	–	1	√
25,29/57,61	–	1	1	–	0	1	√
25,57/27,59	–	1	1	0	–	1	√
25,57/29,61	–	1	1	–	0	1	√

	U	V	W	X	Y	Z	
37,39/45,47	1	0	–	1	–	1	√
37,45/39,47	1	0	–	1	–	1	√
37,45/53,61	1	–	–	1	0	1	√
37,45/45,61	1	–	–	1	0	1	√
41,43/45,47	1	0	1	–	–	1	√
41,45/43,47	1	0	1	–	–	1	√
41,45/57,61	1	–	1	–	0	1	√
41,57/43,59	1	–	1	0	–	1	√
41,57/45,61	1	–	1	–	0	1	√
42,43/58,59	1	–	1	0	1	–	√
42,58/43,59	1	–	1	0	1	–	√
42,58/45,61	1	–	1	–	0	1	√
56,57/58,59	1	1	1	0	–	–	√
56,58/57,59	1	1	1	0	–	–	√
15,31/47,63	–	–	1	1	1	1	√
15,47/31,63	–	–	1	1	1	1	√
27,31/59,63	–	1	1	–	1	1	√
27,59/31,63	–	1	1	–	1	1	√
29,31/61,63	–	1	1	1	–	1	√
29,61/31,63	–	1	1	1	–	1	√
43,47/59,63	1	–	1	–	1	1	√
43,59/47,63	1	–	1	–	1	1	√
45,47/61,63	1	–	1	1	–	1	√
45,61/47,63	1	–	1	1	–	1	√
57,59/61,63	1	1	1	–	–	1	√
57,61/59,63	1	1	1	–	–	1	√

List 3

	U	V	W	X	Y	Z	
5,7/13,15/37,39/45,47	–	0	–	1	–	1	B
5,7/37,39/13,15/45,47	–	0	–	1	–	1	
5,13/7,15/37,39/45,47	–	0	–	1	–	1	
5,13/21,29/37,45/53,61	–	–	–	1	0	1	C
5,13/37,45/7,15/39,47	–	0	–	1	–	1	
5,13/37,45/21,53/29,61	–	–	–	1	0	1	
5,21/13,29/37,45/53,61	–	–	–	1	0	1	
5,21/37,53/13,29/45,61	–	–	–	1	0	1	
5,37/7,39/13,15/45,47	–	0	–	1	–	1	
9,11/13,15/25,29/27,31	0	–	1	–	–	1	√
9,11/13,15/41,43/45,47	–	0	1	–	–	1	√

Table 3–14 continued

	U	V	W	X	Y	Z	
9,11/25,27/13,15/29,31	0	–	1	–	–	1	√
9,4/25,27/41,57/43,59	–	–	1	0	–	1	√
9,13/11,15/25,29/27,31	0	–	1	–	–	1	√
9,13/11,15/41,43/45.47	–	0	1	–	–	1	√
9,13/25,29/11,15/27,31	0	–	1	–	–	1	√
9,13/25,29/41,45/57,61	–	–	1	–	0	1	√
9,13/41,45/11,15/43,47	–	0	1	–	–	1	√
9,13/41,45/25,29/57,61	–	–	1	–	0	1	√
9,25/11,27/13,15/29,31	0	–	1	–	–	1	√
9,25/41,57/11,43/27,59	–	–	1	0	–	1	√
9,25/41,57/13,29/45,61	–	–	1	–	0	1	√
9,41/11,43/13,15/45,47	–	0	1	–	–	1	√
9,41/11,43/25,57/27,29	–	–	1	0	–	1	√
40,41/42,43/56,57/58,59	1	–	1	0	–	–	D
40,41/56,57/42,43/58,59	1	–	1	0	–	–	
11,15/27,31/43,47/59,63	–	–	1	–	1	1	√
11,15/43,47/27,31/59,63	–	–	1	–	1	1	√
11,43/27,59/15,31/47,63	–	–	1	–	1	1	√
13,15/29,31/45,47/61,63	–	–	1	1	–	1	√
13,15/45,47/29,31/61,63	–	–	1	1	–	1	√
13,29/45,61/15,31/47,63	–	–	1	1	–	1	√
25,29/27,31/57,59/61,63	–	1	1	–	–	1	√
25,29/57,61/27,31/59,63	–	1	1	–	–	1	√
25,57/27,29/29,31/61,63	–	1	1	–	–	1	√
41,43/45,47/57,59/61,63	1	–	1	–	–	1	√
41,45/57,61/43,47/59,63	1	–	1	–	–	1	√
41,57/43,59/45,47/61,63	1	–	1	–	–	1	√

List 4

	U	V	W	X	Y	Z	
9,11/13,15/25,29/27,31 41,43/45,47/57,59/61,63	–	–	1	–	–	1	E
9,11/13,15/41,43/45,47 25,29/27,31/57,59/61,63	–	–	1	–	–	1	
9,4/25,27/41,57/43,59 13,15/29,31/45,47/61,63	–	–	1	–	–	1	
9,13/25,29/41,45/57,61 11,15/27,31/43,47/59,63	–	–	1	–	–	1	

List 5

Prime implicant set $= \bar{U}V\bar{W}X\bar{Y},\ \bar{V}XZ,\ X\bar{Y}Z,\ UW\bar{X},\ WZ$

Table 3–15 Prime implicant table with 'don't cares'

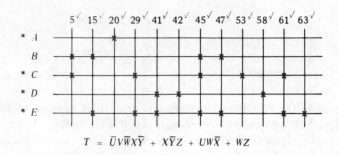

$$T = \bar{U}V\bar{W}X\bar{Y} + X\bar{Y}Z + UW\bar{X} + WZ$$

If the reader draws the Karnaugh map for this problem it will be clear that the map method involves far less computation, and the use of 'don't care' conditions is immediately apparent. However, the strength of the tabular method lies in its easy extension to large-variable problems.

Other tabular techniques have been developed for minimizing Boolean functions, notably those due to Roth,[7] Curtis,[8] and Samson and Mills.[9] The McCluskey method, however, is simple to apply and is well suited for both hand and machine computation.

3–10 Switching tree circuits

We have seen that combinational logic circuits may be designed by setting up a truth-table, deriving the canonical functions, and minimizing these functions. However, there are many occasions when the direct implementation of these minimal equations, either as series/parallel contacts or two-level AND/OR gates, is not the best way of realizing the switching circuit. Though a fuller discussion of this problem will be given in the next chapter, it is useful to consider some of the problems at this stage.

Suppose we wish to design a multi-output circuit in which each input combination has a unique output associated with it, this is called a *tree circuit*. For example, consider a circuit for decoding four-bit pure binary code to ten output-lines each representing one of the ten equivalent decimal numbers 0–9. This could be done quite easily by using normal truth-table methods, and the result would be an array of ten four-input AND gates, one for each combination. However, suppose only two-input logic modules were available, this would mean splitting the input combinations, and the modified circuit would require three two-input AND gates per combination, giving a total of 30 gates. Is there any other way of producing a more economic circuit?

If we take the total number of input variables and divide them as evenly as possible into two integral numbers, continuing until we reach 2 or 3, we obtain

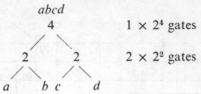

$$
\begin{array}{ccl}
abcd & & \\
4 & & 1 \times 2^4 \text{ gates} \\
\diagup \quad \diagdown & & \\
2 \qquad 2 & & 2 \times 2^2 \text{ gates} \\
\diagup \diagdown \quad \diagup \diagdown & & \\
a \quad b \; c \quad d & &
\end{array}
$$

Each number in the flow diagram represents the total number of variables being switched in all possible combinations at that point. Thus, each 2 represents two variables, say a and b, switched in all four combinations $\bar{a}\bar{b}$, $\bar{a}b$, $a\bar{b}$, and ab. Similarly, 4 represents all possible combinations of the four variables a, b, c, and d. This means that for each number, n, on the diagram, the total number of AND gates required at that point is 2^n, also the lines give the total number of gate inputs. The diagram may be directly related to a logic circuit (except the logic diagram is drawn reverse-way up) as shown in Fig. 3–6(b). The total number of two-input AND gates required has been reduced to 18, a saving of 12 gates. Note that if all the output combinations had to be decoded, 24 two-input AND gates would be needed as against 16 four-input AND gates, and the total number of gate inputs would remain constant at 48.

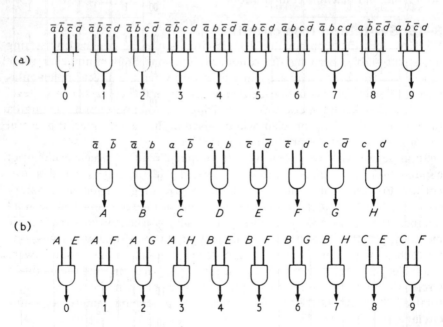

Fig. 3–6 Electronic trees

Table 3–16 Design of relay tree networks

(a)

cd \ ab	00	01	11	10	
00	1	1		1	$\bar{d}$
01	1	1		1	
11	1	1			d
10	1	1			$\bar{d}$

(columns: $\bar{a}$ for 00, 01; a for 11, 10; rows: $\bar{c}$ for 00, 01; c for 11, 10; bottom labels $\bar{b}$, b, $\bar{b}$)

(b)

cd \ ab	00	01	11	10
00	$\bar{a}$ 1	$\bar{a}$ 1		a 1
01	$\bar{a}$ 1	$\bar{a}$ 1		a 1
11	$\bar{a}$ 1	$\bar{a}$ 1		
10	$\bar{a}$ 1	$\bar{a}$ 1		

(c)

cd \ ab	00	01	11	10
00	$\bar{a}\bar{b}$ 1	$\bar{a}b$ 1		$a\bar{b}$ 1
01	$\bar{a}\bar{b}$ 1	$\bar{a}b$ 1		$a\bar{b}$ 1
11	$\bar{a}\bar{b}$ 1	$\bar{a}b$ 1		
10	$\bar{a}\bar{b}$ 1	$\bar{a}b$ 1		

(d)

cd \ ab	00	01	11	10
00	$\bar{a}\bar{b}\bar{c}$ 1	$\bar{a}b\bar{c}$ 1		$a\bar{b}\bar{c}$ 1
01	$\bar{a}\bar{b}\bar{c}$ 1	$\bar{a}b\bar{c}$ 1		$a\bar{b}\bar{c}$ 1
11	$\bar{a}\bar{b}c$ 1	$\bar{a}bc$ 1		
10	$\bar{a}bc$ 1	$\bar{a}bc$ 1		

(e)

cd \ ab	00	01	11	10
00	$\bar{a}\bar{b}\bar{c}\bar{d}$ 1	$\bar{a}b\bar{c}\bar{d}$ 1		$a\bar{b}\bar{c}\bar{d}$ 1
01	$\bar{a}\bar{b}\bar{c}d$ 1	$\bar{a}b\bar{c}d$ 1		$a\bar{b}\bar{c}d$ 1
11	$\bar{a}\bar{b}cd$ 1	$\bar{a}bcd$ 1		
10	$\bar{a}\bar{b}cd$ 1	$\bar{a}bcd$ 1		

(f)

cd \ ab	00	01	11	10
00	$\bar{a}\bar{b}\bar{c}\bar{d}$ 1	$\bar{a}b\bar{c}\bar{d}$ 1		$a\bar{d}$ 1
01	$\bar{a}\bar{b}\bar{c}d$ 1	$\bar{a}b\bar{c}d$ 1		ad 1
11	$\bar{a}\bar{b}cd$ 1	$\bar{a}bcd$ 1		
10	$\bar{a}\bar{b}c\bar{d}$ 1	$\bar{a}bc\bar{d}$ 1		

Let us now implement the circuit in terms of relay logic. It is possible to construct a relay tree making use of transfer or changeover contacts; the full tree for four variables is shown in Fig. 3–7 and may be extended to any number of variables. The contacts within the dotted line are unnecessary in the case of the four-bit decoder, as only the decimal outputs 0–9 are required. In fact, if only these combinations can occur, the others being 'can't happen' conditions, we can also eliminate contacts $\bar{b}$ and $\bar{c}$. Marcus[10] has described

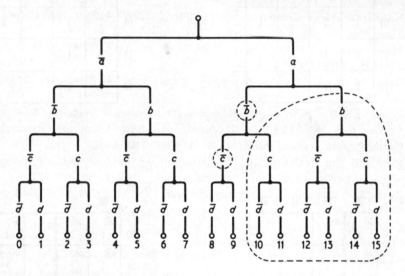

Fig. 3–7 Relay trees

a Karnaugh map technique for designing and minimizing partial trees (as in the case above) to obtain an optimum contact utilization. Briefly, this consists of plotting the required combinations on a Karnaugh map and sub-dividing the map in such a way that the *unused combinations* form a minimum number of sub-groups. The sub-division is commenced [see Table 3–16(b)] by separating the combinations into two groups each dependent on the alternative states of a variable, in this case a, the appropriate literal being inserted in each square. The sub-division is continued, ignoring unused combinations, with variable b, followed by c and d; note that the sub-division is such that the unused combinations form the largest possible groups. In general, there are many alternative ways of sub-dividing, each yielding a feasible tree network though not necessarily an optimum one. The order of subdivision, recorded in each square by the literal term [see Table 3–16(e)] gives the contact path directly, this is identical to Fig. 3–7.

If the combinations required are the only ones that can occur, as could be the case in the four-bit decoder, the procedure can be simplified. The division process is repeated, but only to separate the required combinations; for instance, in Table 3–16(f), the map is sub-divided as before for $\bar{a}$ and a. The $\bar{a}$ group is again divided by b, c, and d, but the a group needs only to be separated by variable d, to yield the final circuit.

References and bibliography

(1) VEITCH, E. W. A chart method for simplifying truth functions. *Proc. Ass. comput. Mach.*, 1952, May, 127–133.

(2) KARNAUGH, M. The map method for synthesis of combinational logic circuits. *Trans. Am. Inst. elect. Engrs Comm. Electron.*, 1953, **72**, 593–599.

(3) McCLUSKEY, E. Minimization of Boolean functions. *Bell Syst. tech. J.*, 1956, **35**, 1417–1444.

(4) QUINE, W. V. The problem of simplifying truth functions. *Am. math. Mon.*, 1952, **59**, 521–531.

(5) PETRICK, S. R. *A direct determination of the irredundant forms of a Boolean function from the set of prime implicants.* Air Force Cambridge Research Center Report, Bedford, Mass. 1956. AFCRC-TR-56-110.

(6) PYNE, I. B. and McCLUSKEY, E. The reduction of redundancy in solving prime implicant tables. *I.R.E. Trans. electron. comput.* 1962, **EC11**, 473–482.

(7) ROTH, J. P. Minimization over Boolean trees. *I.B.M. J. Res. Dev.*, 1960, **5**, 543–548.

(8) CURTIS, H. A. *A new approach to the design of switching circuits.* Van Nostrand, Princeton, N.J., 1962.

(9) SAMSON, E. W. and MILLS, B. E. *Circuit minimization: algebra and algorithm for new Boolean canonical expansion.* Air Force Cambridge Research Center Report, Bedford, Mass. 1954. AFCRC-TR-54-21.

(10) MARCUS, M. P. Minimization of the partially-developed transfer tree. *I.R.E. Trans. electron. comput.*, 1957, **EC6**, 92–95.

(11) DIETMEYER, D. L. *Logic design of digital systems.* Allyn and Bacon, Boston, 1971. Chap. 3.

Tutorial problems

3-1 It is required to design a combinational switching circuit that will perform the functions of both binary addition and subtraction. The circuit has three inputs, x and y (the digits to be added or subtracted), and a carry (or borrow) b/c; the outputs required are the sum (or difference) s/d, and the next carry (or borrow) b/c. A control waveform M determines the mode of operation, i.e. when $M = 1$ the circuit adds, when $M = 0$ it subtracts.

3-2 Convert the relay circuit shown in Fig. 3–8, simplifying if necessary, into a NAND circuit.

3-3 Minimize the following switching functions using Karnaugh maps.

(a) $T(ABCD) = \sum (0, 1, 5, 7, 8, 9, 12, 14, 15)$
'Don't cares' $D = (3, 11, 13)$

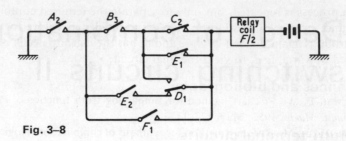

Fig. 3–8

(b) $T(ABCDE) = \sum (1, 2, 4, 5, 9, 10, 11, 15, 16, 18, 19, 21, 22, 25, 27, 31)$
'Don't cares' $D = (0, 8, 13, 17, 24, 26, 29)$

(c) $T(ABCDE) = \prod (5, 6, 8, 11, 12, 19, 21, 22, 23, 24, 25, 28)$
'Don't cares' $D = (2, 10, 13, 14, 20, 26, 29)$

3-4 Minimize the following switching function using the McCluskey tabular technique, and algebraic extraction of the prime implicant set.

$$T(ABCDEF) = \sum (4, 12, 13, 15, 21, 23, 24, 29, 31, 36, 37, 44, 45, 51,$$
$$52, 53, 56, 58, 59, 60, 63)$$
$$\text{'Don't cares'} \quad D = (2, 5, 14, 20, 28, 34, 49, 61)$$

3-5 In a digital servo system an error comparator is required which will compare two three-bit binary numbers, A and B, and give separate outputs for the conditions $A = B$, $A > B$, and $A < B$. Design a combinational logic circuit that will perform this function, and implement the design in terms of NAND logic.

3-6 Design an electronic and relay tree circuit to decode the following combinations:

$$C = (5, 7, 8, 9, 11, 12, 13, 15, 25, 27, 29, 31)$$

3-7 In a numerical machine-tool control system, input from a punched paper-tape reader is stored in a register. The register's capacity is three decimal digits, each represented by five bits in the 1–2–4–8 B.C.D. plus parity bit form. It is required to decode this information so that it may be used in an operator's decimal display unit. The display device uses one digitron tube per decade and requires voltage inputs on separate lines to select the decimal symbols 0–9. Design a suitable combinational switching circuit to perform the decoding for one decimal digit, i.e. one decade only.

4 Design of combinational switching circuits II

4–1 Multi-terminal circuits

So far we have seen how to express logical circuits in the form of a truth-table, with the consequent extraction of canonical Boolean expressions and their reduction to a minimal form. The circuits examined have been of the single-terminal variety, see Fig. 4–1, for which a single output, resulting from a number of inputs, is required. In many practical applications, e.g. encoding or decoding B.C.D. numbers, a multi-terminal output circuit is required.

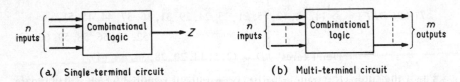

(a) Single-terminal circuit   (b) Multi-terminal circuit

Fig. 4–1 Switching networks

Note that the single-terminal circuit is a special case of the general multi-terminal problem.

In general, the design of multi-terminal circuits follows very closely the procedures already described for single-terminal networks. By deriving from the truth-table separate minimal equations for each output, in terms of the input variables, it is possible to arrive at a perfectly viable solution. However, in so doing, it is very likely that redundancies may occur which could have been avoided if all the output functions were minimized collectively. This may be achieved by comparing Karnaugh maps, or by a modification to the McCluskey tabular method.[1]

4–2 Example of encoder design

The best way of explaining the procedure is by means of an actual example. Suppose we wish to design an encoding circuit to convert pure binary numbers into a binary coded decimal number with the weights 5421. This code is often used to represent numbers in decimal computers; it was used in the Ferranti–I.C.T. Sirius machine, for example. The truth-table is shown in Table 4–1. Note that there are six unused combinations which can be considered as 'don't care' terms for each output function.

Table 4–1 Encoder for 5421 code

a	b	c	d	w	x	y	z
8	4	2	1	5	4	2	1
0	0	0	0	0	0	0	0
0	0	0	1	0	0	0	1
0	0	1	0	0	0	1	0
0	0	1	1	0	0	1	1
0	1	0	0	0	1	0	0
0	1	0	1	1	0	0	0
0	1	1	0	1	0	0	1
0	1	1	1	1	0	1	0
1	0	0	0	1	0	1	1
1	0	0	1	1	1	0	0

a	b	c	d		
1	0	1	0		
1	0	1	1		
1	1	0	0		'Don't
1	1	0	1		care'
1	1	1	0		terms
1	1	1	1		

From the table, the equations for each output condition may be derived, they are:

$$Z_w = \bar{a}b\bar{c}d + \bar{a}bcd + \bar{a}bcd + ab\bar{c}d + ab\bar{c}d$$
$$Z_x = \bar{a}b\bar{c}d + ab\bar{c}d$$
$$Z_y = \bar{a}bcd + \bar{a}bcd + \bar{a}bcd + ab\bar{c}d$$
$$Z_z = \bar{a}b\bar{c}d + \bar{a}bcd + \bar{a}bcd + ab\bar{c}d$$

'Don't care' conditions are

$$Z'_w, Z'_x, Z'_y, Z'_z = ab\bar{c}d + abcd + ab\bar{c}d + ab\bar{c}d + abcd + abcd$$

If we minimize each function separately using Karnaugh maps (see Table 4–2) we get the minimal forms:

$$Z_w = a + bd + bc$$
$$Z_x = ad + b\bar{c}\bar{d}$$
$$Z_y = cd + \bar{b}c + ad$$
$$Z_z = ad + \bar{a}\bar{b}d + bcd$$

These equations when implemented directly in AND/OR, invertor logic require 17 basic elements.

We shall now minimize these equations collectively using a modified form of the McCluskey method. The terms are tabulated, as usual, in groups according to the number of 1's contained in each term, but identifying the

Table 4–2 Karnaugh maps for 5421 encoder

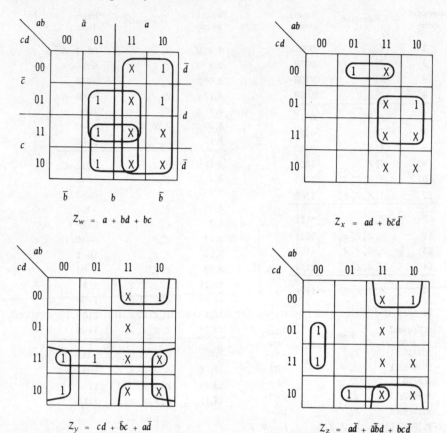

$$Z_w = a + bd + bc$$

$$Z_x = ad + b\bar{c}\bar{d}$$

$$Z_y = cd + \bar{b}c + a\bar{d}$$

$$Z_z = a\bar{d} + \bar{a}bd + bc\bar{d}$$

originating function with each term (Table 4–3). Note that the term $a\bar{b}\bar{c}\bar{d}$ contains one '1' in its binary equivalent 1000, and appears in the output functions $Z_w Z_y Z_z$; thus, this term is placed in group 1 and identified accordingly.

The comparison routine must include the function tags, as well as the eliminated variables (represented by a dash), in its search for changes in one variable only. Referring to Table 4–3, the term Z_z 0001 in group 1 is compared with the first term in group 2, $Z_y Z_z$ 0011, and is found to contain the common function Z_z and to differ in one variable only; the term Z_z 00–1 is formed and used to start a new group in the next listing. The variable c has been eliminated in the process, the common function Z_z is indicated by a tick in the first list. This procedure is repeated until no more terms combine; prime implicant (P.I.) terms are those which contain an unticked function and are identified by a capital letter. It will be seen from Table 4–3

Table 4–3 McCluskey tables for 5421 encoder

Decimal term	Function	Binary term
1	$Z_z^{\vee}$	0001
2	$Z_y^{\vee}$	0010
4	$Z_x^{\vee}$	0100
8	$Z_w^{\vee} Z_y^{\vee} Z_z^{\vee}$	1000
3	$Z_y^{\vee} Z_z^{\vee}$	0011
5	$Z_w^{\vee}$	0101
6	$Z_w^{\vee} Z_z^{\vee}$	0110
9	$Z_w^{\vee} Z_x^{\vee}$	1001
10	$Z_w^{\vee} Z_x^{\vee} Z_y^{\vee} Z_z^{\vee}$	1010
12	$Z_w^{\vee} Z_x^{\vee} Z_y^{\vee} Z_z^{\vee}$	1100
7	$Z_w^{\vee} Z_y^{\vee}$	0111
11	$Z_w^{\vee} Z_x^{\vee} Z_y^{\vee} Z_z^{\vee}$	1011
13	$Z_w^{\vee} Z_x^{\vee} Z_y^{\vee} Z_z^{\vee}$	1101
14	$Z_w^{\vee} Z_x^{\vee} Z_y^{\vee} Z_z^{\vee}$	1110
15	$Z_w^{\vee} Z_x^{\vee} Z_y^{\vee} Z_z^{\vee}$	1111

List 1

Decimal term	Function	Binary term
2,3/10,11	Z_y	−01− E
2,10/3,11	Z_y	−01−
8,9/10,11	$Z_w^{\vee}$	10−−
8,9/12,13	$Z_w^{\vee}$	1−0−
8,10/9,11	$Z_w^{\vee}$	10−−
8,10/12,14	$Z_w^{\vee} Z_y Z_z$	1−−0 F
8,12/9,13	$Z_w^{\vee}$	1−0−
8,12/10,14	$Z_w^{\vee} Z_y Z_z$	1−−0
3,11/7,15	Z_y	−−11 G
3,7/11,15	Z_y	−−11
5,7/13,15	Z_w	−1−1 H
5,13/7,15	Z_w	−1−1
6,7/14,15	Z_w	−11− I
6,14/7,15	Z_w	−11−
9,11/13,15	$Z_w^{\vee} Z_x$	1−−1 J
9,13/11,15	$Z_w^{\vee} Z_x$	1−−1
10,11/14,15	$Z_w^{\vee} Z_x Z_y Z_z$	1−1− K
10,14/11,15	$Z_w^{\vee} Z_x Z_y Z_z$	1−1−
12,13/14,15	$Z_w^{\vee} Z_x Z_y Z_z$	11−− L
11,14/13,15	$Z_w^{\vee} Z_x Z_y Z_z$	11−−

List 3

Decimal term	Function	Binary term
1,3	Z_z	00−1 A
2,3	Z_y	001−
2,10	Z_y	−010
4,12	Z_x	−100 B
8,9	Z_w	100−
8,10	$Z_w^{\vee} Z_y^{\vee} Z_z^{\vee}$	10−0
8,12	$Z_w^{\vee} Z_y^{\vee} Z_z^{\vee}$	1−00
3,11	$Z_y^{\vee} Z_z$	−011 C
3,7	Z_y	0−11
5,7	Z_w	01−1
5,13	Z_w	−101
6,7	Z_w	011−
6,14	$Z_w^{\vee} Z_z$	−110 D
9,11	$Z_w^{\vee} Z_x^{\vee}$	10−1
9,13	$Z_w^{\vee} Z_x^{\vee}$	1−01
10,11	$Z_w^{\vee} Z_x^{\vee} Z_y^{\vee} Z_z^{\vee}$	101−
10,14	$Z_w^{\vee} Z_x^{\vee} Z_y^{\vee} Z_z^{\vee}$	1−10
12,13	$Z_w^{\vee} Z_x^{\vee} Z_y^{\vee} Z_z^{\vee}$	110−
12,14	$Z_w^{\vee} Z_x^{\vee} Z_y^{\vee} Z_z^{\vee}$	11−0
7,15	$Z_w^{\vee} Z_y^{\vee}$	−111
11,15	$Z_w^{\vee} Z_x^{\vee} Z_y^{\vee} Z_z^{\vee}$	1−11
13,15	$Z_w^{\vee} Z_x^{\vee} Z_y^{\vee} Z_z^{\vee}$	11−1
14,15	$Z_w^{\vee} Z_x^{\vee} Z_y^{\vee} Z_z^{\vee}$	111−

List 2

Decimal term	Function	Binary term
8,9,10,11/12,13,14,15	Z_w	1−−− M
8,9,10,11/12,14,13,15	Z_w	1−−−
8,9,12,13/10,14,11,15	Z_w	1−−−
8,9,12,13/10,11,14,15	Z_w	1−−−
8,10,9,11/12,13,14,15	Z_w	1−−−
8,10,9,11/12,14,13,15	Z_w	1−−−
8,10,12,14/9,11,13,15	Z_w	1−−−
8,10,12,14/9,13,11,15	Z_w	1−−−
8,12,9,13/10,11,14,15	Z_w	1−−−
8,12,9,13/10,14,11,15	Z_w	1−−−
8,12,10,14/9,11,13,15	Z_w	1−−−
8,12,10,14/9,13,11,15	Z_w	1−−−

List 4

that there are 14 prime implicants. For example, the expression $Z_w Z_y Z_z$ 1– –0 means that $a\bar{d}$ is a prime implicant of Z_w, Z_y, and Z_z.

The next step in the process is to select the minimal subset. This is done using a P.I. chart as usual, but the four functions $Z_w Z_x Z_y Z_z$ are plotted side by side (Table 4–4). For each prime implicant row, a cross is placed in those columns that contain a term of the original switching function; 'don't care' conditions are ignored. To choose an optimum set, the table is first examined for any column with one entry, marked by a cross, which is an essential P.I. and must be included in the final result for the particular function concerned.

From Table 4–4 it will be seen that prime implicants A, B, D, E, F, G, H, and J are all essential and the rows are marked appropriately. The terms covered by these P.I.'s are then ticked off on the chart, when it then becomes obvious that the functions are completely specified by the essential prime implicants. The minimal equations for the output functions Z_w, Z_x, Z_y and Z_z are given by:

$$Z_w = D + F + H + J \quad = bcd + a\bar{d} + bd + ad$$
$$Z_x = B + J \quad = b\bar{c}\bar{d} + ad$$
$$Z_y = E + F + G \quad = \bar{b}c + a\bar{d} + cd$$
$$Z_z = A + D + F \quad = \bar{a}bd + bc\bar{d} + a\bar{d}$$

Note that a more minimal expression for Z_w (found earlier) is

$$Z_w = a + bd + bc$$

Table 4–4 Prime implicant chart

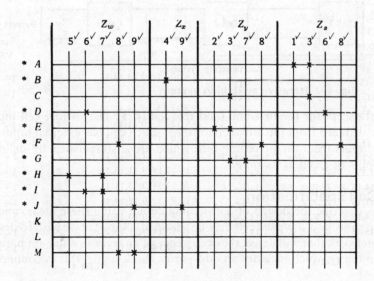

but since the terms $bc\bar{d}$, $a\bar{d}$, and ad are necessary for the other functions it is generally better to represent the function as in Eqn. (1) above.

If the equations above are implemented directly in AND/OR invertor logic only 16 units are required, which gives a saving of one unit compared with the original design. However, the final choice of logic circuit is influenced by many factors; for example, the type of logic system used, the fan-in factor, the possibility of factoring the equations and the availability of logic signals with the system. These points will be considered in more detail in later chapters.

4–3 Iterative circuits

Quite often in combinational logic design, the technique of expressing oral statements for a logic circuit in the form of a truth-table is inadequate. For a simple network, a terminal description will often suffice, but for more complex circuits, and in particular when relay logic is to be employed, the truth-table method can lead to a laborious and inelegant solution. Suppose, for example, a logic system could be decomposed into a number of identical sub-systems, then if we could produce a design for the sub-system, or *cell*, the complete system could be synthesized by cascading these cells in series. The problem has now been reduced to that of specifying and designing the cell, rather than the complete system. In Fig. 4–2 the outputs of one cell form the inputs to the next one in the chain and so on, thus each cell is

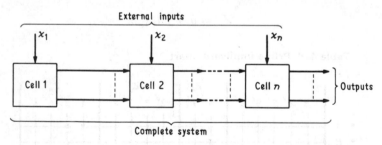

Fig. 4–2 Iterative switching system

identical except for the first one (and frequently the last) whose cell inputs must be deduced from the initial conditions. Each cell has external inputs as well as inputs from the preceding cell, which are distinguished by defining the outputs of a cell as its *state*.

4–4 Cell specification

We now describe the design of a switching circuit using these ideas, and in so doing show how a typical cell may be specified. Suppose we wish to design a logic network that will detect the occurrence of an error in a five-bit parallel binary number which includes an odd-parity check digit; this is commonly

Table 4-5 Truth-table for parity check circuit

x_1	x_2	x_3	x_4	x_5	T
0	0	0	0	0	1
0	0	0	0	1	0
0	0	0	1	0	0
0	0	0	1	1	1
0	0	1	0	0	0
0	0	1	0	1	1
0	0	1	1	0	1
0	0	1	1	1	0
0	1	0	0	0	0
0	1	0	0	1	1
0	1	0	1	0	1
0	1	0	1	1	0
0	1	1	0	0	1
0	1	1	0	1	0
0	1	1	1	0	0
0	1	1	1	1	1
1	0	0	0	0	0
1	0	0	0	1	1
1	0	0	1	0	1
1	0	0	1	1	0
1	0	1	0	0	1
1	0	1	0	1	0
1	0	1	1	0	0
1	0	1	1	1	1
1	1	0	0	0	1
1	1	0	0	1	0
1	1	0	1	0	0
1	1	0	1	1	1
1	1	1	0	0	0
1	1	1	0	1	1
1	1	1	1	0	1
1	1	1	1	1	0

called a parity check circuit. The truth-table is shown in Table 4-5 and it is clear on drawing the Karnaugh maps that no simplification can be effected using standard techniques. A straightforward approach would mean implementing the equations:

$$T = \bar{x}_1\bar{x}_2\bar{x}_3\bar{x}_4\bar{x}_5 + \bar{x}_1\bar{x}_2\bar{x}_3x_4x_5 + \bar{x}_1\bar{x}_2x_3\bar{x}_4x_5 + \bar{x}_1\bar{x}_2x_3x_4\bar{x}_5$$
$$+ \bar{x}_1x_2\bar{x}_3\bar{x}_4x_5 + \bar{x}_1x_2\bar{x}_3x_4\bar{x}_5 + \bar{x}_1x_2x_3\bar{x}_4\bar{x}_5 + \bar{x}_1x_2x_3x_4x_5$$
$$+ x_1\bar{x}_2\bar{x}_3\bar{x}_4x_5 + x_1\bar{x}_2\bar{x}_3x_4\bar{x}_5 + x_1\bar{x}_2x_3\bar{x}_4\bar{x}_5 + x_1\bar{x}_2x_3x_4x_5$$
$$+ x_1x_2\bar{x}_3\bar{x}_4\bar{x}_5 + x_1x_2\bar{x}_3x_4x_5 + x_1x_2x_3\bar{x}_4x_5 + x_1x_2x_3x_4\bar{x}_5$$

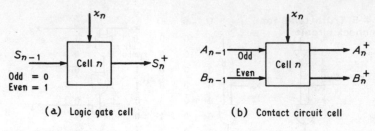

(a) Logic gate cell   (b) Contact circuit cell

Fig. 4–3 Typical cells for parity check circuit

How, then, do we decompose this circuit into an iterative cell configuration? The first step is to decide on the number of state variables and external inputs required. In this case we shall choose one single-bit external input per cell; we could equally well have chosen two bits or even more, there is no absolute rule, except the requirement to keep the number as small as possible compared with the total number of system inputs. The choice of one bit per cell simplifies the design of the cell and produces optimum results. Since we have to distinguish between an odd or even number of 1's in the binary word, a single-bit state variable S is sufficient, and we shall call its two values odd and even; the cell may now be represented as in Fig. 4–3. We now have to express the next output state S_n^+ as a function of S_{n-1} and x_n, and this may be done using a *state transfer table* [Table 4–6(a)] where the entries are the resulting (next) output states. From the table it may be seen that if the input state variable indicates that so far the number of 1's is odd ($\bar{S}$) and if the external input is 0, then the condition is unchanged and the output state of the cell must still indicate an odd number of 1's, i.e. $\bar{S}^+$. Thus we may write

$$S_n^+ = x_n\bar{S}_{n-1} + \bar{x}_n S_{n-1}$$

This equation is the well known exclusive OR logic function, or half-adder, which is available as a basic element in most logic systems. Thus the parity check circuit can be implemented by cascading the cell circuit, i.e. exclusive OR as shown in Fig. 4–4(b). Because the first cell has no state variable input, the external input alone determines the output state, therefore this may be used as the input to the second cell, that is, external inputs $x_1 x_2$ go to the

Table 4–6 State transfer tables for parity check circuit

Input state variable S	External input x_n		Input state variable	External input x_n	
	0	1		0	1
$\bar{S}_{n-1}(0)$	$\bar{S}_n^+(0)$	$S_n^+(1)$	A_{n-1}	A_{n+}	B_{n+}
$S_{n-1}(1)$	$S_n^+(1)$	$\bar{S}_n^+(0)$	B_{n-1}	B_{n+}	A_{n+}

(a) Logic gate implementation   (b) Contact circuit implementation

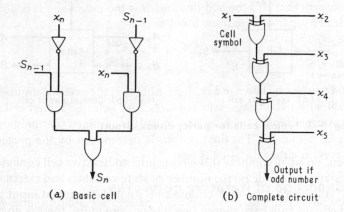

Fig. 4–4 Parity check circuit using logic gates

second cell. This circuit could also have been arrived at by algebraic manipulation of the basic switching equation, but in many cases of this type the algebra involved is tedious.

4–5 Relay implementation
If the design is to be executed in terms of relay logic, the approach must be slightly modified. Again, the choice of state and external inputs is the preliminary step but the representation of these variables, particularly the output states, must be such as to allow a path-closing contact circuit which gives separate voltage outputs. This means in practice that the odd and even states must be on two separate lines, both connected to a voltage source. This can be represented in the state transfer table [Table 4–6(b)] in the same way

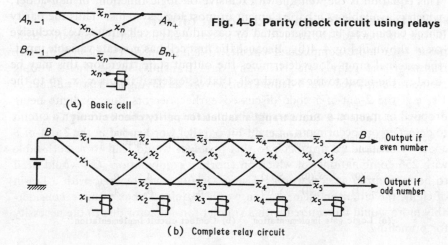

Fig. 4–5 Parity check circuit using relays

as above except that A is the odd line and B is the even line. It is now necessary to derive separate equations for A and B:

$$A_n^+ = \bar{x}_n A_{n-1} + x_n B_{n-1}$$
$$B_n^+ = x_n A_{n-1} + \bar{x}_n B_{n-1}$$

The contact circuit is shown in Fig. 4–5; note that the external inputs energize a relay coil with two change-over contacts. As before, the first cell requires only the external input switching line B, as it is assumed that previous digits are even, i.e. all zeros. The final output is determined by the presence of a voltage level on either the A or B line.

4–6 Advantage of iterative networks

The technique is particularly suitable for pattern recognition, and encoding and decoding circuits with a large number of parallel inputs. Furthermore, circuit specification is simplified and large-variable problems reduced to a more tractable size. Initially, the method was evolved for relay circuitry,[2] but it can be gainfully employed with transistor logic. It should be pointed out though that the speed of the circuit is reduced because of the time required for the signals to propagate along the network; the number of interconnections is also considerably increased. In general, iterative design does not necessarily result in a more minimal circuit. It does however lead to a more flexible circuit, in that the logic system may be extended to handle more external variables by the simple addition of more cells. The parity check circuit, for example, was designed for a five-bit word, but should the requirement change and a 15-bit message be desired, then the circuit could easily be modified by the addition of the appropriate number of exclusive OR circuits. With a conventionally designed system a modification could necessitate a major redesign exercise.

4–7 Iterative design for decoder circuit

Before we conclude the discussion of iterative circuits let us apply the technique to a more complicated circuit, and implement the design in both transistor and relay logic. In many data transmission systems a coding method is employed which defines a codeword as having a certain number of 1's, e.g. the 2-out-of-5 code discussed earlier; errors due to digits being dropped or inserted would corrupt this pattern. We will now design a circuit to detect errors occuring in an eight-bit parallel word coded in the 3-out-of-8 code. The standard approach to this problem would lead to a truth-table with 256 combinations, of which 56 (normal combination $_8C_3$) would need to be recognized as codewords. Using AND/OR invertor logic with a fan-in of eight, the circuit implementation would require 72 basic units; considerably more would be required with a smaller fan-in factor due to the necessity for branching.

In the iterative design, we shall again choose a one-bit external variable, but in this case we have a larger number of state variables. It is necessary to know whether the preceding digits sum to zero, one, two, three, or greater than three digits. The state variable indicating three digits is used to signify a correct codeword. The state transfer table is shown in Table 4–7(b). Since we have five states A, B, C, D, E, we will need three bits (using transistor logic) to represent them, these are x_1, x_2, and x_3; the external input is designated y_n. Note that in assigning the state variables, we have chosen 100 to indicate the correct codeword, i.e. three digits only, this allows us to economize in the final cell, as only x_1 need be examined.

Table 4–7
State transfer tables
for 3-out-of-8 circuit

(a) General table, used for contact circuit.

Input state variables	External input y_n 0	1
A Sum zero	A_+	B_+
B Sum one	B_+	C_+
C Sum two	C_+	E_+
D Sum > three	D_+	D_+
E Sum three	E_+	D_+

(b) Logic gate table

Input state variables			External input y_n	
x_1	x_2	x_3	0	1
A	0	0	0	0 0 0	0 0 1
B	0	0	1	0 0 1	0 1 0
C	0	1	0	0 1 0	1 0 0
D	0	1	1	0 1 1	0 1 1
E	1	0	0	1 0 0	0 1 1
'Don't	1	0	1		
care'	1	1	0		
terms	1	1	1		

The output state equations are obtained by inspecting the transfer table for the conditions that cause the output variables to go to 1. For example x_{1+}, the next output state of x_1, goes to 1 when input states x_1, x_2, x_3 are equal to 010, and the external input goes to 1, i.e. $\bar{x}_1 x_2 \bar{x}_3 y_n$. Similarly, x_{1+} goes to 1 when $x_1 \bar{x}_2 \bar{x}_3 \bar{y}_n$ occurs. Thus we may write

$$x_{1+} = x_1 \bar{x}_2 \bar{x}_3 \bar{y}_n + \bar{x}_1 x_2 \bar{x}_3 y_n$$
$$x_{2+} = \bar{x}_1 \bar{x}_2 x_3 y_n + \bar{x}_1 x_2 \bar{x}_3 \bar{y}_n + x_1 \bar{x}_2 \bar{x}_3 y_n + \bar{x}_1 x_2 x_3 \bar{y}_n + \bar{x}_1 x_2 x_3 y_n$$
$$x_{3+} = \bar{x}_1 \bar{x}_2 \bar{x}_3 y_n + \bar{x}_1 \bar{x}_2 x_3 \bar{y}_n + x_1 \bar{x}_2 \bar{x}_3 y_n + \bar{x}_1 x_2 x_3 y_n + \bar{x}_1 x_2 x_3 \bar{y}_n$$

These equations may be minimized using standard techniques, in this case Karnaugh maps (Table 4–8). It should be pointed out that the way in which the assignment of state variables is made determines to what extent the

**Table 4–8 Karnaugh maps for
3-out-of-8 iterative circuit**

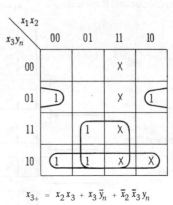

$$x_{1+} = x_1 \bar{y}_n + x_2 \bar{x}_3 y_n$$

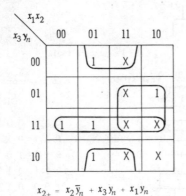

$$x_{2+} = x_2 \bar{y}_n + x_3 y_n + x_1 y_n$$

$$x_{3+} = x_2 x_3 + x_3 \bar{y}_n + \bar{x}_2 \bar{x}_3 y_n$$

equations can be minimized. In the example above, the assignment has been a straightforward allocation of ascending pure binary, but it is conceivable that a different assignment could give a more minimal final set of equations. This problem is identical to that of assigning internal states in a sequential logic circuit, and will be discussed in detail in later chapters on sequential logic. From the Karnaugh maps the minimal expressions are

$$x_{1+} = x_1 \bar{y}_n + x_2 \bar{x}_3 y_n$$

$$x_{2+} = x_2 \bar{y}_n + x_3 y_n + x_1 y_n$$

$$x_{3+} = x_2 x_3 + x_3 \bar{y}_n + \bar{x}_2 \bar{x}_3 y_n$$

These equations are shown implemented in AND/OR invertor logic in Fig. 4–6. The first cell may be simplified, since the preceding sum of digits must be zero and the output states depend only on the value of y_1. The total number of units required is 97, but note that the maximum fan-in required is four,

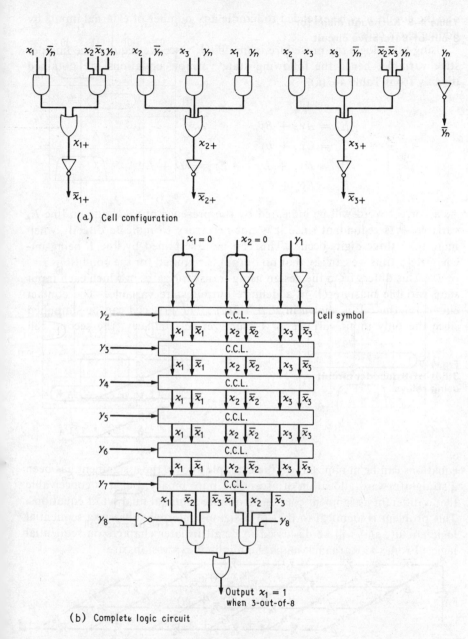

(a) Cell configuration

(b) Complete logic circuit

Fig. 4–6 3-out-of-8 decoder circuit using logic gates

and the circuit may be extended to handle any number of external inputs by adding extra cells.

Using relay logic the procedure is modified, since we require one line per state variable, hence the following state variable equations are obtained directly from Table 4–7(a).

$$A_+ = A\bar{y}_n$$
$$B_+ = Ay_n + B\bar{y}_n$$
$$C_+ = C\bar{y}_n + By_n$$
$$D_+ = Dy_n + D\bar{y}_n + Ey_n = D + Ey_n$$
$$E_+ = E\bar{y}_n + Cy$$

As a correct word will be indicated by the presence of a voltage on line E, variable D is redundant since it is not necessary to indicate directly when more than three digits occur. This can be ascertained by line E being un-energized; thus we can say that no output is required for the conditions Ey_n or D. This differs from the design using transistor gates in which each input state variable must result in a definite output state variable. The contact circuit for the cell is shown in Fig. 4–7(a). The first cell can be simplified since the only input variable is A (sum zero); similarly, the second cell

Fig. 4–7
3-out-of-8 decoder circuit
using relays

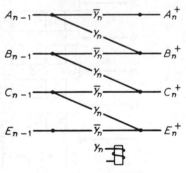

(a) Typical contact cell

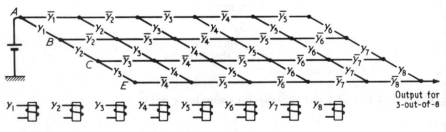

(b) Complete contact circuit

requires only A and B (sum one), and the third requires only A, B, and C (sum two). Furthermore, the last cells in the system can also be simplified, since it is only necessary to retain the final output line E. Thus the last three cells can be contracted as shown in the complete contact circuit shown in Fig. 4–7(b).

4–8 Symmetric functions

From the last part of the preceding design example it is clear that the iterative method is ideal for relay circuit design. Moreover, the final network is in the form of a bridge circuit rather than the series-parallel arrangement obtained by direct truth-table methods. Bridge networks and non-planar circuits (circuits that cannot be drawn without crossing lines) require far less relay contacts and hence are more economical and reliable in use. A further advantage is that it is easy to pick out change-over contacts, in fact the design above can be constructed using 18 change-over contacts and two normally closed contacts. However, the design of such circuits can lead to difficulties in cell specification and to problems in determining the conditions that govern the simplification of the initial and final cells. For certain types of circuit (those which can be represented by a *symmetric logic function*[3]) the design can be greatly simplified.

A symmetric function is a logic function which has the property of remaining unaltered when any two at least of its variables (called the variables of symmetry) are interchanged. For example, the function

$$T = \bar{x}\bar{y}z + \bar{x}y\bar{z} + x\bar{y}\bar{z}$$

is symmetric, since if the variables x and y are interchanged (i.e. replace all x's with y's and all $\bar{x}$'s with $\bar{y}$'s, and vice versa) we obtain

$$T = \bar{y}\bar{x}z + \bar{y}x\bar{z} + y\bar{x}\bar{z}$$

which is identical with the original function. Note that all terms in the function are prime implicants and all three are required in the minimum sum; this is normally the case with symmetric functions. It is also worth noting that the exclusive OR function is, of course, symmetric. The variables of symmetry can also take the complemented form, e.g.

$$T = \bar{x}\bar{y}z + x\bar{y}\bar{z} + xyz$$

is symmetric with the variables x and $\bar{y}$. In this case, we replace x by $\bar{y}$, $\bar{x}$ by y, y by $\bar{x}$, and $\bar{y}$ by x, obtaining the identical function

$$T = yxz + \bar{y}x\bar{z} + \bar{y}\bar{x}z$$

Symmetric functions with uncomplemented variables of symmetry are called *n-out-of-m functions*; that is, the logic function equals 1 when precisely

n variables out of the total m are equal to 1. For example, the decoder circuit designed in Section 4–7 could be described as a symmetric 3-out-of-8 function. The equation

$$T = \bar{x}\bar{y}z + \bar{x}y\bar{z} + x\bar{y}\bar{z}$$

represents a 1-out-of-3 function and can be symbolized as $S_1^3(xyz)$; the decoder circuit would be represented as $S_3^8(y_1y_2y_3y_4y_5y_6y_7y_8)$. The symbology can be extended to functions which equal 1 when, say, two or three of the variables equal 1, i.e. $S_{23}^4(ABCD)$. The parity checking circuit discussed earlier could be described as a $S_{024}^5(ABCD\acute{E})$ function. Furthermore, it can be shown that symmetric functions can be manipulated algebraically, e.g. cascaded circuits, equivalent to logical AND, would be combined:

$$[S_{23}^5(ABCD)][S_{12}^5(ABCD] = S_2^5(ABCD)$$

and in parallel (logical OR):

$$[S_{23}^5(ABCD)] + [S_{12}^5(ABCD)] = S_{123}^5(ABCD)$$

One of the difficulties of using symmetric functions is how to recognize them. This is easy if we start with an n-out-of-m circuit description, but otherwise we need to resort to an identification procedure due to Caldwell.[4]

4–9 Design of symmetric circuits

How then can the recognition and use of symmetric functions assist us in the design of switching circuits? Symmetric functions can be represented by a basic contact network which has one input and which branches out to give $m + 1$ outputs, where m is the number of variables (Fig. 4–8). Tracing through the network it will be seen that all possibilities are covered for the variables $(ABCD)$ in this topological representation; the pattern can of course be enlarged to cover any number of variables. The design of the 3-out-of-8 circuit now becomes very simple. We merely draw the appropriate

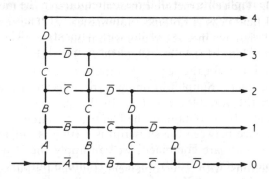

Fig. 4–8 Basic symmetric contact circuit

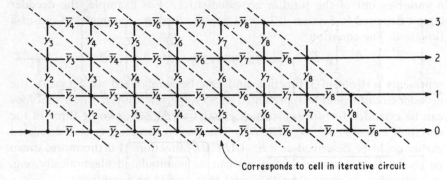

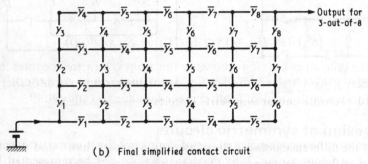

Fig. 4–9 Symmetric contact circuit for 3-out-of-8 decoder

symmetric contact circuit for eight variables, but only include the contacts necessary to give an output when $n = 3$, ignoring all other outputs. If we compare the resultant circuit (Fig. 4–9) with that obtained earlier, we see that they are identical. The cell structure can easily be seen, and the contraction of the initial and final cells is obtained automatically. The same approach may be used to design symmetric circuits with multiple outputs, i.e. circuits represented by functions of the type $S_{024}^5(ABCDE)$. In this case, the circuit for m variables is drawn for the required outputs n_1, n_2, etc., which are then simply joined together. Simplification may be affected by applying the following rules:[5]

(a) If the difference between the subscript is 1 (that is, adjacent outputs) when the outputs are combined, we can apply the $A + \bar{A} = 1$ law. For example, in Fig. 4–10(a) when we combine outputs 1 and 2 they are connected to point X by the contacts $D + \bar{D} = 1$, which can be eliminated.

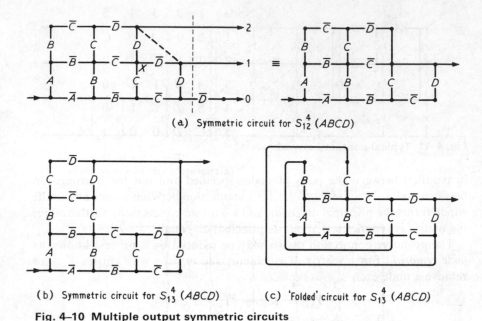

(a) Symmetric circuit for S_{12}^4 $(ABCD)$

(b) Symmetric circuit for S_{13}^4 $(ABCD)$ (c) 'Folded' circuit for S_{13}^4 $(ABCD)$

Fig. 4–10 Multiple output symmetric circuits

(b) If the difference between the subscripts is greater than 1 and they form an arithmetic progression, the network may be 'folded over'—the next term in the progression must be greater than the number of variables.

Suppose we were to implement $S_{13}^4(ABCD)$, we first draw a circuit for 1-out-of-4 (the lowest subscript), then instead of drawing 3-out-of-4 in the normal way to complete the circuit [Fig. 4–10(b)], we 'fold' the circuit over and utilize the common set of contacts in the 1-out-of-4 circuit to get the circuit shown in Fig. 4–10(c).

4–10 Realization of non-series-parallel circuits

The design of combinational circuits using iterative or symmetric techniques leads directly to non-series-parallel circuits. Is it possible, however, to devise bridge networks, starting from the transmission function, for circuits derived from a truth-table approach? In fact several methods have been evolved[6][7] but the technique we shall discuss here is one that employs Boolean matrices due to Hohn and Schissler.[8]

Two-terminal contact circuits can be precisely described using a Boolean matrix. Consider the circuit shown in Fig. 4–11, the *primitive connection* matrix alongside it specifies the identity and location of each contact.

Note that the entries are the actual single contacts (in some cases contacts

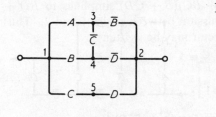

$$\begin{array}{cccccc} \text{Node} & 1 & 2 & 3 & 4 & 5 \\ 1 & \begin{bmatrix} 1 \\ 0 \\ A \\ B \\ C \end{bmatrix} & \begin{matrix} 0 \\ 1 \\ \bar{B} \\ \bar{D} \\ D \end{matrix} & \begin{matrix} A \\ \bar{B} \\ 1 \\ \bar{C} \\ 0 \end{matrix} & \begin{matrix} B \\ \bar{D} \\ \bar{C} \\ 1 \\ 0 \end{matrix} & \begin{matrix} C \\ D \\ 0 \\ 0 \\ 1 \end{bmatrix} \end{array}$$

Fig. 4–11 Typical contact network

in parallel) between the pairs of nodes specified and not the transmission between nodes. Thus we enter a 1 for a connection between a node and itself, which forms the principal diagonal, and a 0 for no connection; furthermore, the matrix is symmetrical about its principal diagonal.

The primitive connection matrix may be reduced by a process known as *node removal*. For a matrix of n columns and m rows with entries Y_{nm}, to remove a node each Y_{nm} is replaced by

$$Y_{nm} = Y_{nm} + (Y_{nx} \cdot Y_{xm})$$

where x is the removed node. To remove node 4 in the matrix above, and by so doing forming a new matrix with four columns and rows, we form the new entries:

$$Y_{15} = Y_{15} + (Y_{14} \cdot Y_{45}) = C + B \cdot 0 = C$$
$$Y_{13} = Y_{13} + (Y_{14} \cdot Y_{43}) = A + B\bar{C}$$
$$Y_{12} = Y_{12} + (Y_{14} \cdot Y_{42}) = 0 + B\bar{D} = B\bar{D}$$
$$Y_{11} = Y_{11} + (Y_{14} \cdot Y_{41}) = 1 + B \cdot B = 1$$

When all the entries have been modified in this fashion, the reduced matrix is

$$\begin{array}{ccccc} & 1 & 2 & 3 & 5 \\ 1 & \begin{bmatrix} 1 & B\bar{D} & A + B\bar{C} & C \\ B\bar{D} & 1 & \bar{B} + \bar{C}\bar{D} & D \\ A + B\bar{C} & \bar{B} + \bar{C}\bar{D} & 1 & 0 \\ C & D & 0 & 1 \end{bmatrix} \\ 2 \\ 3 \\ 5 \end{array}$$

If this process is repeated by removing node 3, and then node 5, we finally arrive at the matrix:

$$\begin{bmatrix} 1 & B\bar{D} + (A + B\bar{C})(\bar{B} + \bar{C}\bar{D}) + CD \\ B\bar{D} + (A + B\bar{C})(\bar{B} + \bar{C}\bar{D}) + CD & 1 \end{bmatrix}$$

Now the expression $B\bar{D} + CD + (A + B\bar{C})(\bar{B} + \bar{C}\bar{D})$ simplifies to $B\bar{D} + CD + A\bar{B} + A\bar{C}\bar{D}$ which is the transmission between nodes 1 and 2. Thus the output matrix of a two-terminal circuit may be written:

$$\begin{bmatrix} 1 & T \\ T & 1 \end{bmatrix}$$

where T is the transmission function of the entire network.

Thus if the transmission function for a required circuit is known, or can be deduced from the truth-table, it can be represented in matrix form and expanded into a primitive connection matrix; in this way a non-series-parallel circuit may be synthesized. Unfortunately, the expansion of an output matrix to a primitive connection matrix does not yield a unique solution, since the result depends on the expansion method and the order employed; furthermore, the resulting circuit is not necessarily minimal. For some circuits it is not possible, or even desirable, to expand to a full primitive matrix. When this happens a *connection matrix* results with a reduced number of nodes, and contacts consequently appear in series.

4–11 Synthesis of bridge networks

To illustrate the arguments above we will synthesize a non-series-parallel circuit starting with the transmission function

$$T = A\bar{C}\bar{D} + ACD + \bar{A}C\bar{D}$$

Before we represent the function in matrix form it is preferable, and sometimes essential, to factorize the equation. This may be done using a mapping technique due to Caldwell.[9] The function is plotted on two Karnaugh maps side by side (Table 4–9) then 1's are inserted in both maps with the object of producing maximal groupings, but each time a 1 is inserted, a 0 must be placed in the corresponding position of the other map. The product of the terms on each map is the factorized function required, in this case

$$T = (\bar{A} + \bar{C}\bar{D} + CD)(A + C\bar{D})$$

This may be expressed in the matrix form

$$\begin{bmatrix} 1 & 0 & \bar{A} + \bar{C}\bar{D} + CD \\ 0 & 1 & A + C\bar{D} \\ \bar{A} + \bar{C}\bar{D} + CD & A + C\bar{D} & 1 \end{bmatrix}$$

Table 4–9
Use of Karnaugh maps in factorization

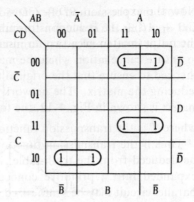

(a) Standard function

$$T = A\bar{C}\bar{D} + ACD + \bar{A}C\bar{D}$$

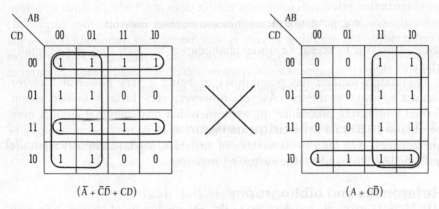

$(\bar{A} + \bar{C}\bar{D} + CD)$ $\qquad$ $(A + C\bar{D})$

(b) Factorized expression

$$T = (\bar{A} + \bar{C}\bar{D} + CD)(A + C\bar{D})$$

Observing that $\bar{D}$ is common to both $\bar{A} + CD + \bar{C}\bar{D}$ and $A + C\bar{D}$ we can expand using this factor:

$$\begin{bmatrix} 1 & 0 & \bar{A} + CD & \bar{C} \\ 0 & 1 & A & C \\ \bar{A} + CD & A & 1 & \bar{D} \\ \bar{C} & C & \bar{D} & 1 \end{bmatrix}$$

Finally, we arrive at the primitive connection matrix:

$$\begin{array}{c c} & \begin{array}{c c c c c} 1 & 2 & 3 & 4 & 5 \end{array} \\ \begin{array}{c} 1 \\ 2 \\ 3 \\ 4 \\ 5 \end{array} & \begin{bmatrix} 1 & 0 & \bar{A} & \bar{C} & C \\ 0 & 1 & A & C & 0 \\ \bar{A} & A & 1 & \bar{D} & D \\ \bar{C} & C & \bar{D} & 1 & 0 \\ C & 0 & D & 0 & 1 \end{bmatrix} \end{array}$$

Note that the method of expansion consists of picking out common factors and applying the reduction formula in reverse. In order to retain the zero entries, it is often necessary to insert other zeros in the appropriate position to ensure cancellation when the matrix is reduced. The final result must be checked to ensure that the original transmission function can be obtained by reducing the matrix. The network obtained by implementing the primitive matrix is shown in Fig. 4–12, the total number of contacts required has been

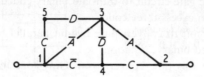

Fig. 4–12 Matrix synthesized contact network

reduced by two to seven, i.e. three change-over contacts and one normally open.

The matrix method has possibilities of being a very powerful tool for contact network synthesis. As yet, however, very little is known about formal minimizing procedures or ways in which near minimal circuits may be obtained. Since a considerable amount of work is involved in manipulating matrices, even for a small number of variables, digital computer methods must be used to handle large switching matrices.

References and bibliography

(1) McNAUGHTON, R. and MITCHELL, B. The minimality of rectifier nets with multiple-outputs incompletely specified. *J. Franklin Inst.*, 1957, **264**, 457–480.

(2) CALDWELL, S. H. *Switching circuits and logical design*. Wiley, New York, 1958, p. 414.

(3) SHANNON, C. E. A symbolic analysis of relay and switching circuits. *Trans. Am. Inst. elect. Engrs.*, 1938, **57**, 713–723.

(4) CALDWELL, S. H. Recognition and description of symmetric switching functions. *Trans. Am. Inst. elect. Engrs. Comm. Electron.*, 1954, **73**, 142–146.

(5) CALDWELL, S. H. *Switching circuits and logical design*. Wiley, New York, 1958, p. 236.

(6) SHANNON, C. E. The synthesis of two-terminal switching circuits. *Bell Syst. tech. J.*, 1949, **28**, 59–98.

(7) McCLUSKEY, E. J. *Algebraic minimization and the design of two-terminal contact networks*. Ph.D. Thesis, Dept. of Elect. Engng, M.I.T., June 1956.

(8) HOHN, F. E. and SCHISSLER, L. R. Boolean matrices and the design of combinational relay switching circuits. *Bell Syst. tech. J.*, 1955, **34**, 177–202.

(9) CALDWELL, S. H. *Switching circuits and logical design*. Wiley, New York, 1958, p. 352.

(10) MARCUS, M. *Switching circuits for engineers*. 2nd edn. Prentice-Hall, Englewood Cliffs, N.J., 1967.

(11) WOOD, P. E. *Switching theory*. McGraw-Hill, New York, 1968.

(12) KOHAVI, Z. *Switching and finite automata theory*. McGraw-Hill, New York, 1970. Chaps 6 and 9.

Tutorial problems

4-1 Design a minimal logic gate circuit to translate binary-coded decimal numbers in the 8 4 2 1 code into excess-three code.

4-2 Devise a logic gate circuit to convert pure five-bit parallel binary numbers to Gray-code, i.e. reflected binary, notation.

4-3 Repeat question 2 but this time convert from Gray-code to pure binary and implement the circuit in NAND logic.

4-4 Design a circuit using the iterative method that will recognize the occurrence of three consecutive 1's in a ten-bit parallel message. Implement the design in both NAND and contact logic. Can this be designed using symmetric functions?

4-5 Repeat question 4 using different state assignments and then using two external inputs per cell.

4-6 Re-design the parity-check circuit discussed in Section 4–4 using symmetric functions, and compare the resulting contact circuit with the one found previously.

4-7 Devise a circuit that will detect whenever the number of 1's contained in a nine-bit parallel message is equal to six or eight.

4-8 Using Boolean matrices synthesize a bridge circuit starting from the transmission function $T = A\bar{C}\bar{D}\bar{E} + \bar{A}\bar{B}C\bar{E} + \bar{A}\bar{C}\bar{D}E + ABCE$.

5 Sequential switching circuits

5–1 Introduction

Up to now we have dealt with the problems of designing combinational logic circuits, that is, circuits in which the output is a function of the present inputs only. However, in a practical system we are concerned with another, more general, type of logical circuit, where the output is a function of both present and *past* inputs. These circuits, variously called *sequential machines* or *finite automata*, are embodied in most digital systems as counters, pattern generators, sequence detectors, etc. A simple example of a sequential machine is the combination lock, which can only be opened if the correct coded sequence of numbers or letters is set up. Perhaps a more familiar example is the G.P.O. telephone system in which a connection is made by dialling code symbols in sequence.

As the output response of a sequential machine is dependent on its present internal state (determined by past inputs) and its present input conditions, it should be apparent that the concepts can be used to describe any dynamic system with finite states. Thus a business organization, a game, or a living organism may be defined in these terms.

Sequential systems are basically combinational circuits with the additional properties of *storage* (to remember past inputs) and *feedback* (Fig. 5–1), note that the output z is a function of inputs x and internal states y. There are two main classes of sequential circuit, synchronous (clocked or strobed) and asynchronous (unclocked or free-running). In the former type the input, output, and internal states are sampled at definite intervals of time, controlled by the fundamental *clock* frequency of the system. Since the clock is generally some form of square wave, synchronous circuits are often referred to as

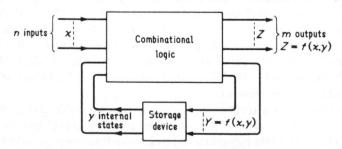

Fig. 5–1 Sequential circuit, Mealy model

pulse circuits, the timing being done by incorporating a clock input to each basic switching module, or bistable element. This type of logic circuit is readily applied to the processing of serial information.

Asynchronous circuits, the most familiar of which is the relay, proceed at their own speed regardless of any basic timing, the outputs of one circuit immediately becoming the inputs to the next. In contrast to pulse signals, active asynchronous logic uses d.c. levels, and is generally used in the processing of parallel data. Due to differences in the inherent delays through signal paths, such circuits can give rise to random operation, requiring special treatment in their design, as we shall see in later chapters. The basic difference between synchronous and asynchronous circuits may be summed up by considering static inputs to each circuit in turn. For the synchronous circuit, if the input combination never changes it will be interpreted as m repetitions (one at each clock pulse) of the input combination. To an asynchronous circuit, however, continued application of a particular input combination appears as a single input.

The rest of this chapter will be devoted to synchronous circuits, and attempts to give a fundamental understanding of the problem, before proceeding to a more formal analysis. In particular we shall consider the design of counter circuits.

5–2 Bistable circuits

It can be seen from Fig. 5–1 that sequential circuits can be represented by a combinational circuit in conjunction with some form of storage or memory element. Before we can begin to design sequential logic circuits, we must examine the properties of these storage devices and derive *characteristic equations* defining their operation.

There is no restriction on the type of storage, and delay lines, ferrite cores, etc. may be used. In practice, however, bistable or flip-flop circuits are extensively used, their two-state properties providing a single bit store. Several types of bistable circuits are available and are classified according to the input conditions available to cause the unit to change state. There is much loose terminology bandied about in connection with bistables, and the only reliable way to specify the logical operation of the device is by means of a truth-table. The more familiar types are the set-reset bistable (SR-FF) the d.c. version of which is also called a toggle or latch; the trigger bistable (T-FF), or divide-by-two circuit; the JK bistable (JK-FF); and the D-type bistable (D-FF) used as a delay element.

Table 5–1(a) shows a truth-table for the *set-reset bistable* giving the next output (or state) Q_+ in terms of the present output (or state) Q and the inputs S and R. The truth-table is constructed by considering the physical action of the circuit shown in Fig. 5–2(a). The operation is such that an input $S = 1$

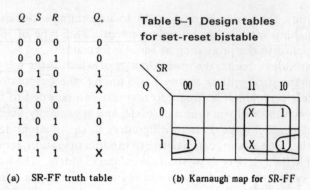

Q	S	R	Q_+
0	0	0	0
0	0	1	0
0	1	0	1
0	1	1	X
1	0	0	1
1	0	1	0
1	1	0	1
1	1	1	X

Table 5–1 Design tables for set-reset bistable

(a)   SR-FF truth table   (b) Karnaugh map for SR-FF

on the set terminal causes an output $Q = 1$, and further inputs have no effect. Similarly, an input $R = 1$ on the reset terminal causes an output $\bar{Q} = 1$; these results are entered in the truth-table. The entries marked with a cross (**X**) correspond to the 'not allowed' or 'don't care' inputs since, under these conditions, when both R and S are present simultaneously, the operation of the circuit becomes uncertain. Note that Q and Q_+ occur in different time intervals, Q_+ occurring *after* Q. That is to say, Q_+ is a delayed version of Q, the delay being caused by the inherent operation time of the bistable store, as the circuit cannot change state instantaneously. This delay is essential in the operation of sequential circuits, and in some cases it is necessary to add further delay to achieve correct logical operation. In a synchronous circuit, Q_+ would be the output in the next sampling interval, or clock pulse. Though Q_+ and Q occur at different times the switching algebra is not affected as they can be treated as two distinct variables.

Thus we can write the *difference equation* as the combinational expression

$$Q_+ = \bar{Q}S\bar{R} + Q\bar{S}\bar{R} + QS\bar{R}$$

The Karnaugh map, shown in Table 5–1(b), gives the minimal *characteristic equation* for the SR-FF element:

$$Q_+ = S + \bar{R}Q$$

Figure 5–2(b) shows the circuit implemented in terms of NAND elements—the

Table 5–2 Design tables for trigger bistable

Q	T	Q_+
0	0	0
0	1	1
1	0	1
1	1	0

T \ Q	0	1
0		1
1	1	

(a)   T-FF truth table   (b) Karnaugh map for T-FF

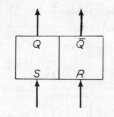

(a) Logic symbol d.c. bistable

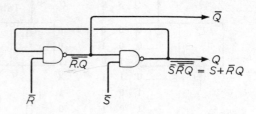

(b) NAND version of *SR-FF*

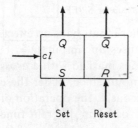

Set   Reset

(c) Logic symbol clocked bistable

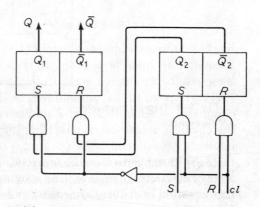

(d) Clocked *SR-FF* using Master-slave bistables

Fig. 5-2 Set-Reset bistable circuits

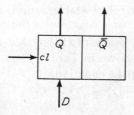

Fig. 5-3 Logic symbol D-type bistable

straightforward hardware circuit in AND/OR logic will not function unless there is some power gain (say, in the form of an invertor) in the feedback loop.

The D-type or delay bistable, shown in Fig. 5.3, has the property of transferring the logic value on input D to the output Q whenever a clock pulse is present. Thus, the characteristic equation for the device is given by:

$$Q_+ = D$$

note that the next state is independent of the present state. This element is equivalent to a 1-bit delay unit, where the bit-time is determined by the clock rate.

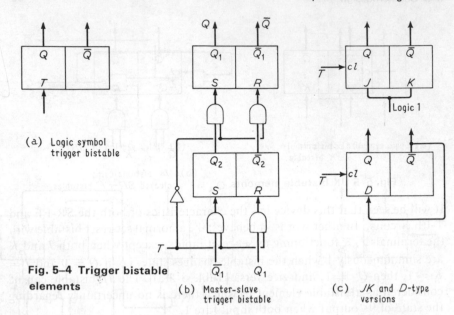

Fig. 5–4 Trigger bistable elements

(a) Logic symbol trigger bistable

(b) Master-slave trigger bistable

(c) JK and D-type versions

The truth-table for the *trigger bistable* is shown in Table 5–2(a). Here the state of the circuit changes each time an input pulse is received. The characteristic equation in this case is the familiar exclusive OR relationship:

$$Q_+ = \bar{Q}T + Q\bar{T}$$

The element is normally engineered as an Eccles-Jordan divide-by-2 counter circuit, using capacitive storage. Alternatively, other bistable types may be interconnected to give the trigger bistable action, as shown in Fig. 5–4(b) and (c).

There are several different versions of JK bistable, particularly in integrated circuit form, one version is shown in Table 5–3(a) and Fig 5–5. From the Karnaugh map, the characteristic equation is

$$Q_+ = J\bar{Q} + \bar{K}Q$$

Q	J	K	Q_+
0	0	0	0
0	0	1	0
0	1	0	1
0	1	1	1
1	0	0	1
1	0	1	0
1	1	0	1
1	1	1	0

(a)   JK-FF truth table

Table 5–3 Design tables for JK bistable

Q \ JK	00	01	11	10
0			1	1
1	1			1

(b) Karnaugh map for JK-FF

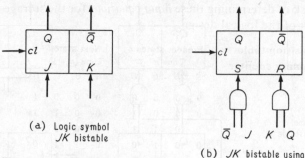

(a) Logic symbol
JK bistable

Fig. 5–5 JK bistable elements

(b) JK bistable using
clocked SR-FF bistables

It will be seen that this device has the characteristics of both the SR-FF and T-FF circuits. In other words, it behaves like a normal set-reset bistable with the terminals J, K functioning as set-reset inputs, except when both J and K are simultaneously 1 when the bistable changes state, i.e. if $Q = 0$ and $J = K = 1$, then $Q_+ = 1$, and vice versa [Table 5–3(a)]. The JK bistable can be considered as a bistable element in which there is no uncertainty regarding the state of its output when both inputs are 1.

The choice of storage element or the particular type of bistable to be used depends entirely on application, availability of devices, cost and reliability. Furthermore, there is always the possibility of using basic logic units such as NOR/NAND to implement the bistable circuits. The advantage here is that the logic element would be readily available and fully toleranced, and it would not add to the number of basic units (and hence spares) required by the system.

It is important to note, however, that d.c. bistable elements cannot control their own inputs using self-feedback from output to input. This is due to the fact that the bistable changes state as soon as the appropriate d.c. level is applied. For example, the JK bistable circuit shown in Fig. 5–5(b) must employ a clocked SR bistable to function correctly.

5–3 Counter design

Before describing the synthesis of synchronous circuits in detail, it is useful to consider the design of a particular class of sequential logic circuit, i.e. the parallel counter.

Example 1. Suppose a counter is required to count incoming pulses up to a maximum of 15, afterwards resetting to zero. The reflected binary system is to be used, each intermediate count being displayed as the count proceeds. This may be considered as a synchronous sequential circuit with the pulse input itself acting as the clock, and gating each stage of the counter. A four-bit store will be required, since there are 16 states, and we shall use SR-FF devices, together with the necessary combinational logic to set and reset the

stores. The task of determining these *input equations* for the storage elements
is a major part of the logical design.

Table 5–4 Transition table for reflected binary counter

	Present states Time n				Next states Time $(n+1)$		
A	B	C	D	A_+	B_+	C_+	D_+
0	0	0	0	0	0	0	1
0	0	0	1	0	0	1	1
0	0	1	1	0	0	1	0
0	0	1	0	0	1	1	0
0	1	1	0	0	1	1	1
0	1	1	1	0	1	0	1
0	1	0	1	0	1	0	0
0	1	0	0	1	1	0	0
1	1	0	0	1	1	0	1
1	1	0	1	1	1	1	1
1	1	1	1	1	1	1	0
1	1	1	0	1	0	1	0
1	0	1	0	1	0	1	1
1	0	1	1	1	0	0	1
1	0	0	1	1	0	0	0
1	0	0	0	0	0	0	0

Table 5–4 shows the truth-table, or more correctly the *transition* or *state-
table* for the counter. In practice, this is a five-variable problem, the variables
being present states A, B, C, and D, and the input x. However, since we are
concerned with changes from one state to another, which only occur when
$x = 1$, we can ignore x. Note that each state may be identified by its four-bit
code, determined in this case by the choice of reflected binary. From the
table, we could write down equations for A_+, B_+, etc., in terms of A, B, C,
and D. These *application equations*, together with the characteristic input
equations for the storage device, form a set of simultaneous Boolean equations:

$$A_+ = f_1(A, B, C, D)$$

$$A_+ = S_A + \bar{R}_A A$$

$$B_+ = f_2(A, B, C, D)$$

$$B_+ = S_B + \bar{R}_B B$$

. . . .

We have now to solve for S_A, R_A, S_B, R_B, etc., in terms of (A, B, C, D), and
thus obtain the input equations for the relevant SR bistables. This may be
done algebraically or by using truth-table methods;[1] we shall use a simpler
approach, however, and deduce the input switching functions directly from
the state-table.

To find S_A, the switching function for setting bistable A, we compare columns A and A_+ in Table 5–4, noting the values of the present state variables for the condition when $A = 0$ and $A_+ = 1$. This value is

$$S_A = \bar{A}B\bar{C}\bar{D}$$

There are also 'don't care' conditions, when no changes are required to take place, which should, if possible, be included in the simplification process. They occur when $A = 1$ and $A_+ = 1$, thus

$$S'_A \text{ (don't care)} = AB\bar{C}\bar{D} + AB\bar{C}D + ABCD + ABC\bar{D}$$
$$+ A\bar{B}C\bar{D} + A\bar{B}CD + A\bar{B}\bar{C}D$$

The corresponding reset conditions occur when $A = 1$ and $A_+ = 0$, and for the 'don't cares' when $A = 0$ and $A_+ = 0$:

$$R_A = A\bar{B}\bar{C}\bar{D}$$
$$R'_A = \bar{A}\bar{B}\bar{C}\bar{D} + \bar{A}\bar{B}\bar{C}D + \bar{A}\bar{B}CD + \bar{A}\bar{B}C\bar{D} + \dot{A}BC\bar{D} + \bar{A}BCD + \bar{A}B\bar{C}D$$

Similarly, comparing columns B and B_+, we have

$$S_B = \bar{A}\bar{B}C\bar{D}$$

and

$$S'_B = \bar{A}B\bar{C}\bar{D} + \bar{A}B\bar{C}D + \bar{A}BCD + \bar{A}BC\bar{D} + AB\bar{C}\bar{D} + AB\bar{C}D + ABCD$$

also

$$R_B = ABC\bar{D}$$

and

$$R'_B = \bar{A}\bar{B}\bar{C}\bar{D} + \bar{A}\bar{B}\bar{C}D + \bar{A}\bar{B}CD + A\bar{B}\bar{C}\bar{D} + A\bar{B}\bar{C}D + A\bar{B}CD + A\bar{B}C\bar{D}$$

Continuing in this manner for the other input switching functions, we arrive at the complete solution, shown plotted on Karnaugh maps in Table 5–5. The maps lead to the reduced set of input equations for S and R shown below.

$$S_A = B\bar{C}\bar{D} \qquad\qquad R_A = \bar{B}\bar{C}\bar{D}$$
$$S_B = \bar{A}C\bar{D} \qquad\qquad R_B = AC\bar{D}$$
$$S_C = D(\bar{A}\bar{B} + AB) \qquad\qquad R_C = D(\bar{A}B + A\bar{B})$$
$$S_D = \bar{C}(\bar{A}\bar{B} + AB) + C(\bar{A}B + A\bar{B}) \quad R_D = \bar{C}(\bar{A}B + A\bar{B}) + C(\bar{A}\bar{B} + AB)$$

Note that $(\bar{A}B + A\bar{B}) = (\overline{\bar{A}\bar{B} + AB})$; in fact this is the exclusive OR function discussed in a previous chapter. The switching functions are shown implemented in terms of AND/OR logic in Fig. 5–6. The input line acts as the clock, and is taken directly to the clock inputs; this is equivalent to logically multiplying all the equations by the input variable. Since the inputs to the setting gates are, in fact, the outputs of the bistable stores, there must be sufficient

Table 5–5 Karnaugh maps for reflected binary counter

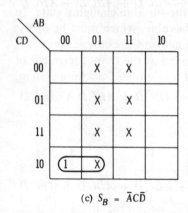

(a) $S_A = B\bar{C}\bar{D}$

(b) $R_A = \bar{B}\bar{C}\bar{D}$

(c) $S_B = \bar{A}C\bar{D}$

(d) $R_B = AC\bar{D}$

(e) $S_C = \bar{A}\bar{B}D + ABD$
$\quad\quad = D(\bar{A}\bar{B} + AB)$

(f) $R_C = \bar{A}BD + A\bar{B}D$
$\quad\quad = D(\bar{A}B + A\bar{B})$

Table 5–5 continued

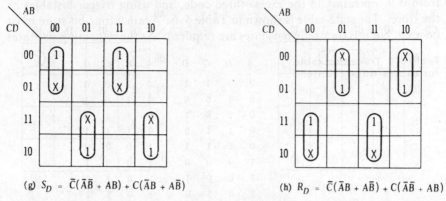

(g) $S_D = \bar{C}(\bar{A}\bar{B} + AB) + C(\bar{A}B + A\bar{B})$

(h) $R_D = \bar{C}(\bar{A}B + A\bar{B}) + C(\bar{A}\bar{B} + AB)$

delay around the feedback-loop to ensure that the input signal has finished before the next internal state appears, due to the bistable changing state. In most cases the inherent response time of the bistable, which must be of the clocked variety, is sufficient (this has been assumed in the example), but if it is not, suitable delaying devices must be employed at the output terminal of the storage device. These can take the form of a two-phase clocking system, single-bit delay elements, bistables, etc.

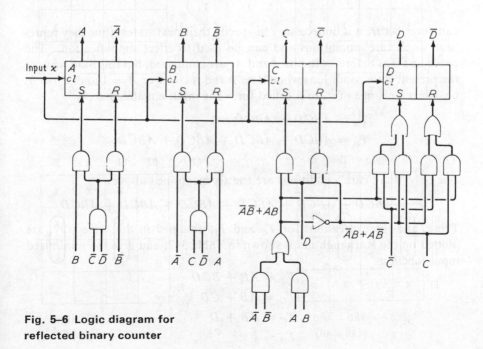

Fig. 5–6 Logic diagram for reflected binary counter

Example 2. Let us now design a binary coded decimal counter, counting from 0–9, operating in the excess-three code, and using trigger bistables as the store. The state-table is shown in Table 5–6. Again a four-bit store must be used, but this time only ten states are required. As the remaining six states

Table 5–6 Transition table for excess-three counter

A	B	C	D		A_+	B_+	C_+	D_+
0	0	1	1		0	1	0	0
0	1	0	0		0	1	0	1
0	1	0	1		0	1	1	0
0	1	1	0		0	1	1	1
0	1	1	1		1	0	0	0
1	0	0	0		1	0	0	1
1	0	0	1		1	0	1	0
1	0	1	0		1	0	1	1
1	0	1	1		1	1	0	0
1	1	0	0		0	0	1	1
0	0	0	0					
0	0	0	1					
0	0	1	0		'Don't care'			
1	1	0	1		terms			
1	1	1	0					
1	1	1	1					

can never occur, it is unnecessary to specify their next states, thus they represent 'don't care' conditions and can be used to effect simplification. The procedure is as before, columns A and A_+ are compared, but this time we note the present state conditions when $A = 0$ and $A_+ = 1$ or $A = 1$ and $A_+ = 0$, i.e. when a change of state is called for. The input equations are

$$T_A = \bar{A}BCD + AB\bar{C}\bar{D}$$
$$T_B = \bar{A}\bar{B}CD + \bar{A}BCD + A\bar{B}CD + AB\bar{C}\bar{D}$$
....

The only 'don't care' conditions are the six mentioned above:

$$T' = \bar{A}\bar{B}\bar{C}\bar{D} + \bar{A}\bar{B}\bar{C}D + \bar{A}\bar{B}C\bar{D} + AB\bar{C}D + ABC\bar{D} + ABCD$$

These, and the expressions for T_C and T_D obtained in the same way, are plotted on the Karnaugh maps shown in Table 5–7, and give the minimized input functions

$$T_A = AB + BCD$$
$$T_B = AB + CD$$
$$T_C = AB + D$$
$$T_D = 1$$

Table 5–7 Karnaugh maps for excess-three counter

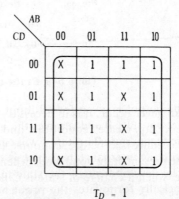

$$T_A = AB + BCD$$

$$T_B = AB + CD$$

$$T_C = AB + D$$

$$T_D = 1$$

which may be implemented in the usual way. Note that the equation $T_D = 1$ means that the trigger bistable changes state for each input pulse.

Both of the designs in these examples could have been achieved using JK bistables which have set (J) and reset (K) inputs identical to those of the SR-FF bistable, but with the added advantage of extra 'don't care' conditions. The input conditions for the JK bistable are:

(a) set (J) transition $Q = 0,$ $Q_+ = 1$

    'don't cares' $Q = 1,$ $Q_+ = 1;$ $Q = 1,$ $Q_+ = 0$

(b) reset (K) transition $Q = 1,$ $Q_+ = 0$

    'don't cares' $Q = 0,$ $Q_+ = 0;$ $Q = 0,$ $Q_+ = 1$

Should the number of variables exceed five, a convenient figure for map manipulation, it is necessary to use tabular methods of simplification as described in Section 3–6.

5–4 Sequential circuits—problem definition

So far we have looked at one particular class of sequential circuit, let us now consider the problem in general. We begin by examining the methods used to clarify and define the initial logical or system requirement—an essential prerequisite to any design problem.

We can represent a sequential circuit by using either a *state-table* (sometimes called a transition table) or *state-diagram*. The truth-table for the JK bistable [Table 5–3(a)] can easily be rearranged to the state-table form (Table 5–8). All bistable circuits are, in fact, examples of simple sequential machines with two internal states. The entries in the state-table are the next states reached by the circuit following any given change of input; similarly,

Present state	Next state				Output			
	00	01	11	10	00	01	11	10
0	0	0	1	1	0	0	1	1
1	1	0	0	1	1	0	0	1

Inputs JK

Table 5–8 State-table for JK bistable

the output is given for all input changes. For example, if the bistable is in present state 0 and receives the inputs JK = 10 (the set condition), a transition from state 0 to state 1 will occur. Since the output in this case is identical with the internal state (which is not usual), the output also goes from 0 to 1. The development of the state-table, from the original circuit specification, logically formulates the problem in the same way as the truth-table for a combinational circuit. It is, in fact, an abstract mathematical representation of a sequential circuit, which lists the outcome of all possible input combinations in terms of the internal states and output states. It has its origins in the function table used in group theory to describe binary operations.

For complicated systems, the table is sometimes difficult to construct because, as no established technique exists, the process is mainly intuitive and relies heavily on past experience. The state-diagram is a useful means of expressing problem requirements before constructing the state-table; it contains exactly the same information but in a more understandable form. The corresponding state-diagrams for the JK bistable are shown in Fig. 5–7. The state-diagram is a directed graph, rather like a signal-flow diagram, representing the states of the circuit by circles (nodes) with directed lines between them showing the transition paths. There are two types of state-diagram called the *Mealy* model[2] and the *Moore* model.[3] In the former,

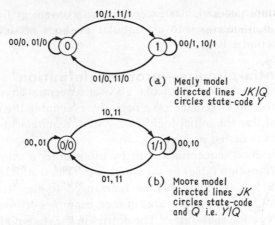

(a) Mealy model
directed lines JK/Q
circles state-code Y

(b) Moore model
directed lines JK
circles state-code
and Q i.e. Y/Q

Fig. 5–7 State diagrams for JK bistables

each path is labelled with the input which causes the transition and the resulting output; the circle contains the code for the internal state. The Moore model differs in that, although the paths are labelled with the inputs which cause the transition, the circles contain both the state-code and the output state, i.e. the output state is a function of the internal states only. When the initial and final states are the same, analogous to a self-loop in signal-flow, we call the transition path a *sling*.

Both models may be used to represent a sequential machine, the choice being one of convenience and personal preference. Note, however, that the Mealy model is more general—the Moore model implies that the output and internal state-codes can be made identical. Once the state-diagram for a sequential circuit has been produced and tested, it is an easy matter to convert it to a state-table. For simple problems, as we saw in the case of counter circuits, it is convenient to proceed directly to the state-table. The concepts of state-tables and state-diagrams apply to sequential systems in general, but slight modifications are necessary when they are used to describe asynchronous logic. Let us now use these techniques to describe a practical problem.

Example 3. A problem that is perhaps more typical of sequential logic is that of pattern recognition. Suppose a circuit is required to recognize a particular three-bit pattern, say 101, and to produce an output whenever it occurs in the continuous serial input to the circuit. For example, in the binary sequence 01110111110111 etc., we would want outputs for the two occurrences of 101 in the sequence. We shall define the problem first by deriving its state-diagram, and second by converting the state-diagram to a state-table. The state-diagram is shown in Fig. 5–8 and the state-table in Table

Table 5–9 State-tables for pattern discriminator

(a)

	Input X			
Present state	Next state		Output	
	0	1	0	1
A	A	B	0	0
B	C	B	0	0
C	A	D	0	1
D	A	B	0	0

(b)

	Input X			
Present state	Next state		Output	
	0	1	0	1
A	A	B	0	0
B	C	B	0	0
C	A	A	0	1

(c)

	Input X			
Present state	Next state		Output	
AB	$X = 0$	$X = 1$	$X = 0$	$X = 1$
	A_+B_+	A_+B_+	A_+B_+	A_+B_+
00	00	01	0	0
01	10	01	0	0
10	00	00	0	1

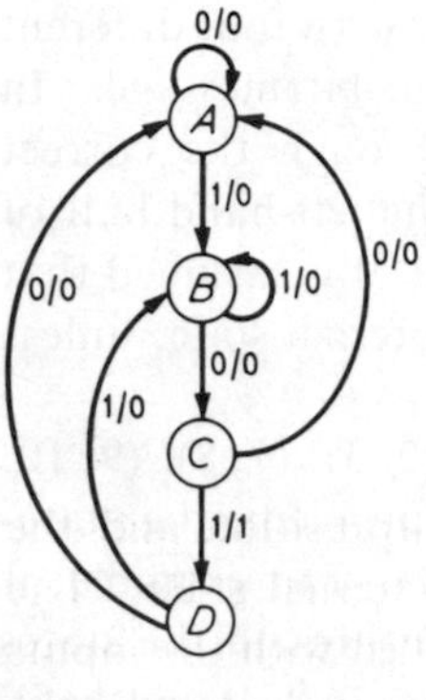

Fig. 5–8 State diagram for pattern discriminator

5–9. Since it is a serial input, we need only consider the inputs that can occur during a clock period, i.e. 0 and 1. Starting from an initial waiting state A, if a 0 is received the circuit stays in the same state (indicated by a sling in the state-diagram). For a 1, however, there is a transition to state B, indicating the start of the required sequence. If, while in this state, a 0 is received, i.e. sequence (10), the circuit changes to state C. When in state C, if a 1 is received, completing the sequence (101), the circuit changes to state D, giving the required output. An input of 0 returns the circuit to state A to await the start of another sequence. When the circuit is in state D, a 1 returns it to state B, and a 0 returns it to state A.

Clearly, state-diagrams and tables are equivalent ways of describing a sequential circuit, there is in fact a one-to-one correspondence between them. However, the state-table is a more convenient form for manipulation and it is used expressly for this reason.

Example 4. Suppose we want to develop the state-diagram and state-tables for a circuit that continuously compares two four-bit serial message channels, on a repetitive basis, and gives an output when coincidence is found. That is, we have two message inputs of the form

1101	1111	1000	1110	0001	etc.	channel A
0001	1101	0011	1111	0001	etc.	channel B
1234	1234	1234	1234	1234	etc.	clock timing

and we want to compare each four-bit word in turn, signalling an output when they are identical, as in the last word above.

The state-diagram is shown in Fig. 5–9, and the corresponding state-table in Table 5–10. In this case we must consider all possible input combinations available on the two signal channels, i.e. 00, 01, 11, 10, at every stage of the process and for every state. Furthermore, we must have at least four different internal states to allow for the examination of the four-bit message. In deriving state-diagrams it is a good idea to follow through the correct sequence of inputs; this, in fact, has been done here, the left-hand half of the diagram being the correct path. Note that, in general, it is assumed that each input combination results in a transition to a new internal state, unless it is obvious that an identical state already exists.

Identical patterns result in a path through states (1), (2, 3), (7, 8), (9, 10, 11, 12) (note that because of the binary nature of the problem, the state-diagram spreads out in the form of a binary, relay, tree). For example, if the pattern 0001 appeared on both input lines, the path through the state-diagram, starting from initial state 1, would be via states 3, 7, 9 and back

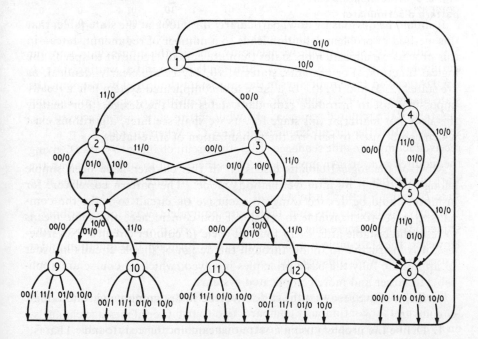

Fig. 5–9 State diagram for pattern correlator

Table 5–10 State-table for pattern correlator

Present states	Next states 00	01	11	10	Outputs 00	01	11	10
1	3	4	2	4	0	0	0	0
2	7	5	8	5	0	0	0	0
3	7	5	8	5	0	0	0	0
4	5	5	5	5	0	0	0	0
5	6	6	6	6	0	0	0	0
6	1	1	1	1	0	0	0	0
7	9	6	10	6	0	0	0	0
8	11	6	12	6	0	0	0	0
9	1	1	1	1	1	0	1	0
10	1	1	1	1	1	0	1	0
11	1	1	1	1	1	0	1	0
12	1	1	1	1	1	0	1	0

(Inputs xy)

to state 1. However, once we have had different inputs, the messages cannot be identical and we must wait for the next word, this is the reason for the delaying path via states 4, 5, 6—it can be entered at any stage of the four-bit comparison.

It should be obvious by now, particularly if we look at the state-table, that this method of problem definition leads to a number of redundant states—in this process we allocate more states than are actually required to specify the logical function. For example, states 9, 10, 11, 12 are clearly identical, as are states (2, 3) and (7, 8). In a large and complicated system it is virtually impossible not to introduce redundant states into the design. Fortunately this does not matter at this stage for, as we shall see later, algorithms exist which can be used to perform the minimization of state-tables.

Most of the logical circuits discussed in this chapter have been simple enough to design by intuitive methods alone. The pattern correlator, for instance, could be devised using an exclusive OR circuit to make the comparison, a set-reset bistable to register a non-coincidence, and some means to reset the bistable after every four-bit cycle (a counter circuit). Nevertheless, it is instructive to follow through the design of simple circuits in order to appreciate fully the basic principles involved, which of course are applicable to larger and more complicated systems.

So far, we have seen that the steps involved in designing synchronous logic circuits are:

1. Define the problem using a state-diagram and/or a state-table.
2. Simplify the state-table by eliminating redundant internal states.

3. Allocate codes to the remaining states.

4. Determine the input switching equations for the selected storage device. Steps 2 and 3, unnecessary in the design of counter circuits since the number of states and their coding were implicit in the problem, will be discussed in some detail in the following chapters.

References and bibliography

(1) PHISTER, M. *Logical design of digital computers*. Wiley, New York, 1958.

(2) MEALY, G. H. A method for synthesizing sequential circuits. *Bell Syst. tech. J.*, 1955, **34**, 1045–1079.

(3) MOORE, E. F. Gedanken-experiments on sequential machines. (Automata Studies.) *Ann. Math. Stud.*, 1955, **34**, 129–153. (Princeton University Press.)

(4) McCLUSKY, E. J. and BARTEE, T. C. *Survey of switching circuit theory*. McGraw-Hill, New York, 1962.

(5) TORNG, H. C. *Logical design of switching systems*. Addison-Wesley, Reading, Mass., 1964.

(6) HURLEY, R. B. *Transistor logic circuits*. Wiley, New York, 1961.

(7) GILL, A. *Introduction to the theory of finite state machines*. McGraw-Hill, New York, 1962.

(8) SPARKES, J. J. Bistable elements for sequential circuits. *Electron. Engng.*, 1966, **38**, 510–515.

(9) DEAN, K. J. The design of parallel counters using the map method. *Radio and Electronic Engineer*, 1966, **32**, 159–162.

(10) ZISSOS, D. A method of designing electronic sequential circuits. *A.T.E. J.*, 1964, **20**, 62–69.

Tutorial problems

5-1 Design a synchronous five-bit ring counter using the design principles discussed in this chapter. Use both T-FF and SR-FF storage elements.

5-2 Derive the input equations for an SR-FF decimal counter counting and displaying the following number sequence:

	5	4	2	1
0	0	0	0	0
1	0	0	0	1
2	0	0	1	0
3	0	0	1	1
4	0	1	0	0
5	1	0	0	0
6	1	0	0	1
7	1	0	1	0
8	1	0	1	1
9	1	1	0	0

5-3 Redesign the reflected binary counter discussed in the text to count and display ten states only using T-FF devices.

5-4 Design a divide-by-five logic circuit using trigger bistable elements. Show that this forms the basis for a divide-by-ten circuit.

5-5 Construct the state-diagram and state-table for a logic circuit that gives an output whenever the sum of the 1's digits in a repetitive five-bit serial input sequence is 2.

5-6 Construct the state-diagram for the counter circuit of Example 2 in the text.

5-7 Derive the state-diagram and state-tables for the clamp-gate or zero-hold circuit used in sampled-data systems. The circuit has two serial inputs x and y and an output z. The characteristics are such that z is made equal to the present value of x if $y = 1$, or to the previous output value if $y = 0$.

  Consider the possibility of reducing the number of internal states in this circuit.

5-8 Derive from first principles the state-diagram and state-tables for a binary serial full-adder circuit.

6 Design of synchronous sequential circuits

6–1 Introduction

We saw in the last chapter that, in general, the formal definition of a sequential problem leads to redundant internal states, that is, the state-table contains more states than are actually required for the interpretation of the problem. The number of internal states of a sequential machine is an important parameter, since it determines the amount of hardware required to represent these states in the final circuit. For an r-state machine using binary storage devices, such as bistables, at least n bistables are required to assign these states, where n is the smallest integer greater than or equal to $\log_2 r$, i.e. $r \leq 2^n$. By reducing r, it is possible that n may also be reduced, thus fewer bistables will be needed in the circuit realization. However, this does not automatically reduce the cost of the system, since using fewer storage elements could increase the number of terms in the input and output equations and hence the amount of combinational logic required. For example, in designing a ring-counter (which requires a unique output for every state of the counter), it is often more economical to use a separate bistable for each state, rather than the minimal number of bistables necessary to represent these states, with suitable decoding and input logic. Thus, since a sequential circuit consists of storage plus combinational logic, for an optimum (and hence an economical) design we must also consider the amount of combinational logic required as well as the number of bistables. Furthermore, the way in which the internal states are assigned an identifying code also determines the amount of combinational logic required. The straightforward approach of allocating each state according to normal ascending binary does not in general lead to an economical solution. It is important to realize that a non-minimal machine will perfectly satisfy all the original design specifications, but the resulting circuit will be costly and, because it contains more components, less reliable.

In this chapter we discuss techniques which have been evolved to search systematically for redundant (or equivalent) states, and we also investigate some of the problems and methods of economical state assignment.

6–2 Reduction of internal states

Let us first consider the problem of state minimization using an intuitive approach. Table 6–1 shows the state-table obtained in the last chapter for the pattern correlator problem. Inspection of this table immediately reveals that internal states (9, 10, 11, 12) and (2, 3) are *identical* in all respects, that

Table 6-1 State-table for pattern correlator

Inputs $x_1 x_2$

Present states	Next state				Outputs Z			
	00	01	11	10	00	01	11	10
1	3^2	4	2	4	0	0	0	0
2	7	5	8	5	0	0	0	0
~~3~~	~~7~~	~~5~~	~~8~~	~~5~~	~~0~~	~~0~~	~~0~~	~~0~~
4	5	5	5	5	0	0	0	0
5	6	6	6	6	0	0	0	0
6	1	1	1	1	0	0	0	0
7	9	6	10^9	6	0	0	0	0
8	11^9	6	12^9	6	0	0	0	0
9	1	1	1	1	1	0	1	0
~~10~~	~~1~~	~~1~~	~~1~~	~~1~~	~~1~~	~~0~~	~~1~~	~~0~~
~~11~~	~~1~~	~~1~~	~~1~~	~~1~~	~~1~~	~~0~~	~~1~~	~~0~~
~~12~~	~~1~~	~~1~~	~~1~~	~~1~~	~~1~~	~~0~~	~~1~~	~~0~~

is, the next-state and output entries in the state-table correspond exactly, one with the other, for every input combination. Thus, we can replace these identical states by one state in the table (conventionally chosen to be the state with the smallest number), modifying all other entries accordingly. Once this is done it is apparent that states (7, 8) are also identical; replacing these states results in the reduced state-table shown in Table 6–2. Using this approach then, we have evolved a minimal description of the machine which requires only seven states, i.e. (1), (2, 3), (4), (5), (6), (7, 8), (9, 10, 11, 12). Note that in the original table internal states (7, 8) were not identical, i.e. they did not have the same next states. When this condition occurs we generally refer to these states as *equivalent* states.

We shall now attempt a more formal definition of the equivalence property,

Table 6-2 Reduced state-table

Inputs $x_1 x_2$

Present states	Next state				Outputs Z			
	00	01	11	10	00	01	11	10
1	2	4	2	4	0	0	0	0
2	7	5	7	5	0	0	0	0
4	5	5	5	5	0	0	0	0
5	6	6	6	6	0	0	0	0
6	1	1	1	1	0	0	0	0
7	9	6	9	6	0	0	0	0
9	1	1	1	1	1	0	1	0

which is due to Moore.[1] Two states are said to be equivalent if, for all sequences of inputs, the sequential machine produces the same output sequence when it is started in either state. Thus it is impossible to distinguish between the two states by the external, terminal, behaviour of the machine. It follows then that the necessary (but not sufficient) condition for two states to be equivalent is that their output states must be identical. Furthermore, two states may be considered equivalent, even though their next states are not the same, providing it is possible to establish an equivalence between the unlike states. This was demonstrated in the example above (Table 6–1) for states (7, 8).

In order to reduce a state-table systematically, we must examine each pair of states having the same output states, and establish if their next states are equivalent. This may be done by direct examination and comparison, e.g. in Table 6–1 we say that $7 \equiv 8$ if $9 \equiv 11$ and $10 \equiv 12$, then by investigating the equivalence of the state-pairs (9, 11) and (10, 12) we can establish if, in fact, $7 \equiv 8$. For a completely specified machine, we can make use of the transitive relationship (if $a \equiv b$ and $b \equiv c$, then $a \equiv c$) in order to ascertain equivalence.

An algorithmic technique for finding equivalent states has been described by Paull and Ungar,[2] which holds for both completely and incompletely specified (i.e. containing 'don't care' conditions) state-tables. In this method an *implication chart* is constructed which shows the necessary conditions or *implications* that exist between all possible equivalent state-pairs. The implication chart for the correlator problem discussed earlier is shown in Table 6–3(a); note that the chart has as many cells as it has possible equivalent state-pairs. To construct the chart, the state-table is first inspected for those state-pairs which cannot possibly be equivalent because of differing output states, and a cross is entered in the appropriate cell, for example $1 \not\equiv 9$, $1 \not\equiv 10$, etc. These non-equivalent state-pairs are called *incompatibles*. Similarly, a tick is inserted in the appropriate cells for identical state-pairs. The chart is completed by considering next each permissable state-pair in turn, say (1, 2), and entering in the chart the necessary equivalent next state-pairs, in this case (3, 7), (4, 5), and (2, 8), required to make the initial state-pair equivalent.

When the chart is completed in this way, it is examined, starting from the extreme right-hand column, for cells containing a cross. In Table 6–3(a), the first cross occurs in column 8 for the state-pair (8, 12). Since these states cannot possibly be equivalent, it follows that any other state-pairs relying on (8, 12) for equivalence [in practice any cell containing (8, 12)] must also be crossed out, e.g. cells (2, 8) and (3, 8). The chart is systematically processed in this way continuing with (8, 11), (8, 10), (8, 9), (7, 12), etc., noting each time which incompatible has been used, until the final column is reached. The process is then repeated ignoring those incompatibles used in previous searches. A convenient method of noting when an incompatible has been

Table 6–3 Implication chart for correlator problem

	1	2	3	4	5	6	7	8	9	10	11
2	3,7 4,5 2,8										
3	3,7 4,5 2,8	√									
4	3,5 4,5 2,5	7,5 8,5	7,5 8,5								
5	3,6 4,6 2,6	7,6 5,6 8,6	7,6 5,6 8,6	5,6							
6	3,1 4,1 2,1	7,1 5,1 8,1	7,1 5,1 8,1	5,1	6,1						
7	3,9 4,6 2,10	7,9 5,6 8,10	7,9 5,6 8,10	5,9 5,6 5,10	6,9 6,10	1,9 1,6 1,10					
8	3,11 4,6 2,12	7,11 5,6 8,12	7,11 5,6 8,12	5,11 5,6 5,12	6,11 6,12	1,11 1,6 1,12	9,11 10,12				
9	X	X	X	X	X	X	X	X			
10	X	X	X	X	X	X	X	X	√		
11	X	X	X	X	X	X	X	X	√	√	
12	X	X	X	X	X	X	X	X	√	√	√

(a)   Initial implication chart

Table 6–3 continued

	1	2	3	4	5	6	7	8	9	10	11
2	3,7 4,5 2,8										
3	3,7 4,5 2,8	✓									
4	3,5 4,5 2,5	7,5 8,5	7,5 8,5								
5	3,6 4,6 2,6	7,6 5,6 8,6	7,6 5,6 8,6	5,6							
6	3,1 4,1 2,1	7,1 5,1 8,1	7,1 5,1 8,1	5,1	6,1						
7	╳ 3,9 4,6 2,10	╳ 7,9 5,6 8,10	╳ 7,9 5,6 8,10	╳ 5,9 5,6 5,10	╳ 6,9 6,10	╳ 1,9 1,6 1,10					
8	╳ 3,11 4,6 2,12	╳ 7,11 5,6 8,12	╳ 7,11 5,6 8,12	╳ 5,11 5,6 5,12	╳ 6,11 6,12	╳ 1,11 1,6 1,12	9,11 10,12				
9	Ⓧ	Ⓧ	Ⓧ	Ⓧ	Ⓧ	Ⓧ	Ⓧ	Ⓧ			
10	Ⓧ	Ⓧ	Ⓧ	Ⓧ	Ⓧ	Ⓧ	Ⓧ	Ⓧ	✓		
11	Ⓧ	Ⓧ	Ⓧ	Ⓧ	Ⓧ	Ⓧ	Ⓧ	Ⓧ	✓	✓	
12	Ⓧ	Ⓧ	Ⓧ	Ⓧ	Ⓧ	Ⓧ	Ⓧ	Ⓧ	✓	✓	✓

(b) After first pass through chart

Table 6–3 continued

2	3,7 4,5 2,8 ⊗									
3	3,7 4,5 2,8 ⊗	✓								
4	3,5 4,5 2,5 ⊗	7,5 8,5 ⊗	7,5 8,5 ⊗							
5	3,6 4,6 2,6 ⊗	7,6 5,6 8,6 ⊗	7,6 5,6 8,6 ⊗	5,6 ⊗						
6	3,1 4,1 2,1 ⊗	7,1 5,1 8,1 ⊗	7,1 5,1 8,1 ⊗	5,1 ⊗	6,1 ⊗					
7	3,9 4,9 2,10 ⊗	7,9 5,9 8,10 ⊗	7,9 5,9 8,10 ⊗	5,9 5,10 ⊗	6,9 6,10 ⊗	1,9 1,10 ⊗				
8	3,11 4,11 2,12 ⊗	7,11 5,11 8,12 ⊗	7,11 5,11 8,12 ⊗	5,11 5,12 ⊗	6,11 6,12 ⊗	1,11 1,12 ⊗	9,11 10,12			
9	⊗	⊗	⊗	⊗	⊗	⊗	⊗	⊗		
10	⊗	⊗	⊗	⊗	⊗	⊗	⊗	⊗	✓	
11	⊗	⊗	⊗	⊗	⊗	⊗	⊗	⊗	✓	✓
12	⊗	⊗	⊗	⊗	⊗	⊗	⊗	⊗	✓	✓	✓
	1	**2**	**3**	**4**	**5**	**6**	**7**	**8**	**9**	**10**	**11**

(c)   Final implication chart

used is to mark the cell by encircling the cross. A number of passes through the chart will be necessary before all the cells have been classified into crossed-out, ticked (identical) or unticked (equivalent) cells. Table 6–3(b) shows the state of the chart after one pass, and the final chart is shown in Table 6–3(c); in practice, of course, only one chart is required.

The final step in the reduction process is to extract the equivalent states, sometimes called *pair-wise compatibles*, from the chart; in this case we have, reading from the right-hand column of Table 6–3(c),

$$11 \equiv 12 \quad 10 \equiv 12 \quad 10 \equiv 11 \quad 9 \equiv 12 \quad 9 \equiv 11 \quad 9 \equiv 10 \quad 7 \equiv 8 \quad 2 \equiv 3$$

These pair-wise compatibles can be grouped into sets of states, each with the same output states and all equivalent to one another, using the transitive relationship, i.e. if $11 \equiv 12$ and $10 \equiv 12$, then $11 \equiv 10$. Thus we may say that the *maximal compatibles* are

$$(9, 10, 11, 12)(7, 8)(2, 3)$$

We can define the terms used more explicitly in the following way. A *compatible* is a set of output-consistent internal states, each of which is equivalent to each of the others. A *maximal compatible* is a set of output-consistent states which form a compatible, and whose states do not form a proper subset of any other compatible. For example, $(11, 12)(10, 12)(10, 11)(9, 12)(9, 11)(9, 10)$ $(9, 10, 11)$ $(10, 11, 12)$ are compatibles, but not maximal, since internal states 9, 10, 11, and 12 may be combined to form the maximal compatible $(9, 10, 11, 12)$.

The internal states of a sequential machine can be represented by a set of maximal compatibles which must include *all* states, thus

$$M = (1)(2, 3)(4)(5)(6)(7, 8)(9, 10, 11, 12) \tag{1}$$

Note that a compatible can consist of one state equivalent to itself. This set of maximal compatibles forms a partition on the set of internal states:

$$S = (1, 2, 3, 4, 5, 6, 7, 8, 9, 10, 11, 12)$$

since the intersection of any block of the partition M is disjoint. Many partitions may be made on the set S; for example, the following are all possible partitions:

$$P = (1)(2)(3)(4)(5)(6)(7)(8)(9)(10)(11)(12)$$
$$P = (1, 2, 3, 4, 5, 6, 7, 8, 9, 10, 11, 12)$$
$$P = (1, 2, 3, 4)(5, 6, 7, 8, 9, 10, 11, 12)$$
$$P = (1, 2, 3, 4, 5, 6)(7, 8, 9, 10, 11, 12)$$

What distinguishes the particular partition we have arrived at from all the others, and is it in fact unique? An obvious factor, of course, is that the blocks of the partition representing the machine must contain states which are equivalent (called *output-consistent*, since all states in the same block must have identical outputs). Another important characteristic, however, is that the partition must be closed (corresponding to the closure property in group theory), thus satisfying all the *necessary implications*. This means that if the equivalent states in a block depend on the equivalence of some other states, these states must belong to a block in the partition. For the partition M [Eqn. (1)], reference to the implication charts in Table 6–3 shows that (7, 8) implies the equivalence of (9, 11) and (10, 12) which are both contained in the same block of the partition. For the case of a completely specified machine, the closed partition obtained for M is the unique minimal description of the internal states. An upper bound on the number of internal states in a minimal machine is the number of maximal compatibles. In the case of a fully specified machine, since the maximal compatibles form a partition, i.e. are disjoint, the number of states is equal to the number of maximal compatibles. Moreover, Ginsberg[3] has pointed out that the number of elements in the largest maximal *incompatible* is a lower bound on the number of rows in the reduced state-table.

The above result is the same as our intuitive result but we now have a routine tabular method, an algorithm, which may be used for any number of internal states, and which is ideal for automatic calculation on a digital computer.

6–3 Example of state minimization

Let us now consolidate our technique by doing an example. Consider the fully specified sequential machine whose state-table is shown in Table 6–4. There are no identical states and an intuitive examination of the state-table leads to a long succession of implications, for example $1 \equiv 2$ if $6 \equiv 3$; $6 \equiv 3$

Table 6–4

	Input x			
Present state	Next state		Output Z	
	0	1	0	1
1	8	3	0	0
2	8	6	0	0
3	8	1	1	0
4	1	8	1	0
5	4	7	0	0
6	4	2	1	0
7	4	5	1	0
8	5	4	1	0

Table 6–5

	1	2	3	4	5	6	7
2	3,6						
3	X	X					
4	X	X	8,1 (crossed)				
5	8,4 3,7	8,4 6,7	X	X			
6	X	X	8,4 1,2	8,4 (crossed)	X		
7	X	X	8,4 1,5	8,4 (crossed)	X	2,5	
8	X	X	8,5 3,4 (crossed)	1,5 8,4	X	4,5 2,4 (crossed)	4,5 (crossed)

if $8 \equiv 4$ and $1 \equiv 2$; $8 \equiv 4$ if $1 = 5$; $1 = 5$ if $8 \equiv 4$ and $3 \equiv 7$; $3 \equiv 7$ if $8 \equiv 4$ and $1 \equiv 5$; therefore $1 \equiv 2$. The tabular approach is much simpler, the final implication chart is shown in Table 6–5. The table shows, reading from right to left, that

$$6 \equiv 7 \qquad 4 \equiv 8 \qquad 3 \equiv 7 \qquad 3 \equiv 6 \qquad 2 \equiv 5 \qquad 1 \equiv 5 \qquad 1 \equiv 2$$

Thus the sequential machine is represented by

$$M = (6, 7)(4, 8)(3, 7)(3, 6)(2, 5)(1, 5)(1, 2)$$

since all internal states are present. However, this is not minimal since we have not derived the maximal compatibles for the machine. Starting from the right-hand side, we can combine equivalent states using the transitive relationship (i.e. $1 \equiv 2$ and $1 \equiv 5$, therefore $2 \equiv 5$) and we may group these together as $(1, 2, 5)$; similarly $3 \equiv 6$ and $3 \equiv 7$, therefore $6 \equiv 7$, giving $(3, 6, 7)$ and finally $(4, 8)$, resulting in the minimal expression for the machine:

$$M = (4, 8)(3, 6, 7)(1, 2, 5)$$

On checking, we find that the closure property is satisfied since $(4, 8)$ implies $(1, 5)$ and $(8, 4)$; $(3, 6, 7)$ implies $(8, 4)(1, 2)(1, 5)$ and $(2, 5)$; and $(1, 2, 5)$ implies $(3, 6)(8, 4)(3, 7)$ and $(6, 7)$, which are all contained in blocks of the partition. Thus we have reduced the original seven-state machine, requiring three bistables, into a three-state machine which may be represented by two bistables. The reduced state-table is shown in Table 6–6, note that the smallest state-number in each block has been used to represent the actual

Table 6–6

Present state	Input x			
	Next state		Output	
	0	1	0	1
1	4	3	0	0
3	4	1	1	0
4	1	4	1	0

states. That is, whenever states 4 and 8 occur in the original state-table, they are replaced by 4; likewise 3, 6, and 7 are replaced by 3; and 1, 2, and 5 are replaced by 1.

6–4 Incompletely specified state-tables

In a practical system it is very likely that some inputs may never occur, so that under these conditions outputs or next states do not matter or are of no consequence. Thus, in these cases, the appropriate entries in the state-table can be filled in any possible way. This does mean, however, that we must slightly modify our approach for the minimization of state-tables. Since it is possible to combine a 'don't care' condition (either next-state or output state) more than once, taking different values each time if necessary, it follows that an internal state can occur in more than one maximal compatible. This means that the final equivalent-states expression is no longer a partition since the blocks (compatibles) can overlap, i.e. the intersection of any two blocks is not necessarily disjoint. In this case the set of maximal compatibles is called a *covering*. Furthermore, the equivalence relationship is not necessarily transitive, i.e. if $a \equiv b$ and $b \equiv c$ it *does not* always follow that $a \equiv c$.

These ideas are best illustrated by means of another example. Consider the incompletely specified state-table shown in Table 6–7. From the implication chart (Table 6–8) the pairwise compatibles are

$$(2, 3)(2, 6)(2, 7)(3, 4)(3, 6)(3, 7)(4, 5)(4, 7)(4, 8)(5, 8)(6, 7)$$

Table 6–7

Present state	Input x			
	Next state		Output Z	
	0	1	0	1
1	2	8	1	1
2	1	7	0	0
3	X	6	0	X
4	4	X	0	1
5	3	4	0	X
6	1	3	X	0
7	X	2	X	X
8	7	5	0	X

The maximal compatibles are found by combining these state-pairs into larger groups with equivalent elements. Now $4 \equiv 7$ and $4 \equiv 8$, but 7 is *not* equivalent to 8, i.e. the transitive relationship does not apply, and $(4, 7, 8)$ is not a maximal compatible. But $4 \equiv 5$, $4 \equiv 8$, and $5 \equiv 8$, therefore we can combine these to give $(4, 5, 8)$; also $3 \equiv 4$, $3 \equiv 7$, and $4 \equiv 7$, therefore we have $(3, 4, 7)$; similarly, we can group $(2, 3, 6, 7)$. Thus the machine may be represented by the expression

$$M = (1)(2, 3, 6, 7)(3, 4, 7)(4, 5, 8)$$

Note that the terms are no longer disjoint, i.e.

$$(2, 3, 6, 7) \cap (3, 4, 7) = (3, 7)$$

and $\qquad\qquad (3, 4, 7) \cap (4, 5, 8) = (4)$

thus the expression M forms a covering on the set of original internal states $S = (1, 2, 3, 4, 5, 6, 7, 8)$.

Now to obtain a minimal solution we need a set of maximal compatibles which include all the original states. The higher bound is seen from M, above, to be four; to find the lower bound we must extract from the chart the set of maximal incompatibles, these are

$$(1, 2, 8)(1, 2, 5)(1, 2, 4)(1, 3, 5)(1, 3, 8)(1, 4, 6)(1, 5, 7)(1, 5, 6)(1, 8, 6)(1, 7, 8)$$

giving a lower bound of three.

It would appear at first glance that the covering

$$M = (1)(2, 3, 6, 7)(4, 5, 8)$$

Table 6–8

	1	2	3	4	5	6	7
2	⊗						
3	⊗	7,6					
4	⊗	⊗	✓				
5	⊗	⊗(1,4/7,4)	⊗(6,4)	4,3			
6	⊗	7,3	✓	⊗	⊗(3,4)		
7	⊗(8,2)	✓	6,2	✓	⊗(4,2)	3,2	
8	⊗	⊗(1,7/7,5)	⊗(6,5)	4,7	3,7 4,5	⊗(1,7/3,5)	⊗(2,5)

Table 6–9

Present state	Next state		Output Z	
	Input x			
	0	1	0	1
A	B	C	1	1
B	A	B	0	0
C	D	C	0	1
D	C or D	B	0	1

would be a minimal description of the machine since all states are present. But we must also check to see if the covering chosen is closed, thereby satisfying all the necessary implications. Now $(2, 3, 6, 7)$ implies $(7, 6)(7, 3)$ $(7, 2)(6, 3)(6, 2)$ and $(3, 2)$ which is valid; but $(4, 5, 8)$, implying $(4, 3)(4, 7)$ $(3, 7)$ and $(4, 5)$, is invalid since $(4, 3)$ and $(4, 7)$ do not occur in the same blocks. Thus the minimal description is given by the covering:

$$M = (1)(2, 3, 6, 7)(4, 5, 8)(3, 4, 7)$$

corresponding to the higher bound of four. The reduced state-table for the machine is shown in Table 6–9. To construct the table, let $A = (1)$, $B = (2, 3, 6, 7)$, $C = (4, 5, 8)$, and $D = (3, 4, 7)$. Now extract from the original state-table (Table 6–7) the next-state conditions for each compatible and note in which block they occur, repeating the process for each input condition. For example, the next-state conditions for $A = (1)$ are (2) for input 0, which is contained in B; and (8) for input 1, which is in C. Again, for $B = (2, 3, 6, 7)$, under input 0 we have $(1, \mathbf{X}, 1, \mathbf{X}) = A$ and for input 1, $(7, 6, 3, 2) = B$; similarly, for $C = (4, 5, 8)$ we have for input 0, $(4, 3, 7) = D$ and for input 1, $(\mathbf{X}, 4, 5) = C$. Finally, for $D = (3, 4, 7)$ we obtain for input 0, $(\mathbf{X}, 4, \mathbf{X}) = C$ or D, and for input 1, $(6, \mathbf{X}, 2) = B$. Note that, due to the 'don't care' condition in the original table, we have a choice of either C or D for the next-state transition of D under input 0.

The minimization of incompletely specified state-tables and the derivation of a reduced state-table are difficult problems, since there is no direct approach. However, by following the exhaustive search routine, and thereby obtaining all possible maximal compatibles, the best use of the 'don't care' entries will be ensured.

In general, the reduction of incompletely specified state-tables results in a set of maximal compatibles (a covering of the machine) from which a minimal subset satisfying the state-table transitions must be chosen. This process of selection is essentially a trial and error technique, as can be seen from the example above, for as yet no systematic method has been evolved.

6–5 Extraction of maximal compatibles
The procedure for extracting the maximal compatibles can be made more

Table 6–10

Column	Compatibles
7	
6	(7,6)
5	(8,5)(7,6)
4	(4,5)(4,7)(4,8)(8,5)(7,6) = (4,8,5)(4,7)(7,6)
3	(3,7)(3,6)(3,4)(4,8,5)(4,7)(7,6) = (4,8,5)(3,4,7)(3,7,6)
2	(2,7)(2,6)(2,3)(4,8,5)(3,4,7)(3,7,6) = (4,8,5)(3,4,7)(2,3,7,6)
1	(4,8,5)(3,4,7)(2,3,7,6)
Final	(1)(2,3,6,7)(3,4,7)(4,8,5)

systematic (essential for large-variable problems), and thus more amenable to machine computation. For example, the expansion into maximal compatibles can be performed column by column, see Tables 6–8 and 6–10, starting from the right-hand column (column 7). At each stage, the pair-wise compatibles are recorded and examined for possible groupings; for example, in column 4 we check to see if $(4, 5)(4, 7)(4, 8)$ can be grouped. We do this by examining the other compatibles, in this case we note that $8 \equiv 5$, or by checking through the implication chart. Thus we ascertain that the group $(4, 8, 5)$ may be formed, which consequently replaces the relevant pairwise compatibles in the table. This procedure is followed through to its natural conclusion on reaching column 1. The final expression is obtained by including those internal states not covered by the maximal compatibles as single-term compatibles.

An alternative approach may be attempted by assuming initially that all the internal states can be accommodated in one grouping, examining the implication chart for contradictions, and splitting the groups where necessary. Referring to Table 6–8, we see that column 1 indicates that state 1 cannot be grouped with states 2, 3, 4, 5, 6, 7, and 8, thus we separate these terms (see Table 6–11). Column 2 shows that state 2 cannot be grouped with states

Table 6–11

Column	Compatibles
	(1,2,3,4,5,6,7,8)
1	(1)(2,3,4,5,6,7,8)
2	(1)(2,3,6,7)(3,4,5,6,7,8)
3	(1)(2,3,6,7)(3,4,6,7)(4,5,6,7,8)
4	(1)(2,3,6,7)(3,6,7)(3,4,7)(4,5,7,8)(5,6,7,8)
	(1)(2,3,6,7)(3,4,7)(4,5,7,8)(5,6,7,8)
5	(1)(2,3,6,7)(3,4,7)(4,5,8)(4,8,7)(8,5)(6,7,8)
	(1)(2,3,6,7)(3,4,7)(4,5,8)(4,8,7)(6,7,8)
6	(1)(2,3,6,7)(3,4,7)(4,5,8)(4,8,7)(6,7)(7,8)
7	(1)(2,3,6,7)(3,4,7)(4,5,8)(4,8)(4,7)
Final	(1)(2,3,6,7)(3,4,7)(4,5,8)

4, 5, and 8, and the group $(2, 3, 4, 5, 6, 7, 8)$ is split into $(2, 3, 6, 7)$ and $(3, 4, 5, 6, 7, 8)$. This process is continued through to the final column; if, as a result of splitting a group, the term obtained can be combined with an existing group, this is done. For example, column 5 splits into groups which include $(8, 5)$ and $(6, 7, 8)$ the former group is already included in an existing group and can therefore be ignored. This technique gives the complete set of maximal compatibles and, furthermore, the systematic procedure is ideally suited for programming on a digital computer.

Another method, an algebraic approach due to Marcus,[4] operates on the incompatible equivalent pairs produced by the implication chart. The incompatible state-pairs for each column are expressed as a Boolean OR function, and then all these terms are combined using the AND operation. Thus we have effectively derived a product-of-sums expression describing the incompatible states in the implication chart. From Table 6–8, the incompatible state-pairs in column 1 are represented as $(1 + 2)(1 + 3)(1 + 4)(1 + 5)$ $(1 + 6)(1 + 7)(1 + 8)$, and in column 2 as $(2 + 4)(2 + 5)(2 + 8)$, which when continued yields the complete expression:

$$MI = (1 + 2)(1 + 3)(1 + 4)(1 + 5)(1 + 6)(1 + 7)(1 + 8)(2 + 4)(2 + 5)$$
$$(2 + 8)(3 + 5)(3 + 8)(4 + 6)(5 + 6)(5 + 7)(6 + 8)(7 + 8)$$

This expression can now be simplified by multiplying out and eliminating redundant terms according to the rules of Boolean algebra. The algebraic work is reduced if the state-pairs are grouped by columns:

$$MI = (1 + 2345678)(2 + 458)(3 + 58)(4 + 6)(5 + 67)(6 + 8)(7 + 8)$$

This follows since, if we multiply out the terms $(2 + 4)(2 + 5)(2 + 8)$ for example, we get:

$$T = 2 \cdot 2 \cdot 2 + 2 \cdot 2 \cdot 4 + 2 \cdot 2 \cdot 5 + 2 \cdot 4 \cdot 5 + 2 \cdot 2 \cdot 8$$
$$+ 2 \cdot 4 \cdot 8 + 2 \cdot 5 \cdot 8 + 4 \cdot 5 \cdot 8$$

Now, according to the rules of Boolean algebra, we can say that $2 \cdot 2 \cdot 2 = 2$ (from $A \cdot A = A$), and $2 + 2 \cdot 4 = 2$ [from $A + AB = A(1 + B) = A$], therefore the expression for T reduces to:

$$T = (2 + 458)$$

Thus, multiplying out and ignoring identical terms we have:

$$MI = (1 + 2345678)(2 + 458)(3 + 58)(4 + 6)(5 + 67)(6 + 8)(7 + 8)$$
$$= (12 + 2345678 + 1458)(34 + 458 + 36 + 586)$$
$$(567 + 67 + 578 + 678 + 568 + 58)$$
$$= (12 + 2345678 + 1458)(34 + 458 + 36 + 586)(67 + 58)$$

$$= 123458 + 2345678 + 13458 + 123658 + 145836 + 12458$$
$$+ 1458 + 12586 + 14586 + 123467 + 1345867 + 12367$$
$$+ 1245867 + 145867 + 125867$$

Hence

$$MI = 2345678 + 1458 + 12586 + 12367$$

Now for each resultant product we write down the missing internal states, and the resulting set is the set of maximal compatibles:

$$M = (1)(2367)(347)(458)$$

6–6 State assignment

Once the reduced state-table has been obtained, the next step in the design procedure is to allocate a binary code to every internal state, or row, in the table so that input equations for the storage elements (JK or SR bistables) may be derived. Any internal variable assignment which allocates a unique binary combination to each internal state will lead to a legitimate circuit, but the particular assignment chosen will have a considerable effect on the amount of hardware required to implement the circuit equations. To attempt the evaluation of all possible assignments for a particular table quickly leads to an insuperable amount of calculation. For a state-table with r rows requiring n state-variables, the number of different possible assignments is given by

$$N = \frac{2^n!}{(2^n - r)!}$$

However, many of these assignments are merely rearrangements or permutations of the variables and could be obtained by simply relabelling the variables. In these cases, no advantage can be gained economically by using a different assignment. For example, the four-row assignments $(00 - 01 - 11 - 10)$ and $(11 - 10 - 00 - 01)$ give the same basic circuits, since the latter can be obtained from the former by inverting the variables.

McCluskey[5] has shown that the number of distinct row assignments for a table with r rows using n state variables is

$$N_D = \frac{(2^n - 1)!}{(2^n - r)!\, n!}$$

This means that for a four-row table requiring two state-variables the number of possible distinct assignments is only three. However, the number of assignments rapidly increases to 840 for an eight-row table with three variables; for a nine-row table using four variables the number exceeds 10^7. Clearly it would be desirable to have some method of determining the best

Table 6–12 Pattern correlator—binary assignment

	Present states y_1 y_2 y_3	Input x_1x_2 Next states 00 01 11 10	Output Z 00 01 11 10
1	0 0 0	001 010 001 010	0 0 0 0
2	0 0 1	101 011 101 011	0 0 0 0
4	0 1 0	011 011 011 011	0 0 0 0
5	0 1 1	100 100 100 100	0 0 0 0
6	1 0 0	000 000 000 000	0 0 0 0
7	1 0 1	110 100 110 100	0 0 0 0
9	1 1 0	000 000 000 000	1 0 1 0
Unused	1 1 1		

state assignment for a particular table, which also took into account the constraints imposed by the particular hardware logic system, and would thus lead to an economical circuit. Unfortunately, no such technique exists at the present time, though considerable research has been done (and is still in progress) on this problem.

Though no systematic technique exists for optimum state assignment there are several useful rules and design methods which can assist in the development of an economical circuit. In the following discussion of these techniques we assume that the best starting point is the reduced state-table. Then, by the appropriate coding of the internal states, we attempt to derive near minimal equations for the combinational logic. As an illustration let us continue with the design of the pattern correlator whose reduced state-table is shown in Table 6–2. Suppose as a starting point we adopt an arbitrary assignment, say pure binary, for the internal states. The fully assigned table is shown in Table 6–12 where every state number in the reduced table has been replaced by a binary code. Note that we have a seven-row table which requires three variables y_1, y_2, and y_3 in order to allocate a unique code to each state or row. It also follows that three storage devices (bistables) Y_1, Y_2, and Y_3 are needed to store these internal states. We shall use set-reset bistables as the internal storage element and derive input equations for the set and reset terminals according to the conditions:

set requires a transition $\quad 0 \rightarrow 1 \quad$ (don't care $1 \rightarrow 1$)

reset requires a transition $\quad 1 \rightarrow 0 \quad$ (don't care $0 \rightarrow 0$)

The Karnaugh maps for the set and reset conditions of bistables Y_1, Y_2, and Y_3 are shown in Table 6–13. These are derived in the manner described in the last chapter, that is, the values of y_1, etc., for present and next states are examined in turn for the set and reset conditions, the appropriate values being entered on the Karnaugh maps. Considering the set conditions of Y_1,

Table 6–13 Karnaugh maps—binary assignment

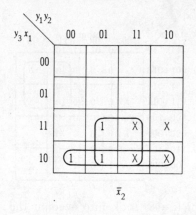

(a) Y_1 Set

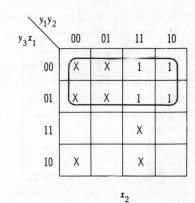

(b) Y_1 Reset

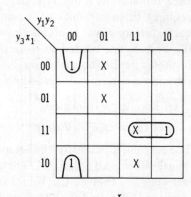

(c) Y_2 Set

Table 6–13 continued

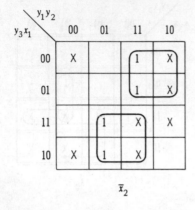

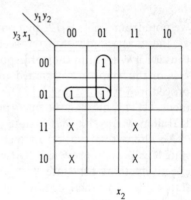

(d) Y_2 Reset

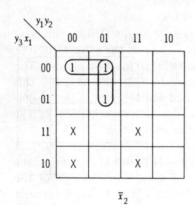

(e) Y_3 Set

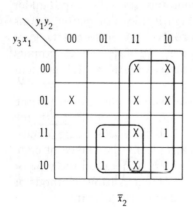

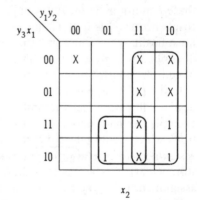

(f) Y_3 Reset

Table 6–13 continued

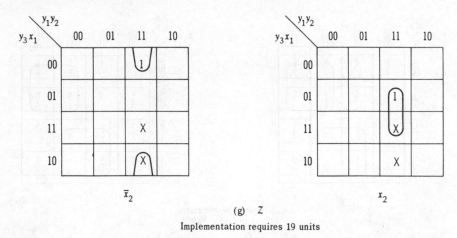

(g) Z

Implementation requires 19 units

we note from Table 6–12, by comparing the present and next state values of y_1, that a set condition is required when $y_1y_2y_3x_1x_2$ takes the value of 00100; thus a 1 is entered in the corresponding Karnaugh map in this position. The rest of the maps are obtained in the same way by following through this procedure for y_1, y_2, and y_3. There is one unused combination in the assignment (111), this can be incorporated as a 'don't care' condition in the Karnaugh maps, since this state can never occur in practice.

An alternative method of including the 'don't care' condition is to treat state 9 as being represented by two combinations—110 and 111. This means effectively that, for state 9, y_3 is a 'don't care' condition throughout the state-table. In practice, however, the set and reset inputs to a SR bistable should never occur together (this would appear on the Karnaugh maps as a 1 in the same square for both reset and set conditions) since the output under these conditions is indeterminate. Thus, though it does not matter in this case whether y_3 is 0 or 1, since either will correctly represent the state, care must be taken to ensure that the simultaneous presence of set and reset inputs does not adversely affect the bistable circuit. The use of a JK bistable element would obviate this problem.

It should be apparent that the particular storage element chosen for the design will also affect the amount of combinational logic required. If, for example, we had used a JK bistable there would be more 'don't care' conditions which could effect the minimization. Thus ideally the choice of code assignment for the internal states should take into consideration the type of storage device to be used. In these examples we compare various methods of assignment using the SR bistable as the standard storage element.

If we extracted the input equations for Y_1, Y_2, and Y_3 from the maps and

132   Design of synchronous sequential circuits

Table 6–14 Effectiveness of internal state assignment

y_3x_1 \ y_1y_2	00	01	11	10
00	1	4	9	6
01	1	4	9	6
11	2	5		7
10	2	5		7

$\bar{x}_2$

y_3x_1 \ y_1y_2	00	01	11	10
00	1	4	9	6
01	1	4	9	6
11	2	5		7
10	2	5		7

x_2

(a) Present states

y_3x_1 \ y_1y_2	00	01	11	10
00	2	5	1	1
01	4	5	1	1
11	5	6		6
10	7	6		9

$\bar{x}_2$

y_3x_1 \ y_1y_2	00	01	11	10
00	4	5	1	1
01	2	5	1	1
11	7	6		9
10	5	6		6

x_2

(b) Next states

implemented them in hardware, we would have a sequential circuit which would correctly satisfy the design specification. Thus:

$$Y_1 \text{ set} \quad = y_2y_3 + \bar{x}_1\bar{x}_2y_3 + x_1x_2y_3$$
$$Y_1 \text{ reset} = \bar{y}_3$$
$$Y_2 \text{ set} \quad = x_1\bar{x}_2\bar{y}_1\bar{y}_2 + \bar{x}_1\bar{x}_2y_1y_3 + x_1x_2y_1y_3 + \bar{x}_1x_2\bar{y}_1\bar{y}_2$$
$$Y_2 \text{ reset} = y_1\bar{y}_3 + y_2y_3$$
$$Y_3 \text{ set} \quad = \bar{y}_1y_2\bar{y}_3 + \bar{x}_1\bar{x}_2\bar{y}_1\bar{y}_3 + x_1x_2\bar{y}_1\bar{y}_3$$
$$Y_3 \text{ reset} = y_1 + y_2y_3$$
$$Z \text{ output} = \bar{x}_1\bar{x}_2y_1y_2 + x_1x_2y_1y_2$$

However, we have no means of knowing if these equations produce a minimal circuit without trying all possible (840) codes! Is there some simple method we can use to ensure at least some degree of minimization? There is, in fact, a simple rule due to Humphrey[6] which is slightly better than choosing a purely arbitrary assignment. But though in general it leads to simpler input equations, there is no question of it producing a unique best state assignment. Consider Table 6–14(a), which is basically a Karnaugh map depicting the present state assignments made above, i.e. pure binary, for all input conditions. Each state appears four times, since there are four possible input conditions. Underneath this map a similar diagram is plotted showing the next states resulting from the prescribed input changes. The positions of the next states in Table 6–14(b) show where the set, reset, and 'don't care' bistable input conditions for a particular state-variable will occur when plotted on the Karnaugh map. This may easily be confirmed by comparing Table 6–13 with Table 6–14. Thus if similar next states were made adjacent in Table 6–14(b), as for example state 1, the input conditions for transitions to that state would be adjacent and hence easily combined and reduced. For example, if we are in present state 6, coded 100, any input transition takes us to state 1, coded 000, thus we need to reset Y_1 under these conditions (in general there will, of course, be other conditions as well). Similarly, we need to reset Y_2 for the transition from present state 9 to next state 1. Since all these conditions are adjacent when plotted on the Karnaugh map [Table 6–13(b) and (d)] they may be combined into a larger group. Note that the

Table 6–15 Pattern correlator—next state assignment

(a)

Next states	Present states
1	6,9
2	1
4	1
5	2,4
6	5,7
7	2
9	7

(b)

Present states	y_1 y_2 y_3	Next states 00	01	11	10	Output Z 00	01	11	10
1	0 0 0	010	110	010	110	0	0	0	0
2	0 1 0	101	100	101	100	0	0	0	0
4	1 1 0	100	100	100	100	0	0	0	0
5	1 0 0	111	111	111	111	0	0	0	0
6	1 1 1	000	000	000	000	0	0	0	0
7	1 0 1	011	111	011	111	0	0	0	0
9	0 1 1	000	000	000	000	1	0	1	0
Unused	0 0 1								

Input $x_1 x_2$

reason these next states are adjacent is that the present states giving rise to them are also adjacent, i.e. present states 9, 6 are adjacent, hence next state 1 is adjacent. Thus we can formulate the following rules: (a) *if two or more states have the same next states, they should be made adjacent in the assignment;* (b) *it is also advisable to give adjacent coding to states if they are both next states of a present state.* For example, in Table 6–2, states 2 and 4 are the next states of 1, and 7, 5 and 9, 6 are the next states of 2 and 7. Thus these states should be made adjacent; that this should be so is apparent from Table 6–14, since the next states of a state are always adjacent. However, should there be any discrepancy between the two rules, the first should always take precedence. If we examine the state-table (Table 6–2) to determine the origin of all the next states we arrive at the result shown in Table 6–15(a). This indicates that states (6, 9), (2, 4) and (5, 7) should have adjacent codes, and as this is identical with the result obtained above for the next states of a state, there is no conflict between the two rules. Table 6–15(b) shows the fully assigned table using these two rules as the basis for coding;

Table 6–16 Karnaugh maps—next state assignment

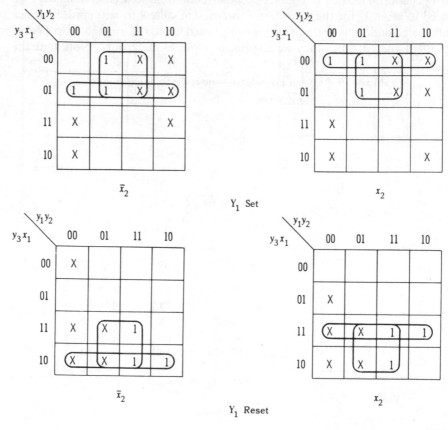

Y_1 Set

Y_1 Reset

notice that states $(2, 4)$, $(7, 5)$ and $(9, 6)$ differ by one bit only—they are adjacent. The Karnaugh maps for the state variables Y_1, Y_2, and Y_3, using this assignment, are shown in Table 6–16, and lead to the equations:

$$Y_1 \text{ set } = y_2\bar{y}_3 + x_1\bar{x}_2\bar{y}_3 + \bar{x}_1x_2\bar{y}_3$$
$$Y_1 \text{ reset } = y_2y_3 + \bar{x}_1\bar{x}_2y_3 + x_1x_2y_3$$
$$Y_2 \text{ set } = \bar{y}_2$$
$$Y_2 \text{ reset } = y_2$$
$$Y_3 \text{ set } = y_1\bar{y}_2 + \bar{x}_1\bar{x}_2\bar{y}_1y_2\bar{y}_3 + x_1x_2\bar{y}_1y_2\bar{y}_3$$
$$Y_3 \text{ reset } = y_2y_3$$
$$Z \text{ output } = \bar{x}_1\bar{x}_2\bar{y}_1y_3 + x_1x_2\bar{y}_1y_3$$

By direct comparison with the maps of Table 6–13, or by examining the equations, it is clear that, using the next state assignment rule, the input functions are much simpler.

Table 6–16 continued

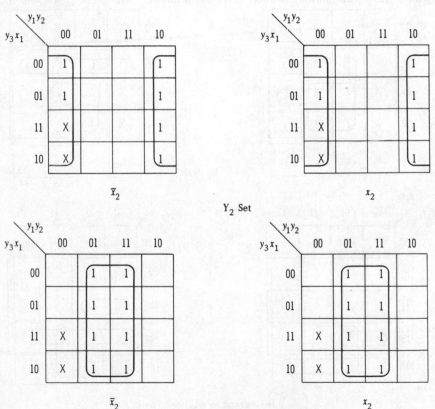

Y_2 Set

Y_2 Reset

Table 6–16 continued

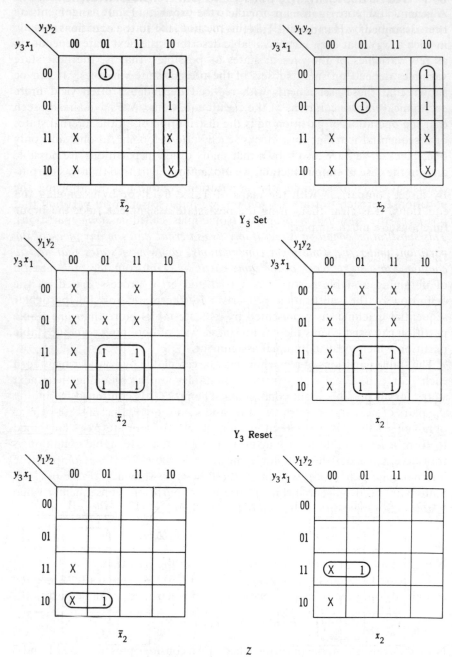

Y_3 Set

Y_3 Reset

Z

Implementation requires 15 units

6–7 State assignment using the partition principle

A general and more rigorous approach to the problem of state assignment has been described by Hartmanis.[7] In this method, the state assignment is made in such a way that each binary variable describing the next state depends on as few variables of the present states as possible; that is, the next state variables depend on small subsets of the present state variables. It can be shown that these assignments with reduced dependence often yield more economical implementations of the circuit equations. We have already seen that the operation of partitioning is the distribution of all the internal states of a sequential machine into blocks, each state belonging to one, and only one, block. We have also shown that many different partitions are possible and, in the case of state reduction, we looked for a partition that was output-consistent and closed under the implication conditions. In applying the partition approach to state assignment, we must search for a partition that possesses the *substitution* property (sometimes called a *stable* partition). *This substitution condition is met if any two internal states in any block of the partition, under the same input combinations, go to next states that are all contained in a single block of the same partition.* Unfortunately, the method of obtaining a stable partition is a trial and error process, based on the definition of the substitution property. Furthermore, for any particular sequential machine (as represented by its state-table) more than one stable partition can exist. Thus there is no simple way of obtaining a unique stable partition which yields a minimal assignment.

The stable partitions of a machine may be calculated by considering in turn each pair of internal states in the state-table, and ascertaining their next states for all possible input conditions. The process is continued by finding the pairs of next states for these pairs, and so on, until a list of state-pairs is obtained. The final list is then examined and appropriate pairs combined to form a *least* stable partition, using the fact that the stable condition is transitive. Consider the state-table shown in Table 6–2. If we compare the internal state-pair $(1, 5)$, we obtain the flow-table shown in Table 6–17(a). State-pairs need only be included once in the partition, consequently when a state-pair repeats it can be ignored. The final list is

$$P = (1, 5)(2, 6)(4, 6)(7, 1)(2, 9)$$

Note that all the internal states are included in the partition.

The pairs $(1, 5)$ and $(7, 1)$, also the pairs $(2, 6)$, $(4, 6)$ and $(2, 9)$, may be combined using the transitive relationship to give the least stable partition:

$$P_1 = (1, 5, 7)(2, 4, 6, 9)$$

Note that this is a stable partition since, if we consider present states 1 and 7 (Table 6–2), for example, the next states for the input conditions 00, 01, 11,

Table 6–17 Extraction of stable partitions

(a)

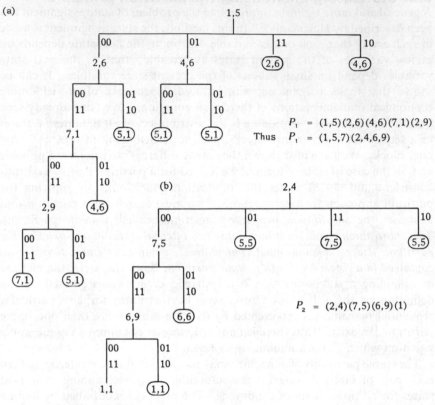

$$P_1 = (1,5)(2,6)(4,6)(7,1)(2,9)$$

Thus $P_1 = (1,5,7)(2,4,6,9)$

$$P_2 = (2,4)(7,5)(6,9)(1)$$

and 10 are $(2, 9)(4, 6)(2, 9)(4, 6)$, which are all contained in a single block of the same partition. For this particular sequential machine, there are only two non-trivial partitions with the substitution property on its set of internal states, they are

$$P_1 = (1, 5, 7)(2, 4, 6, 9)$$

and $P_2 = (1)(2, 4)(7, 5)(6, 9)$

All the rest are trivial in the sense that all the states are contained in one partition:

$$P_3 = (1, 2, 4, 5, 6, 7, 9)$$

The direct examination of state-pairs, as described above, does not necessarily produce the complete set of stable partitions. Fortunately certain algebraic relationships exist between partitions of the same set, and it can be shown that these preserve the substitution property. Thus, once we have found (by examination) all non-trivial partitions, the others may be obtained by algebraic methods without further recourse to the state-table.

Table 6–17 continued

(c)

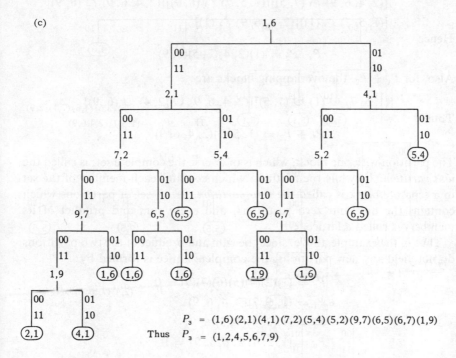

$$P_3 = (1,6)(2,1)(4,1)(7,2)(5,4)(5,2)(9,7)(6,5)(6,7)(1,9)$$

Thus $P_3 = (1,2,4,5,6,7,9)$

If P_1 and P_2 are two partitions of the same set, the algebraic relationships between them may be defined as follows:

(a) P_1 is said to be greater than P_2 $(P_1 \geq P_2)$ if each block of P_2 is contained in a block of P_1.

(b) The sum of two partitions (least upper bound) $(P_1 + P_2)$ is the partition whose blocks are the union of overlapping (i.e. containing common members) blocks of P_1 and P_2.

(c) The product of two partitions (greatest lower bound) $(P_1 . P_2)$ is the partition whose blocks are the intersections of blocks of P_1 with blocks of P_2.

As an illustration, consider the two blocks derived above:

$$P_1 = (1, 5, 7)(2, 4, 6, 9)$$

and $$P_2 = (1)(2, 4)(7, 5)(6, 9)$$

(Note that $P_1 > P_2$). Now taking each block in turn we have:

$$P_1 . P_2 = [(1, 5, 7) \cap (2, 4)][(2, 4, 6, 9) \cap (2, 4)][(1, 5, 7) \cap (7, 5)]$$
$$[(2, 4, 6, 9) \cap (7, 5)][(1, 5, 7) \cap (6, 9)][(2, 4, 6, 9) \cap (6, 9)]$$
$$[(1, 5, 7) \cap (1)][(2, 4, 6, 9) \cap (1)]$$

Hence

$$P_1 . P_2 = (1)(2, 4)(7, 5)(6, 9)$$

Also, for $P_1 + P_2$, the overlapping blocks are:

$$[(1, 5, 7) \cup (1) \cup (7, 5)][(2, 4, 6, 9) \cup (2, 4) \cup (6, 9)]$$

Thus

$$P_1 + P_2 = (1, 5, 7)(2, 4, 6, 9)$$

The partition with one block, which is of course the complete set, is called the *unit partition* (1), while the partition which contains each member of the set in a separate block is called the *zero partition* (0). A set of partitions which contains the unit and zero partitions, and every sum and product of its members is called a lattice.[9][10]

Thus in the example above, since the sum and product of the two partitions do not yield any new partitions, the complete lattice is formed by:

$$P_0 = (1)(2)(4)(5)(6)(7)(9) = 0$$
$$P_1 = (1, 5, 7)(2, 4, 6, 9)$$
$$P_2 = (1)(2, 4)(7, 5)(6, 9)$$
$$P_3 = (1, 2, 4, 5, 6, 7, 9) = 1$$

To sum up, the lattice of stable partitions is obtained by deriving the non-trivial partitions from the state-table, and then generating all other partitions from this set by combining them using the addition operation.

Having now discovered how to obtain stable partitions for a sequential machine, we must next explain how to use them in state assignment. Noting in passing that it is advisable to obtain the complete set of all non-trivial stable partitions and select the ones with the fewest blocks (and/or elements) before commencing the allocation. The first step, then, is to select a suitable partition; suppose in this case we choose

$$P_1 = (1)(2, 4)(5, 7)(6, 9)$$

By inspection, we see that there are four blocks, each block containing a maximum of two elements. Now we also know that for seven internal states, three bits are required for the state-variables, thus two of these can be used to distinguish between blocks, and the remaining bit to distinguish between elements within a block. There are three distinct ways of making this assignment and they should all be investigated. A possible assignment scheme is shown in Table 6–18(a), and the fully assigned state-table is given in Table

Table 6–18 Pattern correlator—partition assignment

(a)

Block	Allocation $y_1\ y_2$
(1)	1 0
(2,4)	0 0
(7,5)	0 1
(6,9)	1 1

(b)

	Present states $y_1\ y_2\ y_3$	Next states (Input x_1x_2) 00	01	11	10	Output Z 00	01	11	10
1	1 0 1	000	001	000	001	0	0	0	0
2	0 0 0	011	010	011	010	0	0	0	0
4	0 0 1	010	010	010	010	0	0	0	0
5	0 1 0	110	110	110	110	0	0	0	0
6	1 1 0	101	101	101	101	0	0	0	0
7	0 1 1	111	110	111	110	0	0	0	0
9	1 1 1	101	101	101	101	1	0	1	0
Unused	1 0 0								

6–18(b). Note that, in using this method, we have arranged that the first two bits of the next state (y_1y_2) can be determined solely from the first two bits (y_1y_2) of the present state and the inputs (x_1x_2). Thus we have a self-dependent subset (y_1y_2) of the state-variables set ($y_1y_2y_3$), also Y_1 set, Y_2 set, Y_1 reset, and Y_2 reset will be, at most, a function of four variables only. However, Y_3 can still depend on $y_1y_2y_3$ and the inputs (x_1x_2).

The Karnaugh maps for this assignment are shown in Table 6–19. This is by far the simplest solution obtained and gives the following input and output equations:

$$
\begin{aligned}
Y_1 \text{ set} &= y_2\\
Y_1 \text{ reset} &= \bar{y}_2\\
Y_2 \text{ set} &= \bar{y}_1\\
Y_2 \text{ reset} &= y_1\\
Y_3 \text{ set} &= y_1y_2 + \bar{y}_3\bar{y}_2\bar{x}_1\bar{x}_2 + \bar{y}_3\bar{y}_2x_1x_2\\
Y_3 \text{ reset} &= \bar{y}_1x_1\bar{x}_2 + \bar{y}_1\bar{x}_1x_2 + y_3\bar{y}_2\bar{x}_1\bar{x}_2 + y_3\bar{y}_2x_1x_2\\
Z \text{ output} &= y_1y_2y_3\bar{x}_1\bar{x}_2 + y_1y_2y_3x_1x_2
\end{aligned}
$$

In this particular case there is no need to plot a map for Z, since the function can be obtained directly from the assigned state-table.

Table 6–19 Karnaugh maps for partition assignment

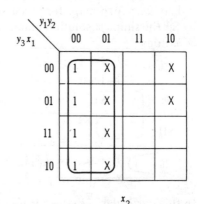

Y_1 Set

Map ($\bar{x}_2$), with columns y_1y_2 = 00, 01, 11, 10 and rows y_3x_1 = 00, 01, 11, 10:

$y_3x_1 \backslash y_1y_2$	00	01	11	10
00		1	X	X
01		1	X	X
11		1	X	
10		1	X	

Map (x_2):

$y_3x_1 \backslash y_1y_2$	00	01	11	10
00		1	X	X
01		1	X	X
11		1	X	
10		1	X	

Y_1 Reset

Map ($\bar{x}_2$):

$y_3x_1 \backslash y_1y_2$	00	01	11	10
00	X			X
01	X			X
11	X			1
10	X			1

Map (x_2):

$y_3x_1 \backslash y_1y_2$	00	01	11	10
00	X			X
01	X			X
11	X			1
10	X			1

Y_2 Set

Map ($\bar{x}_2$):

$y_3x_1 \backslash y_1y_2$	00	01	11	10
00	1	X		X
01	1	X		X
11	1	X		
10	1	X		

Map (x_2):

$y_3x_1 \backslash y_1y_2$	00	01	11	10
00	1	X		X
01	1	X		X
11	1	X		
10	1	X		

Table 6–19 continued

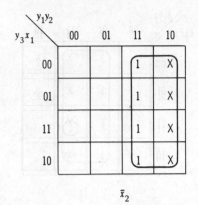

$\bar{x}_2$ (left map) / x_2 (right map)

Y_2 Reset

$y_3 x_1 \backslash y_1 y_2$	00	01	11	10
00			1	X
01			1	X
11			1	X
10			1	X

$y_3 x_1 \backslash y_1 y_2$	00	01	11	10
00			1	X
01			1	X
11			1	X
10			1	X

Y_3 Set

$\bar{x}_2$ (left map) / x_2 (right map)

$y_3 x_1 \backslash y_1 y_2$	00	01	11	10
00	1		1	X
01			1	X
11			1	X
10		X	X	

$y_3 x_1 \backslash y_1 y_2$	00	01	11	10
00			1	X
01	1		1	X
11			X	
10			X	X

Y_3 Reset

$\bar{x}_2$ (left map) / x_2 (right map)

$y_3 x_1 \backslash y_1 y_2$	00	01	11	10
00		X		X
01	X	X		X
11	1	1		
10	1			1

$y_3 x_1 \backslash y_1 y_2$	00	01	11	10
00	X	X		X
01		X		X
11	1			1
10	1	1		

Table 6–19 continued

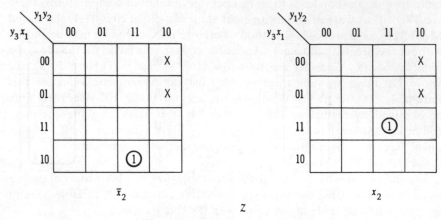

z

Implementation requires 12 units

In the discussion above, the partition approach has been developed using the reduced state-table as a starting point. However, the process of state minimization and state assignment may be combined in the one process for a completely specified machine. To do this we must extract from the normal (unreduced) state-table all the stable partitions which result from the comparison of state-pairs, as described earlier. From this set we select those partitions which are output-consistent (output the same for all states in any block of the partition). If there are no output-consistent partitions, the machine cannot be reduced. These output-consistent partitions must also possess the substitution property, otherwise the resulting machine will not have unique states. The minimal state partition for the machine may be obtained by adding partitions together (using the rule for addition of partitions), and selecting the partition with the fewest blocks.

In some sequential machines, the set of non-trivial stable partitions does not yield a viable assignment (that is, the assignment uses more secondary variables than that required by direct coding). In other cases there are no non-trivial stable partitions for the machine. Stearns and Hartmanis[8] have extended the partition approach to allow assignments, with reduced dependence on the secondary variables, to be obtained from non-stable partitions, using the concepts of *partition pair* algebra.

6–8 Alternative approach to state assignment

A paper by Dolotta and McCluskey[11] has described a technique of state assignment which, though still not producing an optimum design, yields consistently good results and is easier to program for a digital computer than any other known method.

We have seen that to try all the possible distinct codes (N_D) for a state-table assignment soon leads to an insuperable amount of computation—there are 840 distinct ways of coding an eight-state sequential circuit! Dolotta and McCluskey have proposed a method whereby a good encoding may be chosen without the necessity of trying all possible codes; it is based on the idea of a *codable column*. Consider the four-row table 'shown in Table 6–20(a), we know that there are only three possible distinct assignment codes for this state-table: 00–01–10–11; 00–01–11–10; and 00–11–01–10. All others may be obtained by relabelling the variables. It is possible to represent these codings in terms of the codable columns C_1, C_2, and C_3 shown in Table 6–20(a), since they may be combined to give the actual assignments: (C_1, C_2), (C_1, C_3), and (C_2, C_3).

Thus all the possible codings for a state-table may be obtained by choosing suitable subsets of the complete set of codable columns. A codable column for an r-row state-table is any column of 0's and 1's which

(a) is of length r,
(b) has a leading (uppermost) 0,
(c) has not greater than 2^{n-1} 0's, and
(d) has not greater than 2^{n-1} 1's,

where n is the number of state-variables required and is defined by the inequality:

$$2^{n-1} < r \leqslant 2^n$$

In the case of the four-row table, $r = 4$ and $n = 2$. Tables 6–20(b) and (c) show how the codable columns may be generated using the definition above. If the number of codable columns, $C_{(r)}$, for given values of r and n are calculated[12] [Table 6–20(d)] and compared with N_D, we see that they are considerably smaller in value. Thus, if we manipulate the codable columns, and devise a method of choosing an appropriate column subset, the amount of computation required to achieve a good coding will be considerably reduced.

The codable columns for a particular state-table may be represented as a base matrix with r rows and $C_{(r)}$ columns. Furthermore, we may identify each internal state of the table with a row of the base matrix in a one-to-one correspondence. The next states for each input combination may then be represented in the same way; the state-table matrices are shown in Table 6–20(e). Note that the matrix for $x = 0$ is formed by writing down the rows of the base matrix corresponding to the next state values when $x = 0$. In this way, it is possible to see how each codable column maps into the next state column; this is similar in some ways to the Karnaugh map method of determining best assignment which was described earlier. In this technique, however, we can examine all possible codable columns and not just one assignment. By examining each column mapping in turn and evaluating the

Table 6–20 Codable columns

(a)

Present state	Inputs x 0	1	Possible assignment codings			Codable columns C_1	C_2	C_3
1	2	3	00	00	00	0	0	0
2	1	2	01	01	11	0	1	1
3	4	3	10	11	01	1	0	1
4	4	2	11	10	10	1	1	0

(b)

Length $r = 4$, $n = 2$
$C_{(r)} = 3$

```
                     ↓      ↓ ↓
0 0 0 0 0 0 0 0 1 1 1 1 1 1 1 1
0 0 0 0 1 1 1 1 0 0 0 0 1 1 1 1
0 0 1 1 0 0 1 1 0 0 1 1 0 0 1 1
0 1 0 1 0 1 0 1 0 1 0 1 0 1 0 1
```

(c)

Length $r = 5$, $n = 3$
$C_{(r)} = 15$

```
        ↓↓↓↓↓↓↓↓↓↓↓↓↓↓↓
00000000000000001111111111111111
00000000111111110000000011111111
00001111000011110000111100001111
00110011001100110011001100110011
01010101010101010101010101010101
```

(d)

Number of rows (r)	State variable (n)	$C_{(r)}$	N_D
1	0	–	–
2	1	1	1
3	2	3	3
4	2	3	3
5	3	15	140
6	3	25	420
7	3	35	840
8	3	35	840

(e)

Present state	Base matrix			$x = 0$ matrix			$x = 1$ matrix		
1	0	0	0	0	1	1	1	0	1
2	0	1	1	0	0	0	0	1	1
3	1	0	1	1	1	0	1	0	1
4	1	1	0	1	1	0	0	1	1
Octal coding	03	05	06	03	–04	–07	–05	05	–00

result in terms of some suitable minimization criteria, we can determine the best coding method to use. For the convenience of the computation, particularly if programmed for a digital computer, the codable columns are normally represented using octal notation. The least significant digit is taken to be at the bottom, and the column is split up in the normal way with three binary digits being equivalent to one octal digit. Columns which have uppermost 1's are represented as complements, which are obtained by inverting the column (changing 1's for 0's and vice versa) and expressing the result as a negative octal number.

The complete state assignment procedure, including the method of column evaluation using a 'scoring' process developed by Dolotta and McCluskey, is best illustrated by means of an example, and we shall again use the pattern correlator problem. The reduced state-table is shown in Table 6–2 and has seven rows requiring three state variables for its implementation. This means that the base matrix, shown in Table 6–21(a), will consist of 35 codable columns (which may be deduced from the definition) and seven rows. The next state matrices are shown in Table 6–21(b) and (c)—in this particular problem the matrices for the input conditions 00,11 and 01,10 are identical. The next step is to express the codable column matrices in octal terms, and to extract the corresponding next state columns for all input conditions. For example, column 1 in the base matrix may be expressed as octal 007, which maps to 052, 012, 052, and 012 for the changing input conditions 00–01–11–10; the complete tabulation is shown in Table 6–22.

We are now in a position to make the comparison. For each row of Table 6–22 the base entry is compared with the next state entries and allocated a 'score' according to the following criteria established by Dolotta and McCluskey:

(a) An all 0 entry in the row scores 20 marks.
(b) An all 1 entry (complement of all 0) in the row scores 10 marks.
(c) Identical entries in adjacent columns (change of one variable) score 20 marks.
(d) Identical entry to base entry scores 4 marks.
(e) Identical entry to complement of base entry scores 4 marks.

The scores are expressed in octal notation, again to facilitate computer manipulation, and suitable care should be exercised in their handling.

The score 1 column in Table 6–22 is obtained as a result of performing this comparison. Note that row 5 (base vector 017) scores octal 100, since all four identical entries are adjacent, while row 30 (base vector 065) scores octal 120, since all four entries are identical with the base vector complement and are also adjacent. As a result of this comparison, we choose the base vector with the *highest* score (065) as the first codable column. As a consequence of

Table 6–21 Matrix representation of pattern correlator state-table

| | | 10 | 12 | 14 | 16 | 18 | 20 | 22 | 24 | 26 | 28 | 30 | 32 | 34 |
| 1 2 3 4 5 6 7 8 9 | 11 | 13 | 15 | 17 | 19 | 21 | 23 | 25 | 27 | 29 | 31 | 33 | 35 |

Present states

1	0 0 0 0 0 0 0 0 0 0 0 0 0 0 0 0 0 0 0 0 0 0 0 0 0 0 0 0 0 0 0 0 0 0 0
2	0 0 0 0 0 0 0 0 0 0 0 0 0 0 0 0 0 1 1 1 1 1 1 1 1 1 1 1 1 1 1 1 1 1 1
4	0 0 0 0 0 1 1 1 1 1 1 1 1 1 1 0 0 0 0 0 0 0 0 0 0 1 1 1 1 1 1 1 1 1 1
5	0 1 1 1 1 0 0 0 0 1 1 1 1 1 0 0 0 0 1 1 1 1 1 0 0 0 0 0 0 0 1 1 1 1
6	1 0 1 1 1 0 1 1 1 0 0 0 1 1 1 0 1 1 1 0 0 0 1 1 1 0 0 0 1 1 1 0 0 0 1
7	1 1 0 1 1 1 0 1 1 0 1 1 0 0 1 1 0 1 1 0 1 1 0 0 1 0 1 1 0 0 1 0 0 1 0
9	1 1 1 0 1 1 1 0 1 1 0 1 0 1 0 1 1 0 1 1 0 1 0 1 0 1 0 1 0 1 0 0 1 0 0

(a)   Base matrix: $C_{(r)}$ columns and r rows

Next states

2	0 0 0 0 0 0 0 0 0 0 0 0 0 0 0 0 0 1 1 1 1 1 1 1 1 1 1 1 1 1 1 1 1 1 1
7	1 1 0 1 1 1 0 1 1 0 1 1 0 0 1 1 0 1 1 0 1 1 0 0 1 0 1 1 0 0 1 0 0 1 0
5	0 1 1 1 1 0 0 0 0 1 1 1 1 1 0 0 0 0 1 1 1 1 1 0 0 0 0 0 0 0 1 1 1 1
6	1 0 1 1 1 0 1 1 1 0 0 0 1 1 1 0 1 1 1 0 0 0 1 1 1 0 0 0 1 1 1 0 0 0 1
1	0 0 0 0 0 0 0 0 0 0 0 0 0 0 0 0 0 0 0 0 0 0 0 0 0 0 0 0 0 0 0 0 0 0 0
9	1 1 1 0 1 1 1 0 1 1 0 1 0 1 0 1 1 0 1 1 0 1 0 1 0 1 0 1 0 1 0 0 1 0 0
1	0 0 0 0 0 0 0 0 0 0 0 0 0 0 0 0 0 0 0 0 0 0 0 0 0 0 0 0 0 0 0 0 0 0 0

(b)   00 and 11 matrix

Next states

4	0 0 0 0 0 1 1 1 1 1 1 1 1 1 1 0 0 0 0 0 0 0 0 0 0 1 1 1 1 1 1 1 1 1 1
5	0 1 1 1 1 0 0 0 0 1 1 1 1 1 0 0 0 0 1 1 1 1 1 0 0 0 0 0 0 0 1 1 1 1
5	0 1 1 1 1 0 0 0 0 1 1 1 1 1 0 0 0 0 1 1 1 1 1 0 0 0 0 0 0 0 1 1 1 1
6	1 0 1 1 1 0 1 1 1 0 0 0 1 1 1 0 1 1 1 0 0 0 1 1 1 0 0 0 1 1 1 0 0 0 1
1	0 0 0 0 0 0 0 0 0 0 0 0 0 0 0 0 0 0 0 0 0 0 0 0 0 0 0 0 0 0 0 0 0 0 0
6	1 0 1 1 1 0 1 1 1 0 0 0 1 1 1 0 1 1 1 0 0 0 1 1 1 0 0 0 1 1 1 0 0 0 1
1	0 0 0 0 0 0 0 0 0 0 0 0 0 0 0 0 0 0 0 0 0 0 0 0 0 0 0 0 0 0 0 0 0 0 0

(c)   01 and 10 matrix

Table 6–22 Column comparison

	Base	00	01	11	10	Score 1	Score 2	Score 3
1	007	052	012	052	012	0	0	0
2	013	062	060	062	060	0	0	0
3	015	032	072	032	072	0	0	20
4	016	070	072	070	072	0	0	20
5	017	072	072	072	072	100	100*	
6	023	042	−077	042	−077	0	0	2
7	025	012	−065	012	−065	0	30	30
8	026	050	−065	050	−065	0	30	30
9	027	052	−065	052	−065	0	30	30
10	031	022	−017	022	−017	0	0	10
11	032	060	−017	060	−017	0	0	10
12	033	062	−017	062	−017	0	0	10
13	034	030	−005	030	−005	0	0	2
14	035	032	−005	032	−005	0	0	2
15	036	070	−005	070	−005	0	0	2
16	043	−035	000	−035	000	40	40	40*
17	045	−065	012	−065	012	0	30	30
18	046	−027	012	−027	012	0	0	0
19	047	−025	012	−025	012	0	0	0
20	051	−055	060	−055	060	0	0	0
21	052	−017	060	−017	060	0	0	10
22	053	−015	060	−015	060	0	0	0
23	054	−047	072	−047	072	0	0	20
24	055	−045	072	−045	072	0	0	20
25	056	−007	072	−007	072	0	0	20
26	061	−075	−077	−075	−077	0	0	2
27	062	−037	−077	−037	−077	0	0	2
28	063	−035	−077	−035	−077	0	0	2
29	064	−067	−065	−067	−065	0	30	30
30	065	−065	−065	−065	−065	120*		
31	066	−027	−065	−027	−065	0	30	30
32	070	−057	−017	−057	−017	0	0	10
33	071	−055	−017	−055	−017	0	0	10
34	072	−017	−017	−017	−017	100	100	120
35	074	−047	−005	−047	−005	0	0	2

choosing the first column, the scoring procedure must be modified in our search for column two:

(a) The occurrence of an entry corresponding to a chosen column scores 4 marks.
(b) The occurrence of similar entries to those in the chosen column (this is a condition for output sharing in multi-terminal circuits) scores 20 marks.

Again we inspect the table and allocate marks accordingly; these must be added to any existing score, since the marks are cumulative. The score 2 column in Table 6–22 shows the result of this operation—note that row 7 (base vector 025) scores 30 as a result of row similarity and identity with the previously chosen column. We shall choose the base vector 017 as our next codable column (there is an alternative—072). But we must first ascertain if the two columns, 065 and 017, will form a valid code, i.e. can they eventually be combined into a code with 2^n distinct rows, for it is not necessarily true that any set of n codable columns will constitute a valid code? If a code is to be valid the constituent columns, in addition to being codable, must satisfy the following conditions:

1. For each pair of columns, C_1 and C_2 of a set $C_1, C_2, \ldots C_n$, the number of 1's obtained by performing the AND operation between all combinations of the columns $(\bar{C}_1\bar{C}_2, \bar{C}_1C_2, C_1\bar{C}_2, C_1C_2)$ must be less than, or equal to, 2^{n-2} in each case.
2. In general, for a complete code to be valid the same operation must be performed on all columns in all combinations, i.e. for three columns we have $\bar{C}_1\bar{C}_2\bar{C}_3$, $\bar{C}_1\bar{C}_2C_3$, $\bar{C}_1C_2\bar{C}_3$, $\bar{C}_1C_2C_3$, $C_1\bar{C}_2\bar{C}_3$, $C_1\bar{C}_2C_3$, $C_1C_2\bar{C}_3$, and $C_1C_2C_3$, and the sum of the 1's in each case must be less than, or equal to, 2^{n-K}, where n is the number of state variables and K the number of columns.

In this case, for the base vectors 065 and 017, with $n = 3$ and $K = 2$, we have:

$$(\overline{065})(\overline{017}) = 1 \leq 2$$
$$(\overline{065})(017) = 2$$
$$(065)(\overline{017}) = 2$$
$$(065)(017) = 2$$

Thus the two columns can be combined to form a valid three-bit code.

Returning to the scoring array, by choosing column 017 we are able to modify our scoring procedure to include the occurrence of entries which are identical to those obtained by the logical AND or OR of the two previously chosen columns:

Table 6–23 Pattern correlator—'scoring' assignment

	Present state	Next state				Output Z			
				Inputs $x_1 x_2$					
	y_1 y_2 y_3	00	01	11	10	00	01	11	10
1	0 0 0	101	100	101	100	0	0	0	0
2	1 0 1	011	010	011	010	0	0	0	0
4	1 0 0	010	010	010	010	0	0	0	0
5	0 1 0	110	110	110	110	0	0	0	0
6	1 1 0	000	000	000	000	0	0	0	0
7	0 1 1	111	110	111	110	0	0	0	0
9	1 1 1	000	000	000	000	1	0	1	0
Unused	0 0 1								

$$(065)(017) = 005$$
$$(065) + (017) = 077$$

The appearance of these derived vectors is attributed the low priority score
of one mark per entry. Score 3 column (Table 6 22) shows the result of
examining the table and scoring according to the modifications adopted after
choosing the first column, and the extra conditions above. The base vector
with the highest score, 072, unfortunately does not form a valid three-bit
code; the next highest entry which forms a valid code is 043, and this is
taken as our final choice. Thus we have arrived at a set of codable columns,
(065), (017) and (043), and these are used to encode the state-table as shown
in Table 6–23. The Karnaugh maps for the assignment are shown in Table
6–24, and yield the following equations:

$$Y_1 \text{ set} = \bar{y}_1$$
$$Y_1 \text{ reset} = y_1$$
$$Y_2 \text{ set} = y_1 \bar{y}_2$$
$$Y_2 \text{ reset} = y_1 y_2$$
$$Y_3 \text{ set} = \bar{x}_1 \bar{x}_2 \bar{y}_1 \bar{y}_2 + x_1 x_2 \bar{y}_1 \bar{y}_2$$
$$Y_3 \text{ reset} = \bar{x}_1 x_2 y_3 + y_1 y_2 + x_1 \bar{x}_2 y_3$$
$$Z = \bar{x}_1 \bar{x}_2 y_1 y_2 y_3 + x_1 x_2 y_1 y_2 y_3$$

At first sight this technique appears to involve a considerable amount of
work, yet it does still not produce an optimum result. However, both the
Hartmanis and Humphrey procedures would be very difficult to program
for a computer, while this technique could easily be adapted (which has, in
fact, been done). Moreover, the method of scoring could easily be varied
without altering the basic procedure, so we have the possibility of producing

Table 6–24 Karnaugh maps for 'scoring' assignments

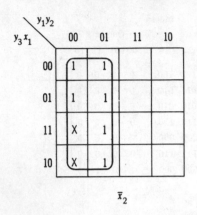

$\bar{x}_2$ x_2

Y_1 Set

$\bar{x}_2$ x_2

Y_1 Reset

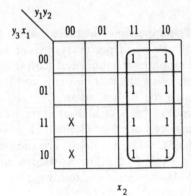

$\bar{x}_2$ x_2

Y_2 Set

Table 6–24 continued

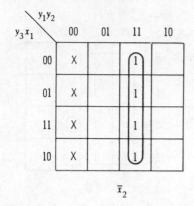

Y_2 map — $\bar{x}_2$

y_3x_1 \ y_1y_2	00	01	11	10
00	X		1	
01	X		1	
11	X		1	
10	X		1	

$\bar{x}_2$

y_3x_1 \ y_1y_2	00	01	11	10
00	X		1	
01	X		1	
11	X		1	
10	X		1	

x_2

Y_2 Reset

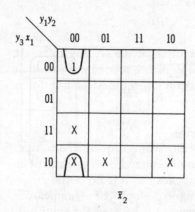

y_3x_1 \ y_1y_2	00	01	11	10
00	1			
01				
11	X			
10	X	X		X

$\bar{x}_2$

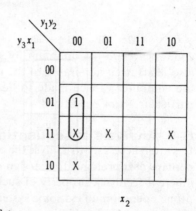

y_3x_1 \ y_1y_2	00	01	11	10
00				
01	1			
11	X	X		X
10	X			

x_2

Y_3 Set

y_3x_1 \ y_1y_2	00	01	11	10
00		X	X	X
01	X	X	X	X
11	X	1	1	1
10	X		1	

$\bar{x}_2$

y_3x_1 \ y_1y_2	00	01	11	10
00	X	X	X	X
01		X	X	X
11	X		1	
10	X	1	1	1

x_2

Y_3 Reset

Table 6–24 continued

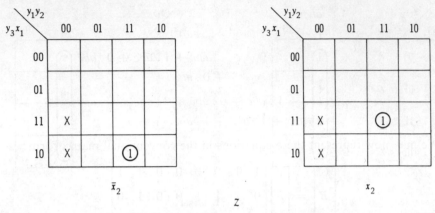

z

Implementation requires 11 units

codes nearer to the optimum by suitable weighting of the scoring rules. It also lends itself admirably to the use of self-optimizing procedures in which the computer can be made to 'learn' how to obtain the best coding for a particular set of conditions.

6–9 Analysis of sequential machines

It is often necessary to analyse the operation of an existing sequential machine, perhaps as a prologue to redesign or simply to understand its functions. The inherent feedback property of such a circuit makes this a tedious and error-prone operation unless some systematic technique is employed. Campeau[13] has described an analytical method, which may also be used for synthesis, which uses Boolean matrices and is excellent for such purposes.

Let us first consider how to represent switching equations in a matrix form. Any Boolean switching function, say $f = (a, b, c)$, may be expressed as a polynomial with coefficients of either 0 or 1. For example, consider the general sequential circuit shown in Fig. 6–1; the following equations may be deduced from the terminal conditions:

$$A = b\bar{c} + ac$$
$$B = b\bar{c} + \bar{a}c$$
$$C = \bar{a}\bar{b} + ab$$

These equations would correspond to the application equations for a sequential circuit, as described in the last chapter. To express these as a set of polynomial equations, we must first expand them into the canonical form, and then denote the presence or absence of actual terms by a 1 or 0 respectively:

$$A = 0 \cdot \bar{a}\bar{b}\bar{c} + 0 \cdot \bar{a}\bar{b}c + 1 \cdot \bar{a}b\bar{c} + 0 \cdot \bar{a}bc + 0 \cdot a\bar{b}\bar{c}$$
$$+ 1 \cdot a\bar{b}c + 1 \cdot ab\bar{c} + 1 \cdot abc$$

$$B = 0 \cdot \bar{a}\bar{b}\bar{c} + 1 \cdot \bar{a}\bar{b}c + 1 \cdot \bar{a}b\bar{c} + 1 \cdot \bar{a}bc + 0 \cdot a\bar{b}\bar{c}$$
$$+ 0 \cdot a\bar{b}c + 1 \cdot ab\bar{c} + 0 \cdot abc$$

$$C = 1 \cdot \bar{a}\bar{b}\bar{c} + 1 \cdot \bar{a}\bar{b}c + 0 \cdot \bar{a}b\bar{c} + 0 \cdot \bar{a}bc + 0 \cdot a\bar{b}\bar{c}$$
$$+ 0 \cdot a\bar{b}c + 1 \cdot ab\bar{c} + 1 \cdot abc$$

We may now represent these equations in the conventional matrix form:

$$\begin{bmatrix} C \\ B \\ A \end{bmatrix} = \begin{bmatrix} c \\ b \\ a \end{bmatrix} \begin{bmatrix} 1 & 1 & 0 & 0 & 0 & 0 & 1 & 1 \\ 0 & 1 & 1 & 1 & 0 & 0 & 1 & 0 \\ 0 & 0 & 1 & 0 & 0 & 1 & 1 & 1 \end{bmatrix}$$

Note that the least significant digit, in this case c, must be at the top. This may be expressed symbolically as

$$\mathbf{F} = \mathbf{BT}$$

where **B** stands for the present state of the sequential system, **F** the next states, and **T** represents the matrix of 1's and 0's relating present and next states. An alternative decimal form may be used for the vector **T**:

$$\mathbf{T} = [1 \quad 3 \quad 6 \quad 2 \quad 0 \quad 4 \quad 7 \quad 5]$$

Let us now define a vector $\mathbf{A}_n$, of order $n \times 2^n$ such that

for $n = 2,$ $\qquad \mathbf{A}_2 = \begin{bmatrix} 0 & 1 & 0 & 1 \\ 0 & 0 & 1 & 1 \end{bmatrix}$

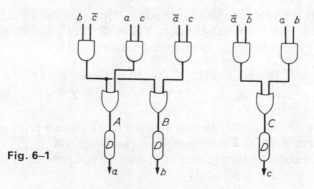

Fig. 6–1

and for $n = 3$, $$\mathbf{A}_3 = \begin{bmatrix} 0 & 1 & 0 & 1 & 0 & 1 & 0 & 1 \\ 0 & 0 & 1 & 1 & 0 & 0 & 1 & 1 \\ 0 & 0 & 0 & 0 & 1 & 1 & 1 & 1 \end{bmatrix}$$

and so on. In decimal form we have

$$\mathbf{A}_3 = [0 \quad 1 \quad 2 \quad 3 \quad 4 \quad 5 \quad 6 \quad 7]$$

$$\mathbf{A}_4 = [0 \quad 1 \quad 2 \quad 3 \quad 4 \quad 5 \quad 6 \quad 7 \quad 8 \quad 9 \quad 10 \quad 11 \quad 12 \quad 13 \quad 14 \quad 15]$$

and so on. Thus the vector $\mathbf{A}$ may be defined as having components a_s, where $a_s = S - 1$ for $S = 1, 2, 3, 4, \ldots, 2^n$, and n is the order of the matrix (and also represents the number of switching variables).

We are now in a position to define a special Boolean matrix multiplication operation. Suppose we wish to find the product of $\mathbf{XY} = \mathbf{Z}$, where $\mathbf{X}$ and $\mathbf{Y}$ are Boolean matrices. The $\mathbf{Z}$ columns are obtained one by one by comparing the $\mathbf{X}$ columns with the appropriate $\mathbf{A}$ matrix, noting which $\mathbf{A}$ column is identical to the $\mathbf{X}$ column. The $\mathbf{Y}$ column corresponding to the number of the identified $\mathbf{A}$ column is the resulting $\mathbf{Z}$ column. For example, suppose we have

$$\underset{\mathbf{X}}{\begin{bmatrix} 1 & 1 & 0 & 0 \\ 0 & 1 & 1 & 0 \end{bmatrix}} \underset{\mathbf{Y}}{\begin{bmatrix} 0 & 0 & 1 & 0 \\ 1 & 1 & 1 & 0 \end{bmatrix}} = \underset{\mathbf{Z}}{\begin{bmatrix} 0 & 0 & 1 & 0 \\ 1 & 0 & 1 & 1 \end{bmatrix}}$$

and for two variables $$\mathbf{A}_2 = \begin{bmatrix} 0 & 1 & 0 & 1 \\ 0 & 0 & 1 & 1 \end{bmatrix}$$

We take the first column of $\mathbf{X}$, $\begin{bmatrix} 1 \\ 0 \end{bmatrix}$, and compare this with the $\mathbf{A}_2$ matrix, where we find that column 2 contains the identical vector. We now use the vector from column 2 of the $\mathbf{Y}$ matrix, $\begin{bmatrix} 0 \\ 1 \end{bmatrix}$, to form the first column of $\mathbf{Z}$. This process is repeated to give the product, shown above, for $\mathbf{Z}$. Note that the operation is not commutative, i.e. $\mathbf{YX} \neq \mathbf{Z}$. The multiplication can be performed throughout using the decimal notation:

$$\underset{\mathbf{X}}{[1 \quad 3 \quad 2 \quad 0]} \underset{\mathbf{Y}}{[2 \quad 2 \quad 3 \quad 0]} = \underset{\mathbf{Z}}{[2 \quad 0 \quad 3 \quad 2]}$$

where $\mathbf{A}_2 = [0 \quad 1 \quad 2 \quad 3]$. In fact, this is a much simpler process, since the required component for $\mathbf{Z}$ is the component in column ($\mathbf{X}_{component} + 1$) of $\mathbf{Y}$.

Let us now consider the problem of finding the components of the vector $\mathbf{F}$

which satisfy the matrix equation $\mathbf{F} = \mathbf{BT}$. The appropriate $\mathbf{A}$ matrix for the three-variable switching equations is

$$\mathbf{A}_3 = \begin{bmatrix} 0 & 1 & 0 & 1 & 0 & 1 & 0 & 1 \\ 0 & 0 & 1 & 1 & 0 & 0 & 1 & 1 \\ 0 & 0 & 0 & 0 & 1 & 1 & 1 & 1 \end{bmatrix}$$

and

$$\mathbf{F} = \begin{bmatrix} C \\ B \\ A \end{bmatrix} = \begin{bmatrix} c \\ b \\ a \end{bmatrix}\begin{bmatrix} 1 & 1 & 0 & 0 & 0 & 0 & 1 & 1 \\ 0 & 1 & 1 & 1 & 0 & 0 & 1 & 0 \\ 0 & 0 & 1 & 0 & 0 & 1 & 1 & 1 \end{bmatrix}$$

In this case we must assume starting values, i.e. present state conditions, for the $\mathbf{B}$ matrix, say $\begin{bmatrix} 0 \\ 0 \\ 0 \end{bmatrix}$. Then, using this value, we derive the next state condition $\mathbf{F}$, using the multiplication rule defined above, this is $\begin{bmatrix} 1 \\ 0 \\ 0 \end{bmatrix}$. The process is then repeated, with the next state value becoming the new present state, until the cycle repeats or goes into a loop. For example,

$$\mathbf{F} = \begin{bmatrix} 0 & 1 & 1 & 0 & 0 & 1 & 1 & 0 & 0 & 1 \\ 0 & 0 & 1 & 1 & 1 & 1 & 0 & 0 & 0 & 0 \\ 0 & 0 & 0 & 0 & 1 & 1 & 1 & 1 & 0 & 0 \end{bmatrix} \cdots \text{ etc.}$$

It will be obvious from inspection that the sequential machine has the characteristics of a cyclic Gray-code counter. It is important to note that the method is applicable only to synchronous (clocked) sequential machines.

If two or more columns of a Boolean matrix are identical, the matrix is said to be *singular*. A singular matrix is said to have a defect of order d, where d is the number of columns of the $\mathbf{A}_n$ matrix which are absent. Providing a Boolean matrix is non-singular, it can be inverted:

$$\mathbf{X X}^{-1} = \mathbf{A}_n$$

The process of inversion is basically the multiplication process in reverse, that is, each column of the $\mathbf{A}_n$ matrix is identified in $\mathbf{X}$, and the corresponding $\mathbf{X}^{-1}$ term is obtained by subtracting 1 from the column number of the identified term in $\mathbf{X}$. The inverse of the matrix $\mathbf{T}$, for a sequential machine, represents a system for which the output cycle is reversed, assuming identical starting conditions.

A special case of a matrix equation is $\mathbf{B} = \mathbf{BT}$, and any vector $\mathbf{B}$ which satisfies this equation is called a *characteristic vector* of $\mathbf{T}$. In practice this means that the **T** matrix has an identical column in the same position as the **A** matrix. Should this condition occur, the sequential machine will automatically lock into a perpetual loop. Thus direct comparison of the **A** and **T** matrices will detect any stable loop conditions in the machine. As an example, consider the equation

$$\mathbf{F} = \begin{bmatrix} Y_1 \\ Y_2 \end{bmatrix} = \begin{bmatrix} y_1 \\ y_2 \end{bmatrix} \begin{bmatrix} 0 & 1 & 0 & 0 \\ 1 & 1 & 1 & 0 \end{bmatrix}$$

and the relevant **A** matrix

$$\mathbf{A}_2 = \begin{bmatrix} 0 & 1 & 0 & 1 \\ 0 & 0 & 1 & 1 \end{bmatrix}$$

It is apparent that a characteristic vector of **T** is $\begin{bmatrix} 0 \\ 1 \end{bmatrix}$ and we would expect

the machine to lock in this condition. Thus starting from $\begin{bmatrix} 0 \\ 0 \end{bmatrix}$, we have

$$\mathbf{F} = \begin{bmatrix} 0 & 0 & 0 & 0 \\ 0 & 1 & 1 & 1 \end{bmatrix} \cdots \text{ etc.}$$

So far we have only considered a system where the output is sampled at every clock pulse. It is also possible, however, to determine the output at alternate (or other multiples) of the clock rate by setting up and solving the equation

$$\mathbf{F} = \mathbf{BT}^n$$

(This assumes of course that the circuit continues to change state normally at every clock pulse.) For example, if

$$\mathbf{T} = \begin{bmatrix} 1 & 1 & 0 & 0 & 0 & 0 & 1 & 1 \\ 0 & 1 & 1 & 1 & 0 & 0 & 1 & 0 \\ 0 & 0 & 1 & 0 & 0 & 1 & 1 & 1 \end{bmatrix} \qquad \mathbf{A}_3 = \begin{bmatrix} 0 & 1 & 0 & 1 & 0 & 1 & 0 & 1 \\ 0 & 0 & 1 & 1 & 0 & 0 & 1 & 1 \\ 0 & 0 & 0 & 0 & 1 & 1 & 1 & 1 \end{bmatrix}$$

then,

$$\mathbf{T}^2 = \begin{bmatrix} 1 & 0 & 1 & 0 & 1 & 0 & 1 & 0 \\ 1 & 1 & 1 & 1 & 0 & 0 & 0 & 0 \\ 0 & 0 & 1 & 1 & 0 & 0 & 1 & 1 \end{bmatrix}$$

and,

$$\mathbf{T}^3 = \begin{bmatrix} 0 & 0 & 1 & 1 & 1 & 1 & 0 & 0 \\ 1 & 1 & 0 & 1 & 1 & 0 & 0 & 0 \\ 0 & 1 & 1 & 1 & 0 & 0 & 1 & 0 \end{bmatrix}$$

and so on. Then assuming the starting condition $\mathbf{B} = \begin{bmatrix} 0 \\ 0 \\ 0 \end{bmatrix}$ we have, for the

Gray-code counter described earlier, at every third clock pulse,

$$\mathbf{F} = \begin{bmatrix} 0 & 0 & 1 & 1 & 0 \\ 0 & 1 & 0 & 0 & 1 \\ 0 & 0 & 1 & 0 & 1 \end{bmatrix} \cdots \text{ etc.}$$

It is apparent that the matrix technique provides a powerful means of analysing clocked sequential systems, and in certain restricted cases, it may also be applied to asynchronous circuits. The use of this technique for synthesis is rather unwieldy and is beyond the scope of this book.

References and bibliography

(1) MOORE, E. F. Gedanken-experiments on sequential machines. (Automata Studies) *Ann. Math. Stud.*, 1955, **34**, 129–153.

(2) PAULL, M and UNGAR, S. Minimizing the number of states in incompletely specified sequential switching functions. *I.R.E. Trans. electron. comput.*, 1959, **EC8**, 356–367.

(3) GINSBERG, S. On the reduction of superfluous states in a sequential machine. *J. Ass. comput. Mach.*, 1959, **6**, 259–282.-

(4) MARCUS, M. P. Derivation of maximal compatibles using Boolean algebra. *I.B.M. Jl Res. Dev.*, 1964, **8**, 537–538.

(5) McCLUSKEY, E. J. and UNGAR, S. H. A note on the number of internal variable assignments for sequential switching circuits. *I.R.E. Trans. electron. comput.*, 1959, **EC8**, 439–440.

(6) HUMPHREY, W. S. *Switching circuits with computer applications.* McGraw-Hill, New York, 1958. Chap. 10.

(7) HARTMANIS, J. On the state assignment problem for sequential machines I. *I.R.E. Trans. electron. comput.*, 1961, **EC10**, 157–165.

(8) STEARNS, R. E. and HARTMANIS, J. On the state assignment problem for sequential machines II. *I.R.E. Trans. electron. comput.*, 1961, **EC10**, 593–603.

(9) BIRKHOFF, G. and MACLANE, S. *A survey of modern algebra.* Macmillan, New York, 1965.

(10) FARR, E. H. Lattice properties of sequential machines. *J. Ass. comput. Mach.*, 1963, **10**, 365–385.

(11) DOLOTTA, T. A. and McCLUSKEY, E. J. The coding of internal states of sequential circuits. *I.E.E.E. Trans. electron. comput.*, 1964, **EC13**, 549–562.

(12) DOLOTTA, T. A. The coding problem in the design of switching circuits. PhD dissertation, Princeton University, 1961.

(13) CAMPEAU, J. O. Synthesis and analysis of digital systems by Boolean matrices. *I.R.E. Trans. electron. comput.*, 1957, **EC6**, 230–241.

(14) BOOTH, T. L. *Sequential machines and automata theory*. Wiley, New York, 1967.

(15) KOHAVI, Z. *Switching and finite automata theory*. McGraw-Hill, New York, 1970.

(16) GILL, A. *Introduction to the theory of finite state machines*. McGraw-Hill, New York, 1962.

(17) MILLER, R. E. *Switching theory—Vol. II Sequential circuits and machines*. Wiley, New York, 1965.

(18) KARP, R. M. Some techniques of state assignment for synchronous sequential machines. *I.E.E.E. Trans. electron. comput.*, 1964, **EC13**, 507–518.

(19) KOHAVI, Z. Secondary state assignment for sequential machines. *I.E.E.E. Trans. electron. comput.*, 1964, **EC13**, 193–203.

(20) HARTMANIS, J. and STEARNS, R. E. *Algebraic structure theory of sequential machines*. Prentice-Hall, Englewood Cliffs, N.J., 1966.

(21) GRASSELLI, A. A method for minimizing the number of internal states in incompletely specified sequential networks. *I.E.E.E. Trans. electron. comput.*, 1965, **EC14**, 350–359.

(22) ARMSTRONG, D. B. On the efficient assignment of internal codes to sequential machines. *I.R.E. Trans. electron. comput.*, 1962, **EC11**, 611–622.

Tutorial problems

6-1 Reduce the state-table shown in Table 6–25 to a minimal form and investigate possible state assignments. Derive the input and output equations for the circuit using SR bistables.

Table 6–25

| Present state | Inputs $x_1 x_2$ | | | | | | | |
| | Next states | | | | Output Z | | | |
	00	01	11	10	00	01	11	10
1	4	2	5	1	1	1	0	1
2	2	5	–	3	0	1	1	–
3	1	3	6	5	1	1	0	1
4	2	–	6	–	–	1	–	1
5	–	2	6	1	0	1	1	1
6	2	4	–	4	0	–	1	1

6-2 Reduce the state-table in problem 5 of Chapter 5 to a minimal form. Carry on and complete the design using JK bistables and derive a logic diagram for the final circuit.

6-3 A synchronous sequential circuit has two inputs x_1, x_2 and an output Z. The output Z is equal to 1 if, and only if, $x_1 = 1$ and the sequence $x_2 = 101$ has occurred immediately after the last time $x_1 = 1$, otherwise the output Z remains equal to 0. Whenever $x_2 = 1$, the output Z is made equal to 0, unless the conditions above are satisfied.

Derive the minimal state-diagram for the circuit and then implement the design using JK bistables. Ensure that the input equations are as near optimal as possible.

6-4 Design a synchronous sequential circuit that will compare two serial inputs, x_1 and x_2, and give an output Z whenever any group of five bits in the same clock sequence correspond exactly.

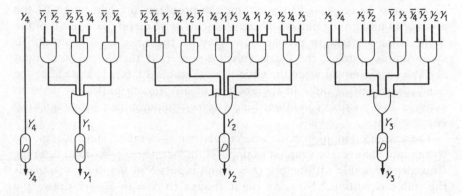

Fig. 6–2

6-5 Analyse the circuit shown in Fig. 6–2 using the matrix technique. Investigate the action of the circuit for all starting conditions, and then consider the outputs obtained after alternate clock pulses. Note that y_1 is the least significant input.

7 Design of asynchronous sequential circuits

7–1 Introduction

In the last chapter we considered synchronous (clocked) sequential circuits; asynchronous circuits are in principle very similar, but special design techniques must be employed to overcome the problems brought about by the absence of any timing pulses. These problems arise mainly as a result of the finite switching time, or propagation delay, of the basic logic modules. In synchronous systems, the clock pulses ensure that the output and input variables are sampled when the circuits have reached a steady state after the delays have settled out. In the absence of any timing pulses, we have to consider two possible conditions for an asynchronous circuit—the *stable* and *unstable* states.

The unstable condition exists when the circuit is changing state in response to an input change, the simplest example is, in fact, the d.c. set-reset bistable. Consider a bistable with output $Q = 1$ and inputs $S = 0$ and $R = 0$, this is the stable condition. Now, an input change to $S = 0$, $R = 1$ causes the output to change to $Q = 0$, but before the circuit reaches this new stable condition, there is a momentary delay (which varies with each circuit) during which there is an unstable condition of $Q = 1$, with inputs $S = 0$ and $R = 1$. In asynchronous systems we always assume that the circuit will eventually arrive at a stable condition, which implies that the duration of the inputs will always be such as to allow this to occur.

Suppose now we had two such bistables in a circuit, and we were causing the outputs of both of them to go from 1 to 0. Because of the inherent switching delays (which would be different for each bistable circuit) there would be no way of predetermining the output states during the unstable period. Thus the outputs might change $11 \to 10 \to 00$; $11 \to 01 \to 00$; or, in the ideal case, $11 \to 00$. Consequently, if these outputs were used as inputs to other circuits, erroneous operation would result if we assumed the ideal change of $11 \to 00$. For this reason, in asynchronous systems all input variable (and also internal state variable) changes are restricted so that only *one* variable can change state at any time. Furthermore, it is also assumed that the internal states have stabilized before another input variable is changed. If these restrictions are ignored circuit 'races' (which may be critical or non-critical) will result; this aspect will be covered in more detail later. A further circuit 'hazard' arises (again from circuit delays) if one assumes that the Boolean expressions $A\bar{A} = 0$ and $A + \bar{A} = 1$ are inviolate under all conditions.

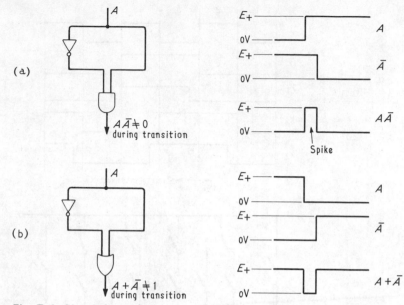

Fig. 7–1 Circuit hazards

That this cannot be so is apparent when we consider that the inverse of a variable is normally produced by using an invertor element, which inserts an additional delay in the signal path (see Fig. 7–1).

As we shall see, many of the design techniques associated with asynchronous logic circuits are concerned with ensuring that these critical race and hazard conditions do not materialize in practice. The design methods which we describe in the rest of this chapter are due mainly to Huffman,[1] and though originally oriented towards relay circuit design are nevertheless applicable to any switching device.

7–2 Problem definition—timing diagrams

Because the design technique was originally concerned with relays, much of the terminology used (and retained here since it is still widely used) is different to that evolved for synchronous systems, though in many cases it means the same. Inputs to an asynchronous circuit are generally called *primaries*, originally referring to primary relays directly controlled by the circuit inputs, the states of which are represented by x. The storage characteristics (internal states) of the sequential circuit, represented by secondary relays, are called *secondaries*, normally symbolized by Y. The equations for next state Y, in terms of present states (y) and input states (x) are called *excitation equations*, and originally represented the contact circuit necessary to energize relay Y. The output states of the sequential circuit we shall call Z.

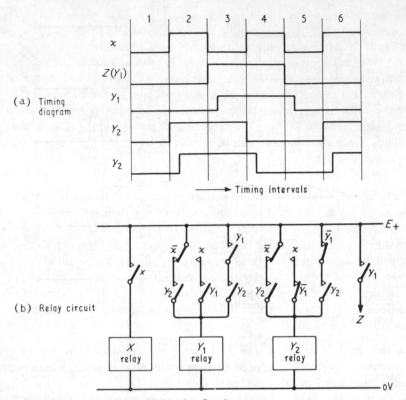

Fig. 7–2 Design for a divide-by-2 relay counter

As with all logic design problems, the first step is to express the oral or written circuit specification in a formal and unambiguous manner. Thus, in earlier chapters, we have used the truth-table and state-diagram/state-table, to design combinational and synchronous logic circuits. Similarly, for asynchronous logic we proceed via a state-diagram (or timing diagram) to a *flow-table*. The flow-table fulfils a similar function to the state-table in that its construction forces the designer to consider all possible modes of circuit operation.

Let us illustrate these ideas by considering the design of a divide-by-two counter, i.e. a circuit which changes its output state on alternate input pulses, which will be used as a running example throughout this chapter. The waveform or timing diagram is shown in Fig. 7–2(a). The timing diagram is the usual starting point in the intuitive design of relay circuits,[2] and it is instructive to consider this approach first and then relate the ideas to asynchronous design theory. In Fig. 7–2(a) the vertical timing divisions, not necessarily equal but drawn so for convenience, represent each state of the relay circuit as it operates in a logical sequence. The horizontal lines represent the conditions, ON or OFF, of the input (x) and the output (Z), which we may also consider, in this particular example, as a secondary (Y_1). Now, in state 1 with input $x = 0$, we require an output $Z = 0$; but with input $x = 0$, in state 3, we also require the output to be 1; this is due to the sequential characteristics of the circuit. Note, moreover, that the actual response of the circuit (y_1) to the excitation Y_1 is delayed, due to the time constant of the relay coil. In fact an unstable circuit condition exists, and this must be taken into account in deriving the excitation equations for Y_1 (i.e. the output Z). Thus, from the timing diagram, we have

$$Y_1 = \bar{x}\bar{y}_1 + \bar{x}y_1 + xy_1$$

Unfortunately, if these equations were implemented it would mean that Y_1 could never be de-energized since the condition for this to occur is $\bar{x}y_1$, one of the conditions we used to switch Y_1 on! It is obvious then that we require some means of distinguishing between these two conditions. This could be provided by an additional secondary relay Y_2 which, in conjunction with x and Y_1, may be decoded to give the correct output conditions. Thus, when two or more states have the same input conditions, but different output conditions, secondaries (equivalent to internal states) must be used to distinguish between them.

The excitation equations for Y_1, Y_2 from the timing diagram are:

$$Y_1 = \bar{x}\bar{y}_1y_2 + \bar{x}y_1y_2 + xy_1y_2 + xy_1\bar{y}_2$$
$$= \bar{x}y_2 + xy_1$$

and
$$Y_2 = x\bar{y}_1\bar{y}_2 + x\bar{y}_1y_2 + \bar{x}\bar{y}_1y_2 + \bar{x}y_1y_2$$
$$= x\bar{y}_1 + \bar{x}y_2$$

also
$$Z = y_1$$

Inspection of the equations for Y_1 and Y_2 suggests that hazard conditions can arise because if

$$Y_1 = \bar{x}y_2 + xy_1$$

and if
$$y_1 = y_2 = 1$$

then
$$Y_1 = (\bar{x} + x) = 1$$

Now if in the implementation we use break-before-make contacts, there will be a delay between $\bar{x}$ and x which will give rise to a transient drop (0) in the output, causing relay Y_1 to de-energize. We must ensure that this can never happen by including the additional terms y_1y_2 to yield the final excitation equations:

$$Y_1 = \bar{x}y_2 + xy_1 + y_1y_2$$

and
$$Y_2 = x\bar{y}_1 + \bar{x}y_2 + \bar{y}_1y_2$$

The full relay circuit is shown in Fig. 7–2(b); in actual relay practice this hazard can be overcome very easily by using make-before-break changeover contacts.

With a simple circuit like this, the design method detailed above is quite successful, but with more complicated circuits involving many variables a more formal approach is desirable, particularly to determine when (and how many) secondaries are required, and to recognize and eliminate hazardous circuit conditions. We now explain how the same circuit may be designed using a more rigorous and versatile procedure.

7–3 Problem definition—state-diagrams and flow-tables

The first step in the design procedure is to draw up a *primitive flow-table* for the counter. In a flow-table [Table 7–1(a)] each entry represents either a stable (circled entry) or unstable internal state of the system (or, alternatively, a 'don't care' condition). A primitive flow-table is simply one in which each stable state is allotted a separate row, implying a different secondary state for each stable state. The output Z is recorded for each stable state row at the side of the table. Each stable state is thus uniquely defined by a combination of primaries (input x) and secondaries (present internal states y) of the machine [see Table 7–1(c)]. An unstable state results when a particular combination of primaries and secondaries (the excitation Y) requires a transition to a new internal state. This is brought about by a change in the input condition, and for a brief period an unstable condition exists during which the internal states do not correspond to those required by the excitation, as we saw, for example, in the relay design of Section 7–2. Thus the primitive flow-table lists all the possible outputs and transitions that can occur when the input variables are changed.

As with synchronous circuits, state-diagrams can also be used as a preliminary aid to formalizing the circuit specifications and writing the primitive flow-table. However, state-diagrams for asynchronous circuits differ from those for synchronous circuits in that each stable state of the circuit must be represented by a *sling*, i.e. a transition path originating and terminating at the same stable state. The reason for this is that, for a synchronous circuit, an unchanging input sequence (say 111 – – – etc.) will be interpreted as repetitions (one for each clock pulse) of the input, whereas for the asynchronous circuit, concerned only with voltage or current levels. it will be regarded as a single input. Thus, whenever a new input combination causes the circuit to assume a new stable state and remain there (while the input is present) the state-diagram must show a sling. The state-diagram may be either of the Mealey or the Moore model form, but we shall see later that an attempt should always be made to relate output and internal states (Moore model) to produce more economical output functions.

When designing a sequential machine, we must initially assume some

Table 7–1 Design tables for divide-by-2 counter

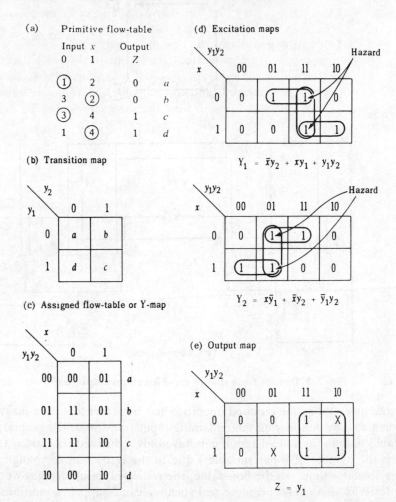

(a) Primitive flow-table

Input x		Output	
0	1	Z	
①	2	0	a
3	②	0	b
③	4	1	c
1	④	1	d

(d) Excitation maps

$$Y_1 = \bar{x}y_2 + xy_1 + y_1y_2$$

$$Y_2 = x\bar{y}_1 + \bar{x}y_2 + \bar{y}_1y_2$$

(b) Transition map

(c) Assigned flow-table or Y-map

(e) Output map

$$Z = y_1$$

starting or resting state; this is conventionally taken as the condition when all the inputs are absent. In practice, provision must be made to reset the machine to this state when switching on. When drawing up the state-diagram (or flow-table) the best plan is to follow through the correct sequence of events to produce the required output. Each time a new input condition occurs, a new internal state is allocated, unless it is obvious that an existing state fulfills the requirements. It is of no consequence at this stage if more states are allocated than are actually required to satisfy the circuit specifications, as these will be found and eliminated at a later stage of the design

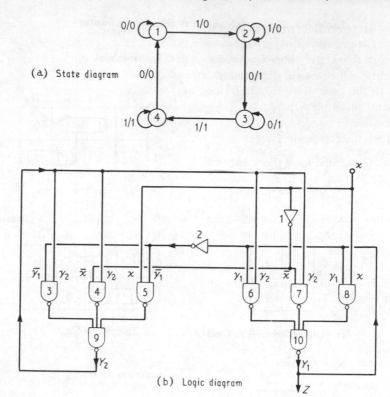

(a) State diagram

(b) Logic diagram

Fig. 7-3 Design for a divide-by-2 electronic counter

procedure. When the required operation has been met, the state-diagram is completed by considering the remaining input transitions. In general, each stable state in the state-diagram can have only n directed transitions (where n is the number of input variables) due to the restriction of changing one variable at a time. In the flow-table, the restricted input changes would be entered as 'don't care' or, more realistically, 'can't happen' conditions.

The Mealey state-diagram for the divide-by-2 counter circuit is shown in Fig. 7–3(a). Starting in stable state 1 with no inputs, i.e. $x = 0$ (note the sling indicating a stable condition), a change of input from $0 \rightarrow 1$ causes a transition to stable state 2, and so on, until in stable state 4, an input change of $1 \rightarrow 0$ returns the counter to the starting condition. It is interesting to observe that the state-diagram or flow-table can, in this case, be obtained directly from the timing diagram, in which the timing intervals represent the necessary internal states; the unstable states are produced by the finite rise and fall times of the waveforms. This result is generally true for the case of counter and shift register circuits, and any other system that can be conveniently represented by a timing diagram.

7–4 Internal state reduction and merging

Once the primitive flow-table has been established it will, in general, contain more stable states than are actually required, so the next step must be to identify and eliminate these redundant states from the table. This is analogous to the process already described for synchronous systems and the same general philosophy holds good. Thus, for two stable states in a primitive flow-table to be identical (or equivalent for the case of incompletely specified tables), the following axioms must be obeyed:

(a) they must have the same output states, and
(b) for all possible input changes, their next-state transitions must result in the same (or equivalent) states.

It is important to note that in this case, a stable state is specified by *both* input and secondary conditions; thus for two states to be identical they must *both be in the same column* of the flow-table. It appears then that this is the identical problem to that encountered with synchronous systems, and consequently it may be solved using the same methods—the implication chart technique.

Let us now consider the primitive flow-table shown in Table 7–2(a). This can be reduced by a simple and exhaustive comparison of the stable states in each column; for example, for the input state $\bar{x}_1\bar{x}_2$ we have ① $\not\equiv$ ⑥ since the output states are different; ① $\equiv$ ⑮ if ② $\equiv$ ⑨, but because their out-

Table 7–2 Flow-table reduction

(a) Primitive flow-table

Inputs x_1x_2				Outputs
00	01	11	10	Z_1Z_2
①	2	–	5	00
15	②	3	–	00
–	4	③	12	00
1	④	11	–	10
6	–	13	⑤	11
⑥	10	–	7	11
16	–	8	⑦	11
–	9	⑧	5	01
1	⑨	14	–	10
1	⑩	11	–	10
–	4	⑪	12	00
6	–	13	⑫	11
–	10	⑬	5	00
–	9	⑭	12	00
⑮	9	–	5	00
⑯	4	–	5	00

(b) Reduced flow-table

	Inputs x_1x_2				Outputs
	00	01	11	10	Z_1Z_2
a	①	2	–	5	00
b	15	②	3	–	00
c	–	4	③	5	00
d	1	④	3	–	10
e	6	–	3	⑤	11
f	⑥	4	–	7	11
g	15	–	8	⑦	11
h	–	4	⑧	5	01
i	⑮	4	–	5	00

Table 7-3 Implication chart

	1	2	3	4	5	6	7	8	9	10	11	12	13	14	15
2	⊗														
3	⊗	⊗													
4	⊗	⊗	⊗												
5	⊗	⊗	⊗	⊗											
6	⊗	⊗	⊗	⊗	⊗										
7	⊗	⊗	⊗	⊗	⊗̶	⊗									
8	⊗	⊗	⊗	⊗	⊗	⊗	⊗								
9	⊗	⊗	11,14 ✓	⊗	⊗	⊗	⊗	⊗							
10	⊗	⊗	⊗	⊗	⊗	⊗	⊗	⊗	⊗						
11	⊗	⊗	✓	11,14 ✓	✓	⊗	6,9 ⊗̶	⊗	14,11	⊗					
12	⊗	⊗	⊗	⊗	✓	⊗	⊗	⊗	⊗	⊗	⊗				
13	⊗	⊗	4,10 5,12	⊗	4,9	⊗	⊗	⊗	⊗	⊗	4,10 12,5	⊗			
14	⊗	⊗	4,9	⊗	⊗	⊗	⊗	⊗	⊗	⊗	4,9	⊗	10,9 5,12		
15	⊗̶	⊗	⊗	⊗	⊗	⊗	⊗	⊗	⊗	⊗	⊗	⊗	⊗	⊗	
16	⊗̶	⊗	⊗	⊗	⊗	⊗	⊗	⊗	⊗	⊗	⊗	⊗	⊗	⊗	9,4

put states are dissimilar ② ≢ ⑨, therefore ① ≢ ⑮ , etc. This is a tedious operation (the reader should attempt this for himself!) and the best approach is to draw up an implication chart, as shown in Table 7–3. There are many more initial incompatibles in this chart (for the number of internal states involved) than is normal for a synchronous system because of the requirement of column comparison only. The incompatibles should be entered first, followed by the identical states, then we use the procedure adopted earlier for synchronous machines to complete the chart. From the chart the following set of maximal compatibles can be obtained:

$$M = (1)(2)(6)(7)(8)(3, 11, 13, 14)(5, 12)(4, 9, 10)(15, 16)$$

As the flow-table was fully specified (the 'don't care' conditions due to the input restrictions will always occur in the same places and thus will never be assigned different values) the final result is a partition and will be unique. Incompletely specified flow-tables will result in a covering of the machine states and should be treated in the normal way. The elimination of redundant stable states allows us to draw the reduced flow-table shown in Table 7–2(b), note that we have simplified the machine to nine stable states, but still expressed in the primitive flow-table form of one stable state to a row. If we assigned a code to each row of the table as it stands we would need four secondary variables; indeed, this is the same number required for the original flow-table before reduction. Can we reduce the number of rows, and hence secondaries, still further? We can if we remember that a stable state is defined by *both* input and secondary conditions—there is no reason why we should not use the same secondary assignment for different internal states. This means that transitions between stable states in the *same row* will be affected by input changes only. Thus, if we can reduce the number of rows by placing more than one stable state per row, we shall automatically reduce the number of secondary variables required to code the rows; this operation is known as *merging*. Rows may be merged, regardless of output states, if there are no conflicting state numbers (irrespective of stable or unstable states) in any columns, 'don't care' conditions being used to represent any state. For example, in Table 7–2(b), row *c* may be merged with row *d* by combining stable and unstable states 4 and 3 (replaced in the merged row by the relevant stable state), and allowing the 'don't care' conditions to assume appropriate values. Thus we obtain, as a result of merging rows *c* and *d*, the row

1 ④ ③ 5

It is interesting to note that during the merging process the circled entries have changed their definition due to our ignoring the output states. In the primitive table they were *internal states* (i.e. state of the feedback loop) concerned only with the input and secondary variables (x, y), whereas in the merged table input, output, and secondary variables are represented and the circled entries have now become *total states*. It is possible to indicate the output states associated with each stable-state on the merged flow-table, but this can become confusing. The best approach is to ignore the output states completely, since they can easily be obtained from the primitive flow-table when required.

Generally, there is more than one way of merging the rows of a flow-table, and the choice can appreciably affect circuit economy. A unique solution is only possible for a fully specified flow-table (one containing no 'don't care' conditions), but this is an unlikely occurrence in practice. In order to ensure that the best choice is made it is advisable to search for all possible mergers. This may be done in a similar way to the determination of state equivalences by methodically comparing each row with every other row and noting the result.

In Table 7–2(b), by comparing row a with rows (b, c, d, e, f, g, h, i), then row b with rows (c, d, e, f, g, h, i), etc., we can obtain the following pairs of mergeable rows:

$$m = (c, d)(c, e)(c, i)(h, i)$$

The final result must be a partition on the set of all flow-table rows, since each row may only be included once. Thus we have

$$M = (a)(b)(c, d)(e)(f)(g)(h, i)$$

Note that the unmergeable rows are included as single element blocks; the fully merged flow-table is shown in Table 7–4.

Mergeable rows may be combined into maximal sets (all rows within a block being combinable) but it is important to realize that the relationship is not transitive. For example, consider the reduced flow-table shown in Table 7–5, a comparative search yields the following mergeable row pairs:

$$m = (1, 2)(1, 3)(2, 3)(2, 4)(3, 6)(4, 8)(5, 6)(5, 7)(5, 8)(6, 7)$$

Table 7–4
Merged flow-table

Inputs x_1x_2			
00	01	11	10
①	2	–	5
15	②	3	–
1	④	③	5
6	–	3	⑤
⑥	4	–	7
15	–	8	⑦
⑮	4	⑧	5

Table 7–5

Inputs x_1x_2				Output
00	01	11	10	Z
①	2	–	3	0
1	②	4	–	1
1	–	–	③	1
–	2	④	5	1
8	–	6	⑤	0
–	7	⑥	–	0
8	⑦	–	–	0
⑧	2	–	5	1

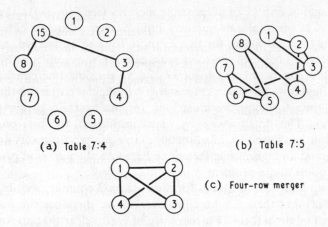

(a) Table 7:4   (b) Table 7:5

(c) Four-row merger

Fig. 7–4 Merger diagrams

These may be combined into maximal sets by examining the row pairs, e.g. rows $(1, 2)$ and $(1, 3)$ can be merged, then if $(2, 3)$ can also be merged (which it can) we may combine to give $(1, 2, 3)$. Applying this technique, we get

$$m = (1, 2, 3)(2, 4)(3, 6)(4, 8)(5, 6, 7)(5, 8)$$

From these sets, we must choose a partition representing all the rows; there are a number of possibilities:

$$M_1 = (1, 2, 3)(4, 8)(5, 6, 7)$$
$$M_2 = (1, 2, 3)(6, 7)(4, 8)(5)$$
$$M_3 = (1)(2, 3)(5, 6, 7)(4, 8), \text{ etc.}$$

The minimal row solution can usually be obtained by including the maximal sets in the partition, though this does not necessarily yield the most economic hardware solution.

An alternative method suggested by Maley and Earle[3] is to merge in such a way as to minimize or eliminate the output gating. This may be achieved by only merging rows with the same output states, and it may be possible to code the feedback loops (i.e. secondaries) in such a way that the outputs may be obtained directly. This is equivalent to designing a Moore machine with identical output and internal states, but this will become clearer when we discuss the derivation of the output equations. An additional advantage, and perhaps a more important one with high speed logic circuits, is that if the output gating can be eliminated circuit delays are reduced. Partition M_3 above is output-consistent in this sense, but results in a four-row flow-table.

Another method of establishing the row mergers, which is useful when dealing with a small number of rows, is to draw a *merger diagram*. This is simply a spatial display of all possible mergers (see Fig. 7–4); the rows are represented by the total state numbers and row mergers are indicated by inter-connecting lines. In order for two or more rows to be merged, all possible interconnections between the rows must exist. For example, in Fig. 7–4(b), rows 1, 2, 3 can be merged together and all possible interconnecting lines between these rows produce a characteristic triangular pattern in the diagram. For four rows to merge we must look for the pyramid pattern shown in Fig. 7–4(c). Thus in this way, by visual inspection, the best possible row mergers can be chosen. Unfortunately, large merger diagrams are difficult to handle and an algorithmic technique based on the partition principle is a better solution to the problem.

Reverting back to our design for a divide-by-2 counter, we observe from Table 7–1(a) that there are no equivalent states, therefore the flow-table is already in a minimal form. Furthermore, it is also clear that no row mergers are possible.

7–5 Secondary state assignment

This is the process of allocating unique states of a bistable (or relay) to each row of the flow-table, or, in other words, assigning a binary code to dis-tinguish between the internal stable states of an asynchronous machine. The procedure is once again analogous to that described for synchronous systems, but with one essential difference: with asynchronous machines, the prime objective of assignment is to produce a workable machine free from circuit 'races' and 'hazards', rather than an economic hardware solution. An arbitrary assignment does not necessarily yield a viable design, as is the case with synchronous machines. In practice of course one tries to optimize both requirements, but the principal aim must always be to achieve a reliable machine.

A further point is to establish exactly what it is we are assigning. In the case of relay circuits there should be no difficulty, since the secondary assignment variables are, in fact, easily identified with the state of the secondary relays in the circuit. But using electronic logic it is perhaps not so easy to appreciate the situation. We have said above that we are assigning the states of a bistable, which is perfectly true, if a little confusing, since we have not as yet mentioned bistable circuits except in a general sense. What, in fact, we are doing is evolving equations for the next state (Y) of the circuit in terms of the present states (y) and inputs (x); this is precisely what we did in Chapter 5 when we found the characteristic equations for a bistable from its truth-table (Section 5–2). As we saw, the principal characteristic of this type of circuit is that of feedback, for we are taking the outputs of the circuit and feeding them back to the input, a process which requires power gain round the loop. Thus, the excitation equations for the secondary variables (Y) must be implemented using a circuit which incorporates some form of

Table 7–6 Circuit 'race' conditions

(a) Assigned flow-table

	Inputs x_1x_2			
y_1y_2	00	01	11	10
00	①	2	③	5
01	1	2	3	④
11	1	②	6	⑤
10	1	⑦	⑥	5

(b) Y-map

	Inputs x_1x_2			
y_1y_2	00	01	11	10
00	00	11	00	11
01	00	11	00	01
11	00	11	10	11
10	00	10	10	11

power gain; the NOR/NAND elements are ideal for this purpose. We shall see later that the configuration inevitably produces some form of bistable storage, hence the analogy to relay circuits is complete.

In the assignment of the secondary variables we must assume, for reasons discussed above, that, during a transition from one stable state to another, only one secondary variable changes at a time. If more than one secondary variable changed simultaneously, a circuit 'race' could ensue which might cause a transition to the wrong internal stable state. Let us now examine these circuit 'race' conditions in more detail.

Suppose we had arbitrarily allocated the secondary variables y_1y_2 to a flow-table as shown in Table 7–6(a). The fully assigned flow-table, or Y-map, is obtained by replacing the stable state entries in the flow-table by the appropriate y_1y_2 row values. The map is then completed by giving the unstable state entries, wherever they occur, the same values as their stable states; the complete Y-map is shown in Table 7–6(b). A *critical race* occurs if, when in state ①, the input (x_1x_2) changes from $00 \rightarrow 10$, and we have the unstable condition in which the present secondary variables show the state 00, but the input variables are dictating a transition to a new stable state (as indicated by the Y-map entry) of 11, i.e. $5 \rightarrow ⑤$. This necessitates the excitation (y_1y_2) to change from $00 \rightarrow 11$ which, due to indeterminate delays in the signal path, can take place in three ways: (a) from $00 \rightarrow 11$, if both y_1 and y_2 change together, giving a correct transition to state ⑤; (b) if y_1 changes first, we have $00 \rightarrow 10 \rightarrow 11$ and a *cycle* via $5 \rightarrow 5 \rightarrow ⑤$; (c) if y_2 changes first, we have $00 \rightarrow 01$ and an incorrect transition to state ④, since the circuit will lock in this stable state. A similar critical race exists if, when in state ①, the inputs change from $00 \rightarrow 01$.

A *non-critical race* is obtained if, when in state ②, the inputs change from $01 \rightarrow 00$, requiring a transition from states $1 \rightarrow ①$, and necessitating the excitation to change from $11 \rightarrow 00$. This time, however, irrespective of which secondary variable changes first, the circuit always cycles to state ①. Since critical races are unpredictable and lead to incorrect or inconsistent operation, they must be avoided at all costs in the design of an asynchronous circuit.

However, non-critical races and cycles can sometimes be used to advantage; for example, the inclusion of a non-critical race (or cycle) in a machine can often effect economies in the excitation logic. Also, the fact that a cycle produces a time-delay between state transitions can sometimes be utilized.

In order to avoid critical races, any rows of the flow-table which have transitions between them must be assigned in such a way that the secondary variables differ in only one variable. Consequently, all possible row-to-row transitions must be examined. A convenient way of doing this is to use a Karnaugh map, called in this application a *transition map*, to plot the row adjacencies. In some cases it may be necessary to include redundant rows, i.e. secondary states, in the flow-table in order to obtain the required change of one variable; this technique will be discussed later.

Continuing with the counter design, each row of the flow-table [Table 7-1(a)] is lettered and then examined for row transitions on the transition map [Table 7-1(b)]. It is apparent that the necessary change of one secondary variable can be obtained by using the normal Gray-code assignment. Thus row *a*, state ①, is arbitrarily assigned $y_1 y_2 = 00$, and the other stable states follow directly from the transition map. Replacing each stable state entry with its row assignment code, and each unstable state with the stable state code, we obtain the fully assigned table shown in Table 7-1(c).

7-6 Secondary excitation and output functions

Having produced the fully assigned flow-table, the next step is to derive the excitation equations. We can do this directly from the flow-table by extracting those combinations of input and present state secondary variables (x, y) that are required to produce the next state secondary variables (Y). For example, in the case of the divide-by-2 counter, examination of the Y-map entries [Table 7-1(c)] reveals that $Y_1 = 1$ for the following condition:

$$Y_1 = \bar{y}_1 y_2 \bar{x} + y_1 y_2 \bar{x} + y_1 y_2 x + y_1 \bar{y}_2 x$$

which is, of course, the excitation equation for Y_1.

For a small number of variables a Karnaugh map approach, called an *excitation map*, may be used to plot these functions directly. This is possible since, in most cases, there is a direct correspondence between the Y-map and the excitation map; compare, for example, Tables 7-1(c) and (d). However, for a large number of variables, greater than five, say, the excitation equations must be obtained directly from the flow-table and minimized using tabular techniques. Furthermore, the excitation equations are, in fact, an example of a multi-terminal circuit and should be treated accordingly.

In obtaining these functions the presence of circuit hazards (due to inherent delaying paths) must always be borne in mind. In fact, the final step in the design procedure is to examine the excitation equations for the possible existence of circuit hazards. For example, the optimized equations for $Y_1 Y_2$ (identical to those obtained for the earlier relay design) are, from Table 7–1(d):

$$Y_1 = \bar{x}y_2 + xy_1$$

and
$$Y_2 = x\bar{y}_1 + \bar{x}y_2$$

As we showed earlier, a circuit hazard exists for Y_1 when $y_1 = y_2 = 1$ and the input variable changes from $x = 1$ to $\bar{x} = 1$. The problem of designing hazardless relay circuits has been investigated by Huffman,[4] and many of the techniques are directly applicable to other forms of switching circuit. The presence of such hazards may be detected (and eliminated) by careful inspection of the Karnaugh map. For example, in the map for Y_1 [Table 7–1(d)] there are two distinct groupings of the functions (i.e. loops) corresponding to the optimized equation given above. Hazards can exist if input changes require a transition between two secondary states (represented by the $y_1 y_2$ value) in different groupings on the Karnaugh map. This hazard can be eliminated by adding redundancy to the circuit in the form of an additional loop embracing the two hazard loops. This connecting group [shown in Table 7–1(d)] is $y_1 y_2$ and results in the final equation:

$$Y_1 = \bar{x}y_2 + xy_1 + y_1 y_2$$

A similar hazard, which responds to the same treatment, exists in the Y_2 excitation map:

$$Y_2 = x\bar{y}_1 + \bar{x}y_2 + \bar{y}_1 y_2$$

We derive the output map from the primitive and assigned flow-tables by plotting the output states as entries in an assigned table. Stable output states are entered first, since the value of unstable output states may be optional, providing they do not cause transient changes in the final output. The latter can be prevented by noting those stable states which, when involved in a transition, have the same initial and final output states. Any unstable states in the transition path must be assigned the same output states. If the initial and final output states are different, the choice of output state for the unstable states is optional. Bearing in mind, however, that if the output is required as soon as possible, it is necessary for the unstable state to have the same output value as the final stable state. The assigned output table can then be regarded as a Karnaugh map and treated accordingly; alternatively, the output functions (including 'don't cares') may be extracted directly.

Thus in the counter output map [Table 7–1(e)], since a transition from stable state ③ → ④ involves no change in output states, unstable state 4 must be output 1. A transition from ④ → ① produces a change in output state from $1 \rightarrow 0$, consequently unstable state 1 can be optional, the choice of output state 1 giving greater simplification. This process is repeated for

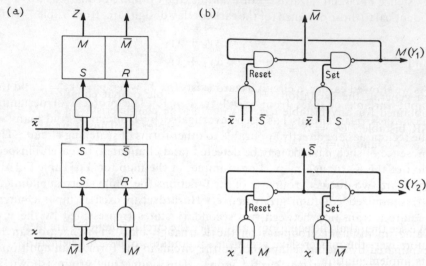

Fig. 7–5 Master-slave bistable

all stable state transitions until the output map is completed. The output equation obtained from the map is

$$Z = y_1$$

Thus the output may be derived directly from the feedback loop and no additional output logic is required.

The final logic circuit for the counter is shown in Fig. 7–3(b), note that the excitation equations have been implemented directly in terms of NAND elements. From the logic circuit diagram one can easily see how the storage property is obtained—NAND gates (8, 10) and (4, 9), due to the feedback loops, act as bistable stores for the secondaries $Y_1 Y_2$.

This circuit configuration is equivalent to the master-slave bistable circuit briefly mentioned in Chapter 5. If we redraw the master-slave circuit in terms of NAND elements (see Fig. 7–5) and then derive the equations for M and S, we have:

$$M = \overline{[(\overline{\bar{x}\bar{s}})(m)][(\overline{\bar{x}s})]} = [(\overline{\bar{x}\bar{s}})m] + \bar{x}s$$

$$= m(x + s) + \bar{x}s$$

Hence $M = mx + ms + \bar{x}s$

Now $m = y_1 \quad \text{and} \quad s = y_2$

thus we have $Y_1 = y_1 x + y_1 y_2 + y_2 \bar{x}$

Similarly for S we have

$$S = \overline{[(\overline{xm})(s)][(x\overline{m})]} = (\overline{xm})s + x\overline{m}$$
$$= s(\bar{x} + \bar{m}) + x\overline{m}$$

Thus
$$S = s\bar{x} + s\bar{m} + x\overline{m}$$

and
$$Y_2 = y_2\bar{x} + y_2\bar{y}_1 + x\bar{y}_1$$

In general, the excitation equations (or bistable output equations) can be obtained for any bistable circuit by using the characteristic equation for a SR bistable: $Q_+ = S + \bar{R}Q$, derived in Chapter 5. Thus if we substitute $S = \bar{x}y_2$ and $R = \bar{x}\bar{y}_2$ in this equation we obtain the same result for Y_1 as before:

$$Y_1 = \bar{x}y_2 + (\overline{\bar{x}\bar{y}_2})y_1$$

Thus
$$Y_1 = \bar{x}y_2 + xy_1 + y_2y_1$$

We see then that the equations, and hence the circuit functions, are identical; moreover, the master-slave arrangement contains one NAND element less in its implementation.

Consideration of this circuit leads us to a quite different approach for implementing asynchronous logic circuits. Instead of deriving excitation equations as described above, an alternative method is to use d.c. bistables for the secondary stores and to deduce the set and reset equations for these elements using the techniques developed for synchronous sequential circuits. Starting with a fully assigned flow-table, say that for the counter [Fig. 7–1(c)], we examine the present and next values of $Y_1 Y_2$ (comparing row assignment and table entries) and determine the conditions required to set and reset a d.c. SR bistable. These conditions are then plotted on a Karnaugh map and minimized in the normal way (see Table 7–7), resulting in the equations:

$$Y_1 \text{ set} = \bar{x}y_2 \qquad Y_1 \text{ reset} = \bar{x}\bar{y}_2$$

and
$$Y_2 \text{ set} = \bar{x}y_1 \qquad Y_2 \text{ reset} = xy_1$$

It will be obvious from the equations that the circuit so obtained is identical to that of the master-slave bistable. An important point to note with this method is that the hazard conditions are automatically accounted for by the inherent characteristics of the d.c. SR bistable, e.g. once $Q = 1$ the set inputs have no effect. This can be shown theoretically by the derivation of the excitation equations from the bistable set-reset input conditions. Since this expression always contains the complete set of prime implicant terms, there is no possibility of logic hazards,[8] as can be shown by plotting these terms on a map and noting that all loops overlap. In the case of electronic logic, then, this alternative method of design sometimes leads to a simpler circuit, particularly when NOR/NAND logic is employed. Also, since many integrated circuit logic systems include gated d.c. bistables (master-slave or

Table 7–7 Set-reset maps for divide-by-2 counter

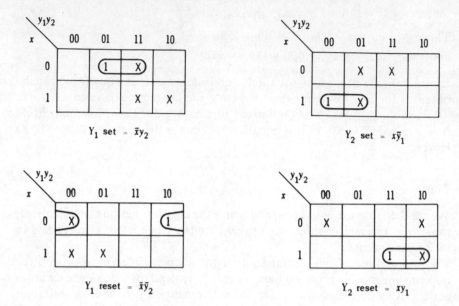

Y_1 set $= \bar{x}y_2$

Y_2 set $= x\bar{y}_1$

Y_1 reset $= \bar{x}\bar{y}_2$

Y_2 reset $= xy_1$

dual latch elements) as standard components, this could be a more convenient method of implementation. In addition, it has the considerable advantage of automatically eliminating circuit hazards of the type so far discussed.

7–7 Design example

The objective of any asynchronous logic design is to evolve optimized hazard-free equations for the secondary excitation and output functions. The process may be divided into several stages:

(a) construction of a primitive flow-table from the oral or written specification—this is generally accomplished with the aid of a state-diagram;

(b) if possible the flow-table is reduced by eliminating redundant internal states, and the resulting table merged;

(c) a secondary state assignment is made, considering the possibility of circuit 'races';

(d) using the derived and primitive flow-tables, equations for the secondary excitation and output are obtained; finally these equations are checked for the presence of circuit 'hazards'. Alternatively, the input equations for a d.c. set-reset bistable may be derived directly from the tables.

Let us consider the following design problem.

A sequential logic circuit is to be controlled by two switches x_1 and x_2. The output Z must go to 1 at the end of the input sequence $00 \rightarrow 01 \rightarrow 11$, which is set up on the switches. This output must be maintained for all input changes until the sequence $11 \rightarrow 10 \rightarrow 00$ occurs, when the output must go to 0.

The circuit has most of the characteristics required of a very simple electronic combination lock. The state-diagram is shown in Fig. 7–6(a) together with the primitive flow-table in Table 7–8(a).

The design follows very closely the procedures described above; the state-diagram is optional—the primitive flow-table gives the same information and may be used as the initial starting point. Note that the input sequences which lead to the required outputs are established first, and the table then completed for all other possible inputs. The primitive flow-table has no equivalent states and therefore cannot be reduced further. Comparing the flow-table rows for possible mergers we get:

$$m = (1, 2)(1, 5)(2, 4)(3, 4)(3, 6)(5, 7)(5, 9)(6, 8)(6, 10)(7, 9)(8, 10)$$
$$= (1, 2)(1, 5)(2, 4)(3, 4)(3, 6)(5, 7, 9)(6, 8, 10)$$

The merger diagram is shown in Fig. 7–6(b). From this, and the set of mergeable pairs above, it is apparent that the best row merge is

$$M = (1, 2)(3, 4)(5, 7, 9)(6, 8, 10)$$

Furthermore, the blocks are output-consistent which will help to reduce the output logic. The merged flow-table is given in Table 7–8(b), together with the output states.

The assignment of rows (which requires two secondary variables), so that each transition involves a change of one variable only, is made by examining a transition map [Table 7–8(c)], the fully assigned table being shown in Table 7–8(d). The derivation of the excitation maps is quite standard, [Table 7–8(e)] and note that Y_1 cannot contain any hazards since the minimal expression consists of overlapping essential prime implicants:

$$Y_1 = y_1 y_2 + y_1 x_2 + y_1 x_1 + x_1 x_2 \bar{y}_2$$

The minimal expression for Y_2 is given by:

$$Y_2 = x_2 \bar{y}_1 y_2 + x_1 \bar{x}_2 \bar{y}_1 + \bar{x}_1 x_2 y_1 + \bar{x}_2 y_1 y_2$$

We now examine the transitions between loops on the excitation map and a convenient way of doing this is to insert the state numbers on the map itself. We find that hazards exist for the transition between $\text{⑦} \rightarrow \text{⑤}$ and $\text{⑥} \rightarrow \text{⑧}$, due to the change in x_2. Thus we must insert two extra terms to ensure hazard-free operation, i.e. $x_1 \bar{y}_1 y_2$ and $\bar{x}_1 y_1 y_2$, which gives:

$$Y_2 = x_2 \bar{y}_1 y_2 + x_1 \bar{x}_2 \bar{y}_1 + \bar{x}_1 x_2 y_1 + \bar{x}_2 y_1 y_2 + x_1 \bar{y}_1 y_2 + \bar{x}_1 y_1 y_2$$

(a) State diagram

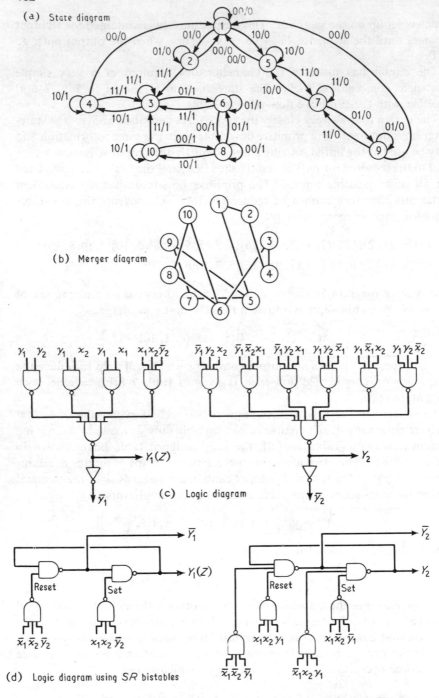

(b) Merger diagram

(c) Logic diagram

(d) Logic diagram using SR bistables

Fig. 7–6 Design example

(a) Primitive flow-table

Table 7–8 Design example

Inputs x_1x_2				Output
00	01	11	10	Z
①	2	–	5	0
1	②	3	–	0
–	6	③	4	1
1	–	3	④	1
1	–	7	⑤	0
8	⑥	3	–	1
–	9	⑦	5	0
⑧	6	–	10	1
1	⑨	7	–	0
8	–	3	⑩	1

(b) Merged flow-table

	Inputs x_1x_2				Output
	00	01	11	10	Z
a	①	②	3	5	0
b	1	6	③	④	1
c	1	⑨	⑦	⑤	0
d	⑧	⑥	3	⑩	1

(c) Row transition map

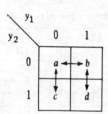

(d) Fully assigned table

	x_1x_2	00	01	11	10
	y_1y_2				
a	00	00	00	10	01
c	01	00	01	01	01
d	11	11	11	10	11
b	10	00	11	10	10

(e) Excitation maps

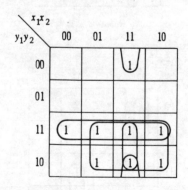

$$Y_1 = y_1y_2 + y_1x_2 + y_1x_1 + x_1x_2\bar{y}_2$$

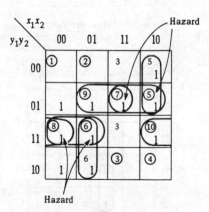

$$Y_2 = x_2\bar{y}_1y_2 + x_1\bar{x}_2\bar{y}_1 + \bar{x}_1x_2y_1$$
$$+ \ \bar{x}_2y_1y_2 + x_1\bar{y}_1y_2 + \bar{x}_1y_1y_2$$

Table 7–8 continued

(f) Output map

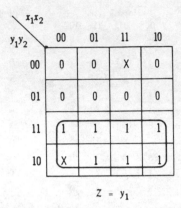

$$Z = y_1$$

(g) SR bistable input equations

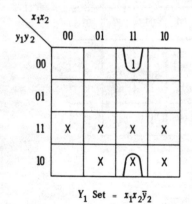

$$Y_1 \text{ Set } = x_1 x_2 \bar{y}_2$$

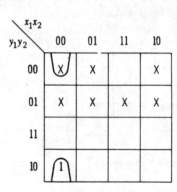

$$Y_1 \text{ Reset } = \bar{x}_1 \bar{x}_2 \bar{y}_2$$

$$Y_2 \text{ Set } = \bar{x}_1 x_2 y_1 + x_1 \bar{x}_2 \bar{y}_1$$

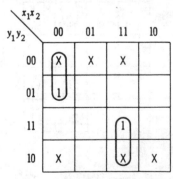

$$Y_2 \text{ Reset } = \bar{x}_1 \bar{x}_2 \bar{y}_1 + x_1 x_2 y_1$$

These are the only loops that need to be interconnected since there are no transitions between $\textcircled{9} \to \textcircled{6}$ and $\textcircled{5} \to \textcircled{10}$. The output map is obtained in the normal way and is plotted in Table 7–8(f); due to the merging, the simple expression $Z = y_1$ results. The complete circuit is implemented in NAND elements in Fig. 7–6(c).

Using the alternative method of implementation and starting with the fully assigned flow-table in Table 7–8(d), the set and reset conditions for $Y_1 Y_2$ are extracted and plotted directly on Karnaugh maps [Table 7–8(g)]. This gives the expressions

$$Y_1 \text{ set } = x_1 x_2 \bar{y}_2 \qquad\qquad Y_1 \text{ reset } = \bar{x}_1 \bar{x}_2 \bar{y}_2$$

$$Y_2 \text{ set } = \bar{x}_1 x_2 y_1 + x_1 \bar{x}_2 \bar{y}_1 \qquad Y_2 \text{ reset } = \bar{x}_1 \bar{x}_2 \bar{y}_1 + x_1 x_2 y_1$$

The implementation of these equations using NAND elements is shown in Fig. 7–6(d), note that only ten NAND's are required in this circuit as against 14 for the previous one. This reduction of units is assisted by the fact that, with NAND elements forming the bistables, it is possible to have multiple set and reset inputs. Let us analyse this circuit to ensure that it operates correctly and, just as important, that it is hazard-free. From Fig. 7–6(d) we can say that

$$Y_1 = \overline{[\overline{(\bar{x}_1 \bar{x}_2 \bar{y}_2)(y_1)}][\overline{(x_1 x_2 \bar{y}_2)}]}$$

$$= [\overline{(\bar{x}_1 \bar{x}_2 \bar{y}_2)(y_1)}] + x_1 x_2 \bar{y}_2$$

$$Y_1 = x_1 y_1 + x_2 y_1 + y_2 y_1 + x_1 x_2 \bar{y}_2$$

which, of course, is the identical excitation equation for Y_1 derived above. Again, we have

$$Y_2 = \overline{[\overline{(\bar{x}_1 \bar{x}_2 \bar{y}_1)(x_1 x_2 y_1)(y_2)}][\overline{(\bar{x}_1 x_2 y_1)}][\overline{(x_1 \bar{x}_2 \bar{y}_1)}]}$$

$$= \overline{(\bar{x}_1 \bar{x}_2 \bar{y}_1)(x_1 x_2 y_1)}(y_2) + \bar{x}_1 x_2 y_1 + x_1 \bar{x}_2 \bar{y}_1$$

Thus $\qquad Y_2 = x_1 \bar{x}_2 y_2 + x_1 \bar{y}_1 y_2 + \bar{x}_1 x_2 y_2 + x_2 \bar{y}_1 y_2 + \bar{x}_1 y_1 y_2$

$$+ \bar{x}_2 y_1 y_2 + \bar{x}_1 x_2 y_1 + x_1 \bar{x}_2 \bar{y}_1$$

If these terms are plotted on a Karnaugh map it becomes obvious that the expression for Y_2 above is the set of all prime implicants and thus no hazards can exist since all loops will interconnect.

7-8 Further aspects of the state assignment problem

So far in the examples of secondary state assignment that we have chosen, it has always been possible to perform the allocation of row variables in such a way that transitions involve a change of one variable only and critical races are avoided. What can we do, though, if this is not possible? Consider the

Table 7–9 State assignment for three-row table

(a) Merged flow-table

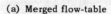

	Inputs x_1x_2			
	00	01	11	10
a	①	②	3	4
b	⑤	2	3	④
c	1	⑥	③	4

(b) Transition maps

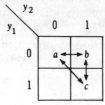
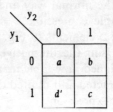

(c) Assigned flow-table

	y_1y_2	Inputs x_1x_2			
		00	01	11	10
a	00	①	②	3	4
b	01	⑤	2	3	④
c	11	1	⑥	③	4
d'	10	1	–	3	–

(d) Y-maps

	Inputs x_1x_2			
y_1y_2	00	01	11	10
00	00	00	10	01
01	01	00	11	01
11	10	11	11	01
10	00	–	11	–

or

	Inputs x_1x_2			
y_1y_2	00	01	11	10
00	00	00	01	01
01	01	00	11	01
11	10	11	11	01
10	00	–	–	–

flow-table shown in Table 7–9(a). This is a three-row table and hence requires a minimum of two secondary variables for row coding. If we examine all the possible state transitions, using the transition map [Table 7–9(b)], we find that there are transitions between all three pairs of rows, thus it is impossible to code the rows so that only one variable changes during a transition. However, secondary assignment can always be obtained for a three-row table using two variables, by making use of the fourth or 'spare' secondary state. Suppose we assign the rows as shown in Table 7–9(c), where we are using the fourth combination $y_1y_2 = 10$ as a buffer state between transition rows. If the circuit is in stable state ② under the input conditions $x_1x_2 = 01$, and a change to $x_1x_2 = 11$ occurs, the machine must go to stable state ③. This is achieved by directing the intermediate secondary changes, using the buffer state, to be $y_1y_2 = ⑩ \rightarrow 10 \rightarrow 11 \rightarrow ⑪$. In other words, we have deliberately created a machine cycle by a suitable choice of the y_1y_2 values for the unstable states. Similarly, if in stable state ⑥ under the input $x_1x_2 = 01$ and x_2 changes to 0, the circuit goes to stable state ① via the directed cycle

$y_1 y_2 =$ ⑪ $\rightarrow 10 \rightarrow 00 \rightarrow$ ⑩ . In some cases it is not necessary to use a buffer state to produce a cycle, for example in Table 7–9(d) the transition ② $\rightarrow$ ③ could have been achieved by coding $y_1 y_2 =$ ⑩ $\rightarrow 01 \rightarrow 11 \rightarrow$ ⑪ .

A secondary assignment without critical races is not always possible for a four-row table using two secondary variables, and consequently three secondaries must be used. This will involve selecting four out of the eight possible combinations to represent the rows, and there are $_8C_4 = 8!/4!\,4! = 70$ ways of achieving this choice! Fortunately, the selection of the four basic combinations is assisted by breaking down the possible combinations into six pattern groups (a full analysis of this problem has been made by Marcus).[5] After this comes the problem of allocating the spare buffer combinations in an appropriate manner to affect the transitions.

The final choice of secondary assignment may be based on circuit economy or on speed of transition. Unfortunately there are as yet no systematic techniques available which give an optimum solution to this assignment problem,[6][7] and the determination of a minimal circuit must depend on experience and 'trial and error' methods, entailing the comparison of Y-maps. As an illustration, consider the four-row flow-table shown in Table 7–10(a). This is again a 'worst-case' condition since there are seven possible transitions between the rows [see Table 7–10(b)i]. Table 7–10(b)ii–vii shows six possible assignments using the spare secondary states, one from each of the Marcus pattern groups; many more variations are possible since in each pattern group the basic row combinations may be permutated in $_4P_4 = 4! = 24$ different ways. Table 7–11(a) shows an assigned flow-table using the first pattern group [Table 7–10(b)ii]. As the unused buffer states are entered as 'don't cares', it follows that an economical solution will be given by the assignment that produces the most 'don't cares' in the table. This can be achieved by ensuring that rows containing a large number of transitions have the smallest cycle or, ideally, are adjacent. In this problem, the majority of transitions occur between rows (a, d) and (c, d) thus, simply by changing the coding of the basic rows according to these ideas [Table 7–10(b)viii], we can arrive at a much better result. Table 7–11(b) shows the assigned table, and the corresponding Y-map is shown in Table 7–12.

Before using spare secondary states, however, it is as well to check whether critical races can be avoided by the insertion of indigenous cycles in the basic flow-table. In this case, due to the existence of a large number of 'don't cares', it is perfectly feasible to use indigenous cycles. As can be seen from Table 7–13, by a suitable choice of row coding and directed cycles we can in fact allocate the four-row tables using the minimum of secondary variables, i.e. two. An alternative coding method for avoiding critical races is *multiple secondary state assignment*. This means that a row in the flow-table is assigned two secondaries, i.e. combinations; this method is, in fact, another means of utilizing the spare secondary states. Using this approach equivalent

Table 7–10 State assignment for four-row table

(a) Merged flow-table

	Inputs $x_1x_2x_3$							
	000	001	010	011	100	101	110	111
a	(A)	E	G	–	(B)	F	C	–
b	–	–	D	–	K	–	(C)	J
c	A	–	(D)	H	–	–	I	–
d	A	(E)	(G)	(H)	(K)	(F)	(I)	(J)

(b) Transition maps

(i)

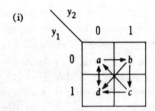

(ii)

y_3 \ y_1y_2	00	01	11	10
0	a	b	c	e'
1	f'	g'	d	

(iii)

y_3 \ y_1y_2	00	01	11	10
0	a	b	c	e'
1	g'	d	f'	

(iv)

y_3 \ y_1y_2	00	01	11	10
0	a	b	c	e'
1		f'	g'	d

(v)

y_3 \ y_1y_2	00	01	11	10
0	a	b	e'	f'
1			c	d

(vi)

y_3 \ y_1y_2	00	01	11	10
0	a	e'	b	g'
1		c	f'	d

(vii)

y_3 \ y_1y_2	00	01	11	01
0	a	b	h'	g'
1	d	c	e'	f'

(viii)

y_3 \ y_1y_2	00	01	11	10
0	a	d	b	e'
1	f'	g'	c	

Table 7–11 Assigned flow-tables

(a)

$y_1y_2y_3$		Inputs $x_1x_2x_3$							
		000	001	010	011	100	101	110	111
a	000	Ⓐ	f'	f'	–	Ⓑ	f'	C	–
b	010	–	–	D	–	g'	–	Ⓒ	g'
c	110	e'	–	Ⓓ	H	–	–	I	–
d	111	g'	Ⓔ	Ⓖ	Ⓗ	Ⓚ	Ⓕ	Ⓘ	Ⓙ
e'	100	A	–	–	–	–	–	–	–
f'	001	A	g'	g'	–	–	g'	–	–
g'	011	f'	E	G	–	K	F	–	J

(b)

$y_1y_2y_3$		Inputs $x_1x_2x_3$							
		000	001	010	011	100	101	110	111
a	000	Ⓐ	E	G	–	Ⓑ	F	e'	–
b	110	–	–	D	–	K	–	Ⓒ	J
c	111	g'	–	Ⓓ	g'	–	–	g'	–
d	010	A	Ⓔ	Ⓖ	Ⓗ	Ⓚ	Ⓕ	Ⓘ	Ⓙ
e'	100	–	–	–	–	–	–	C	
f'	001	A	–	–	–	–	–	–	–
g'	011	f'	–	–	H	–	–	I	–

Table 7–12 Y–map

$y_1y_2y_3$		Inputs $x_1x_2x_3$							
		000	001	010	011	100	101	110	111
a	000	000	010	010	–	000	010	100	–
b	110	–	–	111	–	010	–	110	010
c	111	011	–	111	011	–	–	011	–
d	010	000	010	010	010	010	010	010	010
e'	100	–	–	–	–	–	–	110	–
f'	001	000	–	–	–	–	–	–	–
g'	011	001	–	–	010	–	–	010	–

Table 7–13 Indigenous cycles

(a) Assigned flow-table

		Inputs $x_1x_2x_3$							
y_1y_2		000	001	010	011	100	101	110	111
a	00	Ⓐ	E	G	–	Ⓑ	F	C	–
b	01	A	–	D	–	K	–	Ⓒ	c
c	11	b	–	Ⓓ	H	K	–	I	J
d	10	A	Ⓕ	Ⓖ	Ⓗ	Ⓚ	Ⓕ	Ⓘ	Ⓙ

(b) Y-map

		Inputs $x_1x_2x_3$							
y_1y_2		000	001	010	011	100	101	110	111
a	00	00	10	10	–	00	10	01	–
b	01	00	–	11	–	11	–	01	11
c	11	01	–	11	10	10	–	10	10
d	10	00	10	10	10	10	10	10	10

Table 7–14 Multiple secondary state assignment

(a) Assigned flow-table

		Inputs x_1x_2			
y_1y_2		00	01	11	10
a_1	00	①₁	②₁	3	4
a_2	10	①₂	②₂	3	4
b	01	⑤	2₁	3	④
c	11	1₂	⑥	③	4

(b) Y-map

		Inputs x_1x_2			
y_1y_2		00	01	11	10
a_1	00	00	00	10	01
a_2	10	10	10	11	00
b	01	01	00	11	01
c	11	10	11	11	01

stable states are obtained in different rows, so we have introduced 'redundant' rows in the flow-table. We must have some means of distinguishing between these states and the usual device is to include subscripts on the stable state figures. For example, the flow-table in Table 7–9(a) could be allocated as shown in Table 7–14, where row a has been given two secondaries. The table could equally well have been coded with row c having two assignments; the reason for choosing rows a or c is that a transition is required between these two rows which cannot be obtained [see Table 7–9(b)] using a three-row assignment without changing more than one variable at a time.

In Table 7–14 a transition from stable state ⑥ under the input change $x_1x_2 = 01 \rightarrow 00$ is directed to stable state ①₂ which is in row a_2, involving a change of one variable only. But the transition of stable state $\circled{5}$ for the input change $x_1x_2 = 00 \rightarrow 01$ is directed to stable state $\circled{2_1}$ which is in row a_1, thus again ensuring a change of one variable only. Transitions from stable states in both rows a_1 and a_2 must be suitably cycled to the correct stable states, e.g. $\circled{2_1}$ is cycled to $\circled{3}$ via the directed secondary changes $y_1y_2 = \circled{00} \rightarrow 10 \rightarrow 11 \rightarrow \circled{11}$.

Though we have only considered three- and four-row tables in the examples above, the same arguments must obviously apply to flow-tables containing any number of rows. It is not always possible, for example, to assign an eight-row table with three variables, and we must resort to four variables. Here the number of possible selections increases considerably ($_{16}C_8 = 16!/8!\,8! = 12870$) and an exhaustive trial and error procedure is out of the question.

7–9 Circuit hazards

As we have seen above, circuit hazards arise from differing delays, or propagation times, in the signal paths. The result of this is that the output signals do not respond predictably as defined by a truth-table or flow-table. Hazardous conditions are not confined to sequential circuits—combinational circuits can exhibit the same phenomena but of course since there is no feedback loop the consequences are normally not so serious. Hazards can be classified into two groups:

(a) *Single-variable hazards* due to changes in one variable only. These can be corrected logically or by the insertion of appropriate delays in the circuit. There are three main types: *static*, *dynamic*, and *essential*.

(b) *Multi-variable hazards* occur because of changes in more than one variable, and can also produce static, dynamic and essential hazards. In general they cannot be completely eliminated by logical means or circuit modification, hence the restriction to single-variable changes in asynchronous circuits.

The type of hazard we met in the design example above was the single-variable static hazard, and occurred in the combinational logic governing the feedback signals, i.e. the excitation equations. The characteristic of the static hazard is that it causes a transition in an output, which is required to remain constant at one value, during a variable change. We have seen how this type of hazard can be recognized from the Karnaugh map (or by algebraic manipulation), and logically corrected by the insertion of additional gates using the technique due to Huffman.[4] However, care must be taken to ensure that the hazard correction terms do in fact cover the variable changes. Consider the Y-map shown in Table 7–15, it could appear that the additional loop x_2y_2

Table 7–15

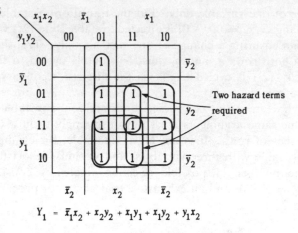

$$Y_1 = \bar{x}_1 x_2 + x_2 y_2 + x_1 y_1 + x_1 y_2 + y_1 x_2$$

is sufficient to cover the hazards since all loops interconnect, and thus the excitation equations would be:

$$Y_1 = \bar{x}_1 x_2 + y_2 x_2 + x_1 y_1 + x_1 y_2$$

But if a transition is required for the conditions $x_1 = x_2 = y_1 = 1$ and $y_2 = 0$, when $x_1 \to 0$ the hazard condition is not covered, and an additional loop is required: $y_1 x_2$. Thus it is essential that all possible transitions are examined on the Y-map and, where necessary, loop terms covering the initial and final states of the transitions should be added. Static hazards can also occur when the output, instead of remaining constant at 0, changes from $0 \to 1 \to 0$ due to a change in a single variable—these are called zero hazards. Huffman has proved, however, that the logical elimination of one type of hazard (either 0 or 1) will automatically correct for the other. Even though static hazards have been eliminated, it is still possible for multi-variable input changes to produce logical hazards. It is worth bearing in mind, though it has in fact been stated earlier, that in order to eliminate all logical hazards in a two-level circuit, whether arising from either single or multi-variable input changes, the complete set of prime implicants must be included in the solution.

The dynamic hazard, which also occurs in combinational circuits, causes an output to change three or more times instead of only once, and so produce sporadic outputs because of a single-variable change. Thus an output required to change from $1 \to 0$ would, due to a dynamic hazard, change $1 \to 0 \to 1 \to 0$ (note the minimum three changes of output). Should the duration of the output transition be long enough to cause any following circuits to switch over, for example if connected in a feedback loop, the circuit could malfunction.

Dynamic hazards are caused by the existence in the circuit of three or more different signal paths for the same variable, each with differing delay times.

Table 7–16 Dynamic hazard

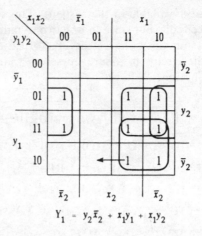

$$Y_1 = y_2\bar{x}_2 + x_1y_1 + x_1y_2$$

In practice this is generally the result of factoring electronic gates, or using long lead connections in fast logic circuits; in relay circuits, contacts with different closure times can produce the same effect. NOR/NAND logic in particular gives rise to this problem, since each unit includes an invertor amplifier with a significant propagation time. Consider the Y-map shown in Table 7–16, there are no static hazards since all prime implicants are present and the excitation equation is given by:

$$Y_1 = \bar{x}_2 y_2 + x_1 y_1 + x_1 y_2$$

Now if this equation was implemented directly using three-input NAND gates, the circuit would function perfectly correctly. However, suppose it is necessary to factorize the equations, so that existing gates (part of a much larger logic system) can be used, then a dynamic hazard could arise. Figure 7–7 shows one possible way of factorizing the circuit, assuming gate C giving

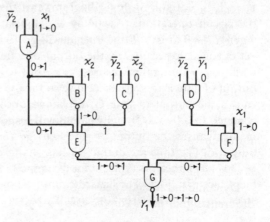

Fig. 7–7
Dynamic hazard
caused by factoring

$\bar{y}_2\bar{x}_2$ is already available in the system. This is not the best way of implementing the circuit, but since in practice dynamic hazards arise mainly from careless, and sometimes unnecessary, factorization it provides a good example. Analysing the circuit to assure ourselves that it faithfully reproduces the switching equation, we have

$$Y_1 = \overline{\{\overline{[(\overline{(\bar{y}_2 x_1)}(x_2)][\overline{(\bar{y}_2 x_1)}][\overline{(\bar{y}_2 \bar{x}_2)}]\}\{[\overline{(\bar{y}_2 \bar{y}_1)}(x_1)]\}}}$$

$$= \overline{[\overline{(\bar{y}_2 x_1)}(x_2)][\overline{(\bar{y}_2 x_1)}][\overline{(\bar{y}_2 \bar{x}_2)}]} + [\overline{(\bar{y}_2 \bar{y}_1)}(x_1)]$$

$$= [(\bar{y}_2 x_1) + \bar{x}_2][y_2 + \bar{x}_1][y_2 + x_2] + x_1 y_2 + x_1 y_1$$

$$= (\bar{y}_2 y_2 x_1 + \bar{y}_2 x_1 \bar{x}_1 + y_2 \bar{x}_2 + \bar{x}_1 \bar{x}_2)(y_2 + x_2) + x_1 y_2 + x_1 y_1$$

$$= y_2 \bar{x}_2 + y_2 \bar{x}_2 x_2 + \bar{x}_1 \bar{x}_2 y_2 + \bar{x}_1 \bar{x}_2 x_2 + x_1 y_2 + x_1 y_1$$

Hence $Y_1 = y_2 \bar{x}_2 + x_1 y_2 + x_1 y_1$

Now suppose the circuit is in the stable condition $x_1 = x_2 = y_1 = 1$ and $y_2 = 0$, and let x_1 change to 0. The output Y_1 is initially at 1 and when $x_1 \rightarrow 0$ it should go to 0 and stay there. However, from Fig. 7–7, there are three paths, each of different length, from the input signals x_1 to the output gate:

1. via gates F, G,
2. via gates A, E, G and
3. via gates A, B, E, G.

Thus we can expect dynamic hazards to occur. A convenient way of analysing and appreciating the operation of NAND circuits is to invoke the basic logic properties of the gate. That is, the output will only be logical 0 when all its inputs are logical 1, thus a 0 on any input will always cause the output to go to 1. Now, if we insert the initial truth-values of the variables ($x_1 = x_2 = y_1 = 1$, $y_2 = 0$) on the logic diagram, and then let $x_1 \rightarrow 0$, we can easily see the circuit operation. Assuming equal delays through the NAND elements, when $x_1 \rightarrow 0$ at gate F the output will go to 1, the output of gate E has not yet changed, consequently the output of gate G will go from $1 \rightarrow 0$. Meanwhile, $x_1 \rightarrow 0$ at gate A causes its output to go to 1, this in turn causes the output of gate E to go to 0 because so far the output of B is unchanged. This causes the output of gate G to change once again to 1, thus so far it has changed $1 \rightarrow 0 \rightarrow 1$. Finally gate B will respond, its output going to 0, which in turn causes the output of gate E to go to 1, giving a final change at the output of G; thus the output Y_1 has changed $1 \rightarrow 0 \rightarrow 1 \rightarrow 0$.

This mechanism is typical of a dynamic hazard and is primarily caused by inept factorization. The hazard cannot be overcome by basic logical design, since the fault arises from the circuit structure; the only remedy is to refactor the circuit. It is good practice always to avoid dynamic hazards where possible because, even if the output transitions are of very short duration, they still have the effect of introducing 'spikes', or noise, in the system which is very undesirable in low level logic circuits such as integrated circuits.

The *essential hazard* is pertinent only to asynchronous sequential systems, and is basically a critical race between an input signal change and a secondary signal change. The hazard can only exist, for reasons which will be apparent later, in systems with at least two secondaries.

Let us demonstrate this hazard by means of an actual circuit, using the master-slave divide-by-two counter (Fig. 7–8) as our example. We shall use the same descriptive method to explain this hazard as we used for the dynamic hazard, i.e. consideration of the basic logic inputs. Figure 7–8(a) shows the counter circuit with the stable state ① conditions $y_1 = y_2 = x = 0$ entered on the logic diagram. In the normal operation of the counter we assume, quite rightly in the majority of cases, that the delay through gates H, I and E, F (the input gates and the Y_2 SR bistable) is very much longer than the delay through the invertor G. This means that when $x \to 1$, corresponding to the unstable state, the output of gate G responds first and goes to 0, which in turn makes the output of gate C go to 1, gate D output being unchanged. Thus the state of Y_1, since the bistable is already reset, is also unchanged. Meanwhile, $x \to 1$ at gate H has no effect, but at gate I the output goes to 0. This in turn causes the output of gate F to go to 1, thus setting the bistable, and Y_2 goes to 1. The Y_2 output is fed back to gate E whose output then goes to 0, resulting in stable state ② with $y_1 y_2 = 01$. This corresponds to the correct action for the counter as dictated by the flow-table shown in Table 7–17.

Now suppose that, due to circuit delays, the response of input gates H, I and the bistable E, F is very much faster than the response of the invertor loop G. (If both circuits have similar responses, we have the condition where a 'critical race' exists between the input signal and the secondary circuit for Y_2.) In this case, the output of gate F, and hence Y_2, will have changed before the input change due to $x \to 1$ has reached gates C and D, consequently the Y_1 secondary circuit will behave as if it were in the state $y_1 y_2 = 01$ with input $x = 0$. Reference to Table 7–17 shows that this will be unstable state 3 directing $y_1 \to 1$. The circuit action is then, from Fig. 7–8(b), $\bar{Y}_2 \to 0$ causes the output of gate C to go to 1, and $Y_2 \to 1$ will cause the output of gate D to go to 0 since $\bar{x}$ is as yet unchanged and equal to 1. The change in output of gate D will, in turn, cause the output of gate B (Y_1) to go to 1, which is then fed back to gate A producing a 0 output and thus maintaining Y_1. When the input change $x \to 1$ eventually reaches gates C and D it will have no effect since the bistable has already been set.

Meanwhile, as the outputs of Y_1 are fed back to Y_2 secondary circuits, the circuit will change again, responding as if it were in unstable state 4, i.e.

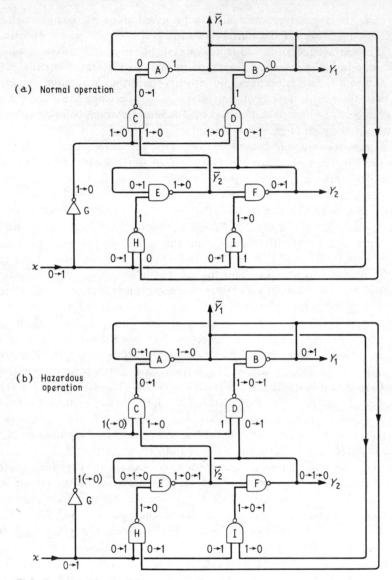

Fig. 7–8 Essential hazard in master-slave counter

$y_1y_2 = 11$ and input $x = 1$. Thus the output of gate H goes to 0, which in turn causes gate E output to go to 1. Since the output of gate I has also changed to 1, the output of gate F (Y_2) goes to 0 and a final stable state is reached with $y_1y_2 = 10$ and $x = 1$, i.e. stable state ④ in the flow table. This, of course, is incorrect!

Table 7–17 Essential hazards

(a) Flow-table

Input x

y_1y_2	0	1
00	①	2
01	3	② hazard
11	③	4
10	1	④

(b) Y-map

Input x

y_1y_2	0	1
00	00 → 01	
01	11 ↙ 01	hazard
11	11 → 10	
10	00	10

(c) Flow-table

Input x

y_1y_2	0	1
00	①	2
01	3	②
11	③	2
10		

(d) Y-map

Input x

y_1y_2	0	1
00	00 → 01	
01	11 ↙ 01	
11	11 → 01	
10		

The action of the circuit is difficult to understand, and to explain, and the reader is advised to redraw Fig. 7–8 with the initial stable conditions, and then insert the changing values as he reads through the description of the circuit action.

The essential hazard cannot be corrected logically, since it is inherent in the logical structure, as well as depending on the circuit characteristics. The only way of eliminating it is to insert delaying elements (or some form of clock pulse system) in the circuit to ensure that the input signal always wins the 'race'. In the example we considered this would entail a delay in the x signal path to the Y_2 secondary circuit. Ungar[8] has defined the essential hazard in terms of a flow-table and has also proved that if a flow-table contains an essential hazard, at least one delay element is essential if it is to operate reliably.

The hazard is effectively caused by three changes of input, initially in the counter circuit we had $x = 1$ and secondary Y_2 changed accordingly, giving $y_1y_2 = 01$; then secondary Y_1 responded with $x = 0$ (due to the input delay) giving $y_1y_2 = 11$; finally, Y_2 again changed due to $x = 1$ and the new value of Y_1, giving the final circuit condition of $y_1y_2 = 10$. Furthermore, if we examine the flow-table for the counter circuit, it is apparent that if the next state of the circuit after the hazard occurred (stable state ④ via unstable state 4 with $y_1y_2 = 11$ and $x = 1$) had in fact been the same as the starting state (stable state ② via unstable state 2) we would have eventually arrived back at the correct stable state. This structure is shown in Table 7–17(c) and (d). Putting these two facts together, we may now define how an essential hazard may be recognized from the flow-table. If, starting from one stable state in the flow table, the state reached after one input change is different to that reached after three changes of the same input, an essential hazard could occur.

This type of flow-table structure occurs in counters, shift registers, etc., which are extensively used in logic systems, hence the reason for examining this hazard in some detail. Fortunately though, using medium speed logic circuits with switching times in the order of microseconds, the hazard seldom arises in practice. However, with high speed nanosecond logic systems using integrated circuits, signal delays along a connecting wire may be appreciably longer than the actual switching time of the logic unit, and essential hazards could easily materialize. With large-variable switching problems it is essential to have some more systematic method of detecting the presence of hazards in a sequential or combinational circuit. Both McCluskey[9] and Huffman[4] have described methods of detecting and eliminating hazards arising from single input-variable changes, and these ideas could be developed into an algorithmic procedure. However, the best approach to date is due to Eichelberger[10] who describes a method which can be used to detect any type of hazard arising from both single- and multi-variable input changes. This uses ternary algebra (i.e. a three-valued Boolean algebra) to describe the transient behaviour of the input switching waveforms. The technique could easily be implemented into a digital computer program which would then be capable of analysing very large logic systems.

References and bibliography

(1) HUFFMAN, D. A. The synthesis of sequential switching circuits. *J. Franklin Inst.*, 1954, **257**, 161–190 (March), 275–303 (April).

(2) APPELS, J. and GEELS, B. *Handbook of relay switching technique.* Macmillan, New York, 1966.

(3) MALEY, G. A. and EARLE, J. *The logic design of transistor digital computers.* Prentice-Hall, Englewood Cliffs, N.J., 1963. Chap. 8, et seq.

(4) HUFFMAN, D. A. The design and use of hazard-free switching networks. *J. Ass. comput. Mach.*, 1957, **4**, 47–62.

(5) MARCUS, M. *Switching circuits for engineers.* 2nd edn. Prentice-Hall, Englewood Cliffs, N.J., 1967. Chap. 16.

(6) LIU, C. N. A state-variable assignment method for asynchronous sequential switching circuits. *J. Ass. comput. Mach.*, 1963, **10**, 209–216.

(7) TRACEY, J. H. Internal state assignment for asynchronous sequential machines. *I.E.E.E. Trans. electron. comput.*, 1966, **EC15**, 551–560.

(8) UNGAR, S. H. Hazards and delays in asynchronous sequential switching circuits. *I.R.E. Trans. Circuit Theory*, 1959, **CT6**, 12–25.

(9) McCluskey, E. J. Transients in combinational logic circuits. From *Redundancy techniques for computing systems*, R. H. Wilcox and W. C. Mann (Eds). Spartan Book Co., Washington, D.C., 1962, pp 9 et seq.

(10) Eichelberger, E. B. Hazard detection in combinational and sequential switching circuits. *I.B.M. Jl. Res. Dev.*, 1965, **9**, 90–99.

(11) McCluskey, E. J. *Introduction to the theory of switching circuits.* McGraw-Hill, New York, 1965. Chap. 7.

(12) Ungar, S. H. *Asynchronous sequential switching circuits.* Wiley Interscience, New York, 1969.

(13) Hill, F. J. and Peterson, G. R. *Introduction to switching theory and logical design.* Wiley, New York, 1968.

Tutorial problems

7-1 Design an asynchronous circuit that has two inputs, $x_1 x_2$, and one output Z. The circuit is required to give an output whenever the input sequence (00), (01), and (11) is received, but only in that order.

7-2 Derive the excitation and output equations for an asynchronous three-bit Gray-code counter which has one input x and three outputs Z_1, Z_2, and Z_3. Implement the design in terms of NAND elements. Redesign the circuit by extracting the set and reset equations for d.c. SR bistables and then compare and comment on the two circuits.

7-3 Design one stage of an asynchronous shift register, which is a circuit having two inputs x_1 and x_2 and one output Z. Input x_1 is the output of the preceding shift register stage, and x_2 is the shift pulse. When $x_2 = 1$, Z remains unchanged; when $x_2 = 0$, Z takes the previous value of x_1 when $x_2 = 1$.

Derive the excitation equations in NAND logic, and then in terms of input equations for master-slave bistables.

Confirm that the circuit may be connected in cascade to form a multistage shift register and, in so doing, explain its action.

7-4 In a numerical machine tool control system an optical Moiré fringe device is used to digitize the linear motion of the work piece. The relative movements

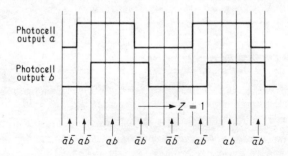

Fig. 7–9 Tutorial problem 7–4

of the gratings produce light and dark fringes which are detected photoelectric-ally using two photocells spaced $\lambda/4$ apart. A waveform diagram is shown in Fig. 7–9, a and b are the squared outputs of the photocells; note that due to the spacing of the cells the outputs cannot change together.

Design an asynchronous circuit with inputs a and b and output Z, which will detect the direction of motion, left or right, of the workpiece. (*Hint:* note that the sequence is $\bar{a}\bar{b} \rightarrow \bar{a}b \rightarrow ab \rightarrow a\bar{b} \rightarrow \bar{a}\bar{b}$ in one direction and is reversed for the other direction.)

7-5 Design an asynchronous circuit that has two inputs x_1 and x_2 and an output Z. Input x_1 is a repetitive square-wave or 'clock' pulse signal, and input x_2 origi-nates from a noise-free button. The action of the circuit is such that when x_2 is pressed at any point in the clock cycle, the output Z must transmit the next complete clock pulse of x_1. This circuit is called a single-shot generator and its function is to produce one clock pulse each time the button x_2 is pressed, irrespective of the duration of x_2.

Assume that x_1 and x_2 cannot occur together.

7-6 Design an asynchronous version of the clamp-gate circuit described in problem 7 of Chapter 5, and implement the design using master-slave bistables. Compare the relative merits of the synchronous and asynchronous circuits.

8 Circuit implementation

8–1 Introduction
In the preceding chapters we have attempted to explain the principles and techniques of logical design without being too specific as to the actual type of switching circuit used. We have done this so as not to obscure with unnecessary detail the basic fundamentals of switching theory which are completely general in application. However, before we can attempt the design of a digital system, the first problem to be overcome is the choice of the actual components. This is not easily resolved since there are various types of logic systems available on the commercial market; furthermore, at the time of writing, a quick survey revealed some sixty different manufacturers of logic elements! In this chapter we describe, in general terms, the various types of logic circuit available, and review the factors to be considered when comparing or selecting a logic system before implementation. The logic circuits available may be broadly classified as follows:

1. Electronic devices
   (a) modular elements comprising discrete components
   (b) integrated circuits
2. Fluid logic (pneumatic, hydraulic switching elements)
3. Relays, particularly dry-reed relay logic
4. Magnetic logic

We now describe briefly the main characteristics of each type of system.

8–2 Electronic devices
As we have seen, a logical switching system requires a minimum of an invertor and either an AND or OR gate; alternatively the NAND/NOR gate may be used. All these basic logic elements are possible and available with electronic circuitry. Transistors are used almost exclusively in these circuits, operating in the switching mode,[1] i.e. working between the cut-off and saturated regions of the characteristic curve. Some earlier systems had separate AND/OR gates, using passive diode-resistor circuits, combined with transistorized emitter followers, invertor amplifiers, and bistable circuits. The majority of present day systems, however, are built up around a basic NOR/NAND logic unit, generally including a.c. and d.c. bistable elements. The reason for this is that, with passive AND/OR circuitry, the constraints imposed on the logic design by the actual circuits themselves are numerous. For example, it is not possible to cascade AND/OR circuits freely as the loading

of each unit produces attenuation of the logic signals, and it is necessary to insert some form of power amplifier such as an emitter follower or invertor to reinstate the logic levels. This leads to complex loading tables for the logic elements which must be taken into account in the logic design. The use of NAND/NOR logic overcomes this disadvantage, since each element contains an amplifier giving voltage or current gain, and thus the rules for interconnection are very simple and reduce to observation of the maximum permitted number of inputs (fan-in) and outputs (fan-out) for the element.

In active logic circuits (in contrast to path-closing logic, i.e. relays), the binary variables 0 and 1 are usually represented by voltage levels (or pulses). When the 1 level is more positive than the 0 level the circuit is called a positive logic system, and when the 0 level is more positive than the 1 level, it is called a negative logic system. Due to the duality of logic functions, the same physical circuit may be both OR/AND or NOR/NAND according to the choice of logic convention, and this has led to the concept of dual-polarity logic which will be discussed later.

Since any logical system consists of a large number of identical units performing the logical operations of AND, OR, INVERT, etc., it is extremely important that these circuits should have the same operating characteristics, independent of any variation in power supply or component value. To achieve this, the design technique must take into account any component tolerances in the circuit configuration and a circuit must be evolved which can accommodate these changes while still maintaining the required input/output specification. This technique is known as 'worst-case' design.[2] However, since this assumes that all the circuit tolerances conspire at the same time to degrade the characteristics—a most pessimistic and unlikely situation—statistical design methods have emerged using 'Monte-Carlo' techniques.[3]

Electronic logic circuits may be constructed using discrete miniature components mounted on printed circuit boards and encapsulated in epoxy resin. Each logic 'brick' performs a particular logic function, say NAND, and a digital system can be built up using these bricks mounted on a larger 'mother' board, with wired interconnections on the back. The bricks are normally rectangular in shape, and have an approximate maximum size of 1 in × 2 in × $\frac{3}{4}$ in. Plated connection leads are brought out to one side, normally spaced 0·1 in, 0·15 in or 0·2 in between centres, to allow easy assembly to a mother board.

The alternative logic circuit, which is rapidly superseding discrete modules in many applications, is the micro-electronic circuit.[4][5] Various forms of micro-circuit are in existence, for example:

(a) *Semi-conductor integrated circuits* in which all the passive and active elements, including conductors, required to perform a specified logic function are formed in, or on, a semiconductor substrate by diffusion and/or epitaxial growth processes; they are also called monolithic circuits.

(b) *Multiple-chip circuits* are a variant of the above devices; instead of forming the circuits on one large substrate, several semiconductor substrates (chips) are used, which are subsequently interconnected within a single component package. This enables the isolation of critical components and prevents parasitic oscillations occurring.

(c) *Thin-film circuits* have all the passive components and conductors formed on an inert substrate such as glass, by evaporating, spluttering, plating, etc. The active devices, transistors and diodes, are added afterwards, as discrete components to this circuit.

(d) *Hybrid circuits* use semiconductor integrated circuits for the active elements with thin film passive devices added as overlays.

Integrated circuits (I.C.'s) are by far the most developed and widely used of the micro-circuit family, and we shall confine our comments to this type of circuit only.

There are a large number of packages available, but the most common is the T05 style. This is basically a transistor mounting can ('header') of approximately 0·325 in diameter with the connections (8–12) brought out from the base. Another method of packaging is the so called flat-pack; this can be any rectangular capsule, having the approximate dimensions of $\frac{1}{2}$ in $\times$ $\frac{1}{4}$ in $\times$ $\frac{1}{8}$ in, with the connections brought out straight from the edges. A cheaper method of encapsulation, which is also much easier to assemble on printed boards, is the dual-in-line (DIL) package. This is rectangular in shape, much larger than the flat-pack, but with the connections (up to 16) brought out at right angles from both sides and spaced 0·1 in apart for easy mounting.

The principal advantages of integrated logic circuits over discrete component logic are:

(a) reliability, which depends mainly on bonding and encapsulation of the device and not on the components or circuit configuration;
(b) weight and size;
(c) reduced power consumption;
(d) speed of operation: 0·5 MHz–65 MHz compared to 10 kHz–5 MHz for discrete component modules.

Initially, integrated circuits were very expensive but, with large scale production, certain types are now very much cheaper than their discrete component logic counterparts. We are almost at the stage when the use of integrated logic circuits can be justified solely on economic grounds, and one would require very good reasons for using discrete component modules. This state of affairs is certainly true today for very large digital systems. The disadvantages of integrated circuits arise mainly from the low logic levels, 0·8 V–2 V compared to 6 V–24 V for the discrete modules, and their consequent susceptibility to d.c. noise. Noise may have many causes, e.g. electromagnetic radiation from other equipment, power supply pick-up, adjacent contactor circuits, etc. Internal noise injection from the system can also occur, for example, due to bistable transients and large earth currents. This can generally be overcome by screening, by the use of common earth planes connected to all circuits with the shortest possible leads, and by careful component and wiring layouts.

Many different circuit configurations have been developed to reproduce the required logical functions, and in most cases there are both discrete and integrated versions of the same circuit. However, some of the circuits to be described below have been developed for exclusive use in integrated circuit form and mainly use transistors and very few other components. The reason for this is that with integrated circuits it is just as easy, and no more expensive, to form transistors as it is diodes or resistors. In fact, it is easier to fabricate a transistor than a close tolerance or high value resistor, consequently transistors are often used to replace resistors acting as constant-current sources or collector loads. Let us now examine some of the major types of electronic logic circuit.

(a) *Diode logic* (*DL*)
Figure 8–1 shows typical passive networks incorporating diodes and resistors which perform the logical operations of AND and OR. Figure 8–1(a) is an AND gate for positive logic (OR gate for negative logic) and Fig. 8–1(b) shows the OR gate. If any diode is conducting (i.e. biased in the forward direction with the anode more positive than the cathode) the output takes up the level of the input to that diode (less the voltage drop across the diode). Thus for the AND gate, if all inputs are positive, i.e. logic 1, the diodes are reverse-biased and do not conduct and the output stays at E_+. If, however, any one

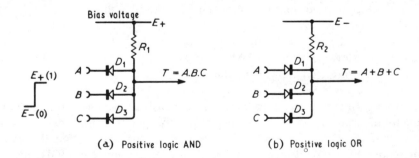

(a) Positive logic AND   (b) Positive logic OR

Fig. 8–1 Diode-resistor logic

of the inputs goes negative, the appropriate diode will conduct, and the output will follow and go negative, i.e. logic 0. It will be apparent that if we reverse the logic convention (positive voltage is logic 0) the circuit functions as an OR gate. It is possible to choose the bias voltage to be more positive than logic 1 (generally five times the output swing) and under this condition all diodes will conduct when the inputs are present together, clamping the output to the logic 1 level.

If circuits are cascaded, the input drive current to the circuit must be provided by the preceding stages. In general, this means that the bias resistors must be reduced in value in order to maintain the required drive currents. This is not possible in practice unless different types of AND/OR gates are available in the system, and buffer amplifiers are used instead.

(b) *Diode-transistor logic (DTL)*

This is a natural extension of diode logic, since, in order to overcome many of the drawbacks, the obvious solution is to incorporate a transistor invertor amplifier after every diode gate. Figure 8–2 shows the circuit diagram of this well-tried and reliable logic configuration, which is available in both discrete and integrated circuit forms. It was one of the first logic elements to be fabricated as an integrated circuit, since all the circuit design rules[6] had previously been well established using discrete components.

Basically the operation is as follows. Any input going positive (equivalent to logic 1) will cause the base of the transistor to go positive with respect to the emitter and hence the transistor will go into the cut-off region. This means that no current flows in the collector circuit and the output goes negative, i.e. E_- equivalent to logic 0. When all the inputs are negative (logic 0) the base of the transistor will be negative and hence goes into saturation with the collector output approaching the emitter value, i.e. 0 V equivalent to logic 1. As we saw before, changing the logic convention produces the dual function—the NAND operation. When logic circuits are referred to as

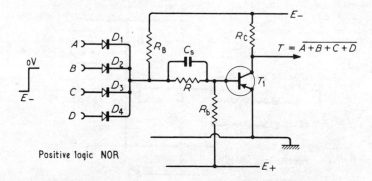

Fig. 8–2 Diode-transistor logic

NAND/NOR it is *generally* to be assumed that positive logic convention is indicated.

The capacitor C_s in the base circuit produces a capacitive overdrive current to switch the transistor on quickly without unduly increasing the stored base charge. Resistors R_B, R and R_b form a level-setting potentiometer chain to ensure that when any diode conducts the base of the transistor will be sufficiently positive to cause cut-off. Typical values of power supplies would be $E_+ = +10$ V, $E_- = -10$ V; fan-in is limited by the diode input circuits and typically would be of the order of 5–10. The limitation on fan-out is governed solely by the transistor amplifier; it could be 5 direct, or up to 25, using an extra emitter-follower output stage.

The discrete component circuit has been well proved in the computer industry and, suitably designed, provides a reliable logic element capable of operating up to 2 MHz with very good noise immunity. A direct copy of DTL logic has been fabricated using integrated circuits and is made by most manufacturers. This operates at speeds of 2 MHz–20 MHz with logic levels between 0·5 V–5 V; power supplies vary between 3 V–6 V. But, though very fast and reliable, the integrated version did not fully achieve the predicted speed for this type of circuit. Furthermore, the circuit was not easy to produce economically, and this led consequently to the development of transistor-transistor logic (TTL or T²L) which we shall consider later.

(c) *Resistor-transistor logic* (*RTL*)

Since, using discrete components, resistors are very much cheaper than diodes, it is obviously more economical to use resistors for the AND/OR logic network. Figure 8–3 shows the circuit for a positive logic NAND element. The operation is essentially the same as for DTL—any input going negative (logic 0) will cause the transistor to conduct (into saturation) and the output will go to earth (logic 1). When all the inputs are positive (logic 1), the transistor will stay cut-off and the output will be negative, i.e. E_- equivalent

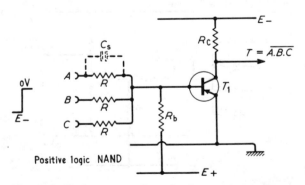

Fig. 8–3 Resistor-transistor logic

to logic 0. The effect of R_b and the E_+ power supply is to ensure that the transistor remains cut off if the collector leakage current I_{co} increases at high temperatures, but leakage current can often be ignored if silicon transistors are used. The circuit design is straightforward and leads to a well toleranced circuit.[7][8] If capacitors are used in parallel with the input resistors to enhance the switching speed, C_s in Fig. 8–3, the circuit is called an RCTL circuit. The major advantages of this circuit over DTL are enhanced speed and cheapness, but it has relatively poor fan-out and noise immunity due to the resistive coupling.

Again, like the DTL circuit, integrated circuit versions have been made, but have not proved very popular and are marketed by relatively few manufacturers. In integrated circuit form, it has low logic levels of about 1 V, using 3 V–4 V power supplies.

(d) *Direct coupled transistor logic (DCTL)*

In this type of circuit, the logic is carried out entirely by transistors acting as basic switches. It has the advantage of requiring only one low voltage supply with a very small power dissipation, and fast switching speeds are attainable. The configuration is ideally suited to integrated circuit techniques as very few components other than transistors are required. Figure 8–4 shows typical circuits for the positive logic NAND and NOR functions. The operation is very simple for the NAND circuit: if any input goes negative (E_- equivalent to logic 0) the transistor will saturate and the output will fall to earth (logic 1). With all the inputs at logic 1 (earth), all the transistors will be cut-off and the output will be negative (E_- equivalent to logic 1). Thus we have the typical NAND function; the NOR circuit works in a similar way. The circuits are

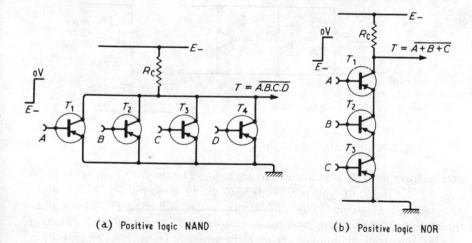

(a) Positive logic NAND   (b) Positive logic NOR

Fig. 8–4 Direct coupled transistor logic

principally limited by the leakage current through the transistors in the off condition—if the leakage currents are too high the difference between the two output levels is not large enough to operate a succeeding stage. Since each input requires its own transistor, this will also limit the fan-in (and fan-out) factor for the circuit. Furthermore, the circuit demands uniform transistor parameters, particularly V_{BE}, the voltage between base and emitter. Better results can be obtained using planar, epitaxial silicon transistors, though the circuits were originally developed for use with germanium devices.

Most of these disadvantages are overcome in the integrated circuit version, but the main disadvantage, the poor noise immunity of the element, still remains.

(e) *Current mode logic (CML)*

This is an alternative method of using transistors only in a logic circuit, in which a constant current is switched from one transistor to another. Because the transistors are not allowed to saturate fully, the circuits are capable of working at very high speeds, with switching times in the order of 1 nanosecond or less. A further advantage is that, since each unit draws a constant current, there are no sudden demands on the power supply when the element (or elements) is switched on (or off), thereby removing one of the major sources of d.c. noise.

The operation of the circuit (Fig. 8–5) is as follows. The bias voltage maintains a constant current through the transistor T_4 if all the inputs are

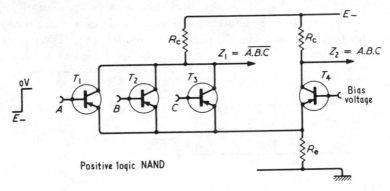

Positive logic NAND

Fig. 8–5 Current mode logic

at a positive level (0 V equivalent to logic 1). The output at Z_1 will thus be negative E_- (logic 0), and positive 0 V (logic 1) at output Z_2. If any input goes negative E_- (logic 0), the relevant transistor will conduct and the additional current through R_e will cause transistor T_4 to cut-off, the constant current now being maintained through the switched transistor. Thus, output Z_2 goes negative E_- (logic 0) and Z_1 goes to earth (logic 1). It will be apparent that, as well as giving the NAND function at output Z_1, the normal AND function is also obtained at Z_2. The main drawbacks to this type of circuit are the fairly heavy power requirements, and the large number of components used. This is outweighed, however, by the very good noise immunity and high speed properties of the device.

The configuration is also known as emitter-coupled transistor logic, ECTL.

(f) *Transistor-transistor logic (TTL)*

This circuit configuration is possible in both discrete and integrated circuit form, though the latter form has the greatest possibilities. The main difference between this circuit and others in which the logic is performed by transistors is that it makes use of a common base connection in place of the more usual common emitter. A typical circuit is shown in Fig. 8–6(a), and the integrated circuit version, using a multiple emitter transistor, is shown in Fig. 8–6(b). The characteristics of the logic circuit are very similar to DTL, though in general the TTL circuit is about twice as fast (4 MHz–50 MHz)

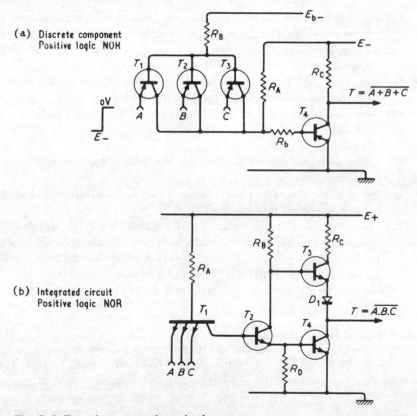

Fig. 8–6 Transistor-transistor logic

and cheaper to produce. Its circuit configuration is similar to DTL, with the input transistors effectively replacing the normal diode logic network.

The operation of the positive logic NOR circuit [Fig. 8–6(a)] is as follows. Any input going positive (logic 1) will cause the appropriate transistor to conduct (since the emitter will be positive with respect to the base), consequently the base of transistor T_4 will go positive and cut-off, driving the collector output negative (E_- equivalent to logic 0). All inputs must be negative (logic 0) for the output to go positive (logic 1), thus we have the typical NOR function.

This particular logic configuration in integrated circuit form is becoming increasingly popular, especially with computer manufacturers, since it is cheap (using plastic DIL packages also reduces the cost), relatively fast and has a good noise immunity (equal to DTL for similar conditions).

As well as basic logic modules, such as NOR/NAND elements, most manufacturers also market logic sub-systems. These are available in both discrete component and integrated circuit systems. Typical sub-systems would include:

(a) *d.c. and a.c. bistables*—JK, SR and clocked bistable circuits, also master-slave (dual latch) bistables found particularly in TTL systems;
(b) *half-adder (exclusive OR) circuits*—for use as basic binary arithmetic elements, etc;
(c) *registers*—used for storing and manipulating digital data; single or multiple stage shift registers are also available;
(d) *counters*—binary, B.C.D. serial and parallel counter stages;
(e) *level changers*—devices for interfacing one logic system to another by changing logic levels;
(f) *analogue-digital converter elements*—used for the conversion of analogue signals to logic voltage levels;
(g) *line drivers*—power amplifiers to drive peripheral equipments like relay contactors, paper tape readers, etc;
(h) *expanders*—some logic elements have expander terminals (for example, in the case of a DTL NAND circuit, a direct connection would be made to the base) which can be used to increase the fan-in factor by connecting external clusters of diodes or resistors to this terminal. The fan-out factor can also be increased by the use of separate buffer amplifiers.

8–3 Fluid logic devices

In these devices, the logic functions are performed by minute jets of air, gas, or liquid. The basic theory of the devices has been established by Tesla, Coanda and Reynolds,[9][10] and later papers[11][12] have described practical applications based on these ideas. The elements normally use air as the switching medium, requiring a main air pressure power supply of between

3 lb/in²–30 lb/in². There are three main types of fluid logic element at present available on the market:

Mechanical. In this type, the physical movement of certain components within the element itself controls a flow or jet of air. For example, one such element employs spring-tensioned levers, resting on a pressure operated diaphragm, to control the escape of supply air from the device. In the normal position, with no external inputs to the diaphragm, the supply air flow is prevented from escaping and the resulting back pressure which is set up in the device provides the logic output signal. Any external air inputs (logic signals) to the diaphragm chamber cause it to expand and move the levers, thus allowing air to escape and the back pressure (logic output) to fall. On reflection, it is easy to see that this simple device has all the characteristics of the logical NOR function. Other devices have been made utilizing the flapper-nozzle-diaphragm principles normally employed in three-term process controllers.

Interacting jet devices. These do not rely on moving parts for their operation, but simply on the alteration of the direction of one air flow by the opposing pressure of another air flow. Figure 8–7 gives a schematic diagram of the device. The supply pressure P causes a normal air flow through the element and out again at outlet Z_1; however, input pressure from jet A will cause

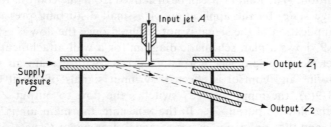

Fig. 8–7 Flow deflection device

the air stream to deflect and pass out from outlet Z_2. The air flow from jet A must be maintained if a bistable action is required, and by using more than one input jet it is also possible to construct a NOR unit.

A special form of interacting jet device is the *turbulence amplifier*. This works on the principle (first discovered by Reynolds) that a laminar or streamline fluid flow can easily be converted into a turbulent flow by the application of a very small external disturbance. Since in all laminar flow some turbulence already exists, the effect is to produce amplification of the turbulence by the disturbing signal, hence the name turbulence amplifier. The operation is simple: streamline flow is established in the device between the supply and

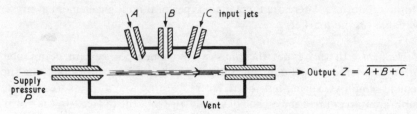

Fig. 8–8 Turbulence amplifier NOR unit

output tubes (Fig. 8–8) and, so long as this is maintained, the output pressure is not much lower than the input supply pressure, about 0.3 lb/in². However, if the stream is made turbulent by a jet of air from any one of the inputs, the flow becomes disturbed and the output pressure drops very nearly to zero. Only a very small input flow is required to trigger the device from the stream-line to turbulent states, and to produce a large output change.

Coanda or wall attachment devices. These devices show the most promise, and current research and development is very active in this area. The device is basically derived from the work of Coanda, who demonstrated the ability of a gas or air stream to cling to a suitably contoured wall or surface. A fluid flow can be made to follow a contour in the device (the contour physically takes the form of an accurately shaped recess or channel) and establish a stable flow condition. The fluid flow can be dislodged from one contour to another, (i.e. change state) by the application of a small disturbing pressure; continuous application of the signal is not required once the flow is established. Figure 8–9 shows a plan schematic diagram for a wall attachment NOR and bistable element. The device normally operates with a main air supply of about 2 lb/in² and control is effected by input signals of about 0.2 lb/in². In Fig. 8–9(a), the input signal S switches the flow to output Z_1, and R switches the flow to output Z_2. In the NOR unit, the main air is biased to output Q_2 and the application either of signal A or signal B switches the flow to output Q_1.

Practical logic systems employing all these techniques have been produced. The 'solid state' (no moving parts) devices tend to be favoured since they are intrinsically more reliable and faster in operation. The majority of the systems are, as with electronic logic, based on the NOR/NAND function, but some systems also include bistable and shift register modules. As with normal logic NOR elements, the units may be cascaded directly, the output of one unit feeding into the input of another. The typical fan-out for a turbulence amplifier or wall attachment device is about 4–6, while that for the mechanical types is slightly higher, in some cases up to 20. Since the output pressures from fluid logic devices are generally very low, it is necessary to provide some

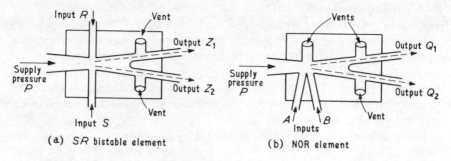

Fig. 8–9 Wall attachment devices

means of amplification so that normal pneumatic controllers and valves may be operated. These devices may be pneumatic, hydraulic, or electrical, depending on the requirements of the input-output interface and peripheral equipment. In the simplest case, a pneumatic step-relay is generally used which gives a pressure amplification of about 1000 to 1.

In fluid logic systems at present switching speeds are very low compared with electronic systems, and are certainly no greater than 1 kHz. For example, a typical turbulence amplifier NOR unit would switch on in 2 ms, and turn-off in 5 ms, giving a reversal time of 7 ms. For mechanical types, the switching speed is even lower, in the order of 10 ms. Wall attachment devices and the miniaturization of fluid modules will increase the switching speeds, but there is a fundamental limit to the speed that can be obtained. The speed gap between electronic and fluid devices can be compared to the difference between the speed of light and the speed of sound.

The most significant advantage of this type of logic element is its extreme reliability, and the fact that it is impervious to adverse environmental conditions. For example, the devices may be used in nuclear radiation areas, explosive atmospheres, electrically noisy systems, etc. Furthermore, they are easy to understand and service, particularly for instrument technicians already familiar with pneumatic systems. Even so, due care must be taken in their installation to avoid long interconnections (which give rise to undesirable delays and pressure drops) and bends in the connecting path which can cause stray turbulence effects.

At the moment they tend to be slightly more expensive than conventional electronic systems, but this does depend on whether or not an air power supply is already available. The provision of a dry, clean (filtered), air supply for the logic system can be expensive, but is essential for reliable operation, since dirt in the main air supply can cause intermittent faults. Typical applications so far have been in machine tool control systems, computer interfaces for electro-mechanical data processing equipment, general control and materials handling techniques.

8–4 Relay logic

The use of relay contact circuits is well established[13][14][15] and has already been discussed in the text. However, in many applications the conventional electro-magnetic system has many disadvantages: large power supplies are required; unwanted audio and electrical noise are generated; it has a low speed of operation (5 ms–20 ms); and a high contact resistance. There are, in addition, reliability and routine maintenance problems as a result of the physical size and weight of the system.

Many of these problems can be overcome by using the *dry-reed* relay. The reed-relay (Fig. 8–10) consists of two nickel alloy reeds with gold plated contacts mounted in a glass tube about 1 in long by $\frac{1}{4}$ in diameter and filled with an inert gas. The normally open contacts can be closed by a magnetic field, by inserting the contacts inside a coil; or, by adding a bias magnet, it is possible to convert them to normally closed contacts. The relays have a

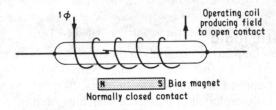

Fig. 8–10 Dry reed relay

(a) AND element $T = A.B$ (b) OR element $T = A + B$

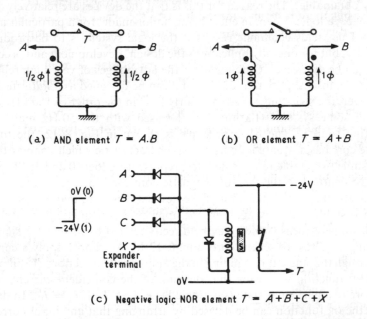

(c) Negative logic NOR element $T = \overline{A + B + C + X}$

Fig. 8–11 Reed relay logic

maintenance-free life longer than about 10^8 operations, very low noise since there are no large voltage or current transients, and a maximum power rating of 10 W. Power rating can be increased to 250 W if relays with mercury-wetted contacts are used; the voltage range is 50 V–200 V and the speed of operation is 0·5 ms–1 ms.

The reed-relay can be used as the basis of a logic module, and provides all the usual logic functions, including bistables and counter circuits. Figure 8–11 shows typical logic units employing reed relays; the NOR element has a nominal fan-in of 4 or 5 logic inputs which can be increased with the expander terminal X. Fan-out is in the order of 25 logic inputs, with a switching time of 500 μs, though the output bounce can be a further 200–500 μs. The unit is usually encapsulated in a modular form for easy assembly into a digital system. The reed-relay is also often used as a stepping, or sampling, switch in analogue-to-digital converter systems.

8–5 Magnetic logic

The use of square loop ferrite materials in the form of torroids, multi-aperture devices, transfluxors, LADDIC, etc., for logic purposes has been extensively investigated and applied in computer technology.[16][17][18] As yet, however, it has not been fully exploited in industrial switching, and no complete logic systems are commercially available, though the components themselves are freely obtainable. The reason for this is that the devices are relatively difficult to use, each logic system in effect being 'tailor-made' for a particular application. This yields economic results if the logic system is to be produced in quantity, but for one-off applications the design, development and production time can be excessive. Core logic has the advantages of very high reliability, low noise, insensitivity to radiation and can be designed as a fail-safe system. However, the switching speeds are fairly low, in the order of 100 kHz or less, in fact some systems (LADDIC) can be used with the 50 Hz mains as the clocking source. The basic principle is shown in Fig. 8–12, the torroidal ferrite core has a square loop hysteresis characteristic which enables the core to assume two stable remanent states, representing logic 0 and 1. The ferrite core is identical to the type of magnetic core used in core storage systems, which was the first application of the device. The core may be set to one of the two stable states by applying the appropriate magnetic intensity H_C, or $(AT)_C$ ampere-turns (which may be directly related to current for single turn windings). Thus, to set the core [Fig. 8–12(b)] we simply apply a current of I_C through the single turn winding in the appropriate direction. To implement the AND function we ensure that the sum of the coincident currents will set the core to a particular state (say, logic 1) i.e. $I_1 + I_2 + I_3 = I_C$. In the same way, the OR function can be devised by arranging that any input current can set the core. Negation, or inhibition, can be performed by using oppositely

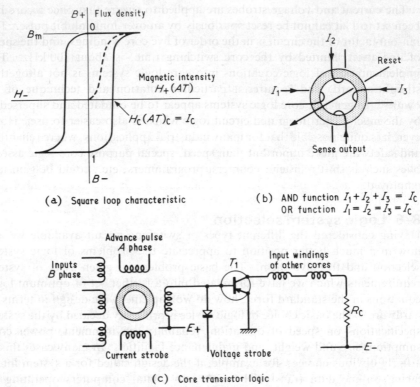

(a) Square loop characteristic

(b) AND function $I_1 + I_2 + I_3 = I_c$
     OR function $I_1 = I_2 = I_3 = I_c$

(c) Core transistor logic

Fig. 8–12 Core logic systems

wound (current in opposing direction) windings. So that the state of the cores may be sampled, they must be reset to the opposite state, in this case logic 0, after each operation. If the core has been set to logic 1, the reset operation will cause a change of flux which will induce a voltage in the sense winding, consequently, the logic is normally arranged as a clocked serial system. In practice, the system is complicated owing to the necessity of interconnecting the cores, and the fact that the logic output voltages are transitory. In some systems, the core logic output signal is sampled and stored in a second core during one clock pulse, and then used at a later clock pulse period; this necessitates at least a two-phase clock pulse system. One of the most success-ful current logic systems uses transistors as inter-stage amplifiers, and it is known as core-transistor logic (CTL). Figure 8–12(c) shows the basic circuit. Inputs are applied during the time of the B clock phase; the advance pulse, which occurs during the A clock phase, resets the core and gives an output if the core is set and this turns the transistor on. The transistor saturates, giving a defined current set by the resistor R_C, which is passed to the input windings of the following stages.

The current and voltage strobes are applied to ensure that once a core has been set to 1, it cannot be reset spuriously by an over-long inhibit pulse. The fan-out factor of the circuit is in the order of five core windings, and the speed of operation, limited by the core switching time, is about 100 kHz. The implementation of logic equations into core logic systems is not altogether straightforward, and requires a particular notation and technique of its own.[19] In general, core logic systems appear to be outdated and superseded by the much faster integrated circuit logic which is also easier to use. However, it is quite possible that for many industrial applications, where reliability and safety are more important than speed, special purpose core logic assemblies such as shift registers, counters, programmers, etc., could be gainfully employed.

8–6 Logic system selection

Having considered the different types of switching circuit available we are now in a much better position to appreciate the problems of logic system selection and to solve them. The basic problem is, given a set of system requirements which we have formulated into a further set of optimum logic equations in the standard form, how do we implement the design in terms of hardware? The basic choice of logic device is primarily decided by the system specifications on speed of operation, reliability, environment, power consumption, size and weight, and maintenance facilities. In many cases this is a fairly obvious choice; for example, if the design called for a system interfacing on-line data transfers between two digital computers operating at 1 MHz, there would be no alternative but to use electronic logic, either in discrete component or integrated circuit module form. But we are still faced with the problem of selecting the type of electronic circuit, so the next step is to examine the various devices on the market[20] to find the device which can best fulfil the specifications at the lowest cost.

When comparing electronic systems the following parameters should be considered:

(a) *Type of logic:* DTL, RTL, TTL, etc.
(b) *Fan-out/fan-in factors*, and if expander terminals are provided.
(c) *Speed:*

   (i) Binary speed, i.e. the minimum switching rate of simple set-reset bistables (also called the toggle-rate), which can vary from 500 kHz–65 MHz for integrated circuits and 10 kHz–5 MHz for discrete component modules.

   (ii) Propagation delay, i.e. the time delay through the element between input and output waveforms, which can vary with loading (fan-out), temperature and collector supply voltage. Typical values for delay are 3 ns–100 ns for integrated circuits, and 20 ns–8 μs for discrete component modules.

(d) *Supply voltages:* it is necessary to consider

  (i) logic levels, whether positive or negative logic convention, and maximum terminal rating, i.e. limiting values before damage to component ensues;

 (ii) supply line voltages and tolerances;

(iii) power taken from supply line, which can vary with fan-out;

(iv) maximum power that can be delivered to an external source.

(e) *Package:* size of module and whether T05, DIL, flat-pack or encapsulated module, pin spacing, number of connections, etc. Ease of assembly into hardware system, and replacement problems.

(f) *D.C. noise sensitivity:* defined as the difference between the logic output voltage and the input voltage that will just maintain the output voltage level.

(g) *Failure rate:* difficult to assess since data are not always available, particularly on new devices.

(h) *Logic functions:* whether NOR/NAND or otherwise, types of bistable available (JK, SR, master-slave, etc.); logic sub-systems included in the system (counters, shift-registers, etc.). Some logic systems, but not emitter-follower or emitter-coupled devices, will permit the direct connection of logic outputs to give a wired OR function. Thus units can be saved by simply connecting together outputs which are required to be 'OR'ed' together.

However, a direct comparison of the electrical and logical properties does not always result in the ideal device. On these grounds alone, one might be tempted to choose a new device which is made by one, relatively unknown, manufacturer only and which possesses the ideal characteristics. This could be very risky, and is certainly unsound systems practice, because very little would be known about the reliability of the device. Furthermore, should the manufacturer discontinue production, the entire project might need to be re-engineered if no direct equivalent could be found. Thus we must also take into consideration the following points when selecting a logic system, and these, of course, could apply equally well to any component.

(a) Devices must have been in production long enough to have been adequately 'debugged' of design and production faults.

(b) The delivery of devices, particularly in bulk, must be guaranteed.

(c) Design advice and assistance from manufacturers must be available, also the device should be adequately documentated.

(d) Consider if the device will become cheaper in the near future, due to increased demands and mass production techniques.
(e) Alternative manufacturers should be available, for example, DTL logic is manufactured by several companies and it is possible in many cases to get direct equivalents.
(f) One should select a logic system so that the minimum of interface circuitry is required.

In the particular problem we have considered above, the best choice of logic system would be that used in the actual computers. This would mean that the logic levels and power supplies of the interface and computer logic would be compatible, and there would be no proliferation of different logic modules. This last factor is important from the point of view of spares and maintenance.

Let us now consider another system—the design of some control logic for a digital servo system. The inputs, originating from digital encoders, have to be decoded and compared and the output used to control contactor circuits. The required speed of operation of the system is 10 kHz, with input logic levels of 10 V; the current required to energize the contactor coils being in the order of 100 mA. Again it is fairly obvious that electronic logic is required in order to achieve the specified speed. An initial appraisal of the available devices could suggest that, on cost grounds alone, the use of integrated circuits would be justified. However, using integrated circuits in this application could lead to some nasty problems. First, since the input level is 10 V, and the logic levels required for the integrated circuit is only 1 V–3 V, a level-changing circuit must be provided; if this is available as a standard module, the solution is simple, but this is seldom the case and more often than not a special circuit must be designed to perform this function. Second, on the output side we have much the same problem—unless suitable line drivers are available in the system, special power amplifier circuits must be designed to drive the contactors. Thus we have a situation in which almost as much special circuitry is needed at the interfaces as actual logic, and the whole point of using a modular logic system is lost. Furthermore, the use of fast integrated circuit logic at speeds well below the nominal working range, and in a noisy environment, leads to unnecessary cross-talk (electrical interference between adjacent signal paths) and pick-up problems. Most of these problems can be solved by the use of a suitable medium-speed discrete component module with logic levels compatible with the input signals (in the order of 10 V), and power units capable of driving inductive loads. The higher cost of the logic module is counteracted by the saving gained by not having to provide the special interface circuits.

As a final example, suppose we wish to design a logic circuit for use in a process plant manufacturing an explosive chemical. The requirements are that the system must be highly reliable, safe, robust, easy to maintain and capable of operating at 100 Hz. Relays would be too slow and dangerous in this application; discrete component electronic circuits with suitable flame-proof enclosures could be used, but the best system would be fluid logic, particularly since the pneumatic power supply would already be available for the process control instruments on the plant. The switching speed, 5 ms–10 ms, would be adequate, and what little servicing was required could easily be handled by the existing instrument technicians.

Once the type of basic switching device has been selected the next step is to see how it affects the actual form of the logic equations. The most obvious effect is that of fan-in, which determines the number of inputs, and hence the type and degree of factoring required. The implementation should also take into consideration what logic signals, if any, are already available in the system. Other factors to consider are the existence or otherwise of a wired OR connection, and the fan-out factor which, if too small, may mean the introduction of extra or more powerful units. In the near future, when ultra-fast integrated logic circuits with propagation delays of 1 ns or less come into use, the number of interconnections in a circuit may well prove to be more important than the number of elements. This is because the logic speed is limited by the delays caused by the length of the interconnecting paths, due to lead inductance and stray capacitance; the more paths there are, the greater is the risk of cross-talk. Even at the present time, fast logic circuits necessitate the use of transmission line techniques (ground planes, twisted pairs, etc.) to eliminate and reduce the undesirable effects produced by the interconnections. Moreover, the cost of system wiring is becoming more significant than the cost of producing logic gates. In the near future, we may well optimize a logic circuit to conserve connections rather than logic gates. At the moment this means that the use of logic units with a very large fan-in (or additional expander terminal) may be preferable to factoring equations so that gates with small fan-in factors can be used.

This philosophy leads quite naturally to the concept of large scale integrated circuits (LSI), and the possibility of producing multi-logic circuits, say a complete central processor, in a single integrated device. This could well mean that the logical design approach of thinking in basic logic units (like NOR/NAND) may become obsolete, and logic design and circuit design will of necessity merge into one discipline. This is apparent in the more sophisticated applications of metal-oxide-silicon (MOS) arrays[21] now being developed, and the growing interest in threshold logic.[22] Nevertheless, at the present time, the majority of logic design is still performed using NOR/NAND elements, and we shall consider the implementation of this very important form of logic in the next section.

8–7 NOR/NAND **implementation**

All the logical techniques described in the previous chapters have evolved logic functions in terms of the basic AND/OR or OR/AND equations, i.e. the product-of-sums or sum-of-products form. Since most of the logic manufacturers have standardized on NOR/NAND circuits, for reasons explained above, it is necessary to transform these equations into a form suitable for implementing in this type of logic. In the literature, the NOR and NAND functions are often referred to as the *Pierce* or *Dagger* function and *Sheffer stroke* function, respectively.

There are basically two approaches to the problem of NOR/NAND implementation, and we will consider each in turn and discuss their relative merits.

Algebraic and Karnaugh map factoring technique[23][24][25]

The NAND/NOR equivalents of the AND and OR logic functions are shown in Figs. 8–13(a) and (b); the single input NOR/NAND unit acts as a simple invertor. Direct implementation of the function $T = AB + C$, assuming positive logic convention throughout, in NAND/NOR produces the circuits shown in Fig. 8–13(c). Note that, for the NAND element, odd levels function as OR gates with the variables complemented, and even levels as AND gates; level 1 is assumed to be the output gate. The same circuit configuration [Fig. 8–13(d)], using NOR gates and complementing the inputs to odd levels, gives the function $T = (A + B)C$. Thus, for the NOR unit, odd levels act as AND gates, and even levels as OR gates. For both types of circuit, when counting the levels, which is a necessary operation in any transform process, single input invertors are not counted as levels. Thus, in order to implement NOR/NAND circuits, the sum-of-products equations (AND/OR form, with OR as the final output gate) must be used for NAND logic, and product-of-sums (OR/AND form) for NOR logic. For two-level circuits, the direct transform is very simple and, assuming that both the variables and their complements are available ('double rail' working), is the most economic form. Furthermore, the minimality of the original equations will always be retained in two-level NOR/NAND equivalent circuits, but this does not always follow for factored forms of the equation.

Now consider the exclusive OR function:

$$T = A\bar{B} + \bar{A}B$$

or in the product-of-sums form:

$$T = (\bar{A} + \bar{B})(A + B)$$

Both these functions may be implemented directly in two-level circuits (see Fig. 8–14) and five NAND/NOR elements will be required if variable complements are not available. Is it possible, though, by suitable factoring of the

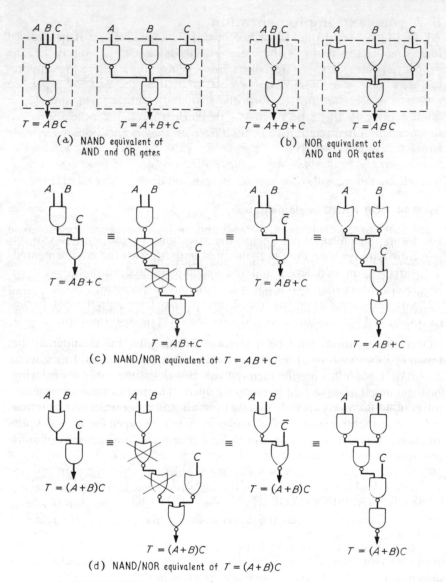

$T = ABC$

$T = A+B+C$

(a) NAND equivalent of AND and OR gates

$T = A+B+C$

$T = ABC$

(b) NOR equivalent of AND and OR gates

$T = AB+C$ ≡ $T = AB+C$ ≡ $T = AB+C$

$T = AB+C$

(c) NAND/NOR equivalent of $T = AB+C$

$T = (A+B)C$ ≡ $T = (A+B)C$ ≡ $T = (A+B)C$

$T = (A+B)C$

(d) NAND/NOR equivalent of $T = (A+B)C$

Fig. 8–13 NOR/NAND implementation

circuit to produce a more economical result, which does not rely on complements always being available? In general it is possible if the equations can be manipulated so that the complemented variables occur on odd levels, and the uncomplemented on even levels. Collecting all these facts together we may state the following transform rules:

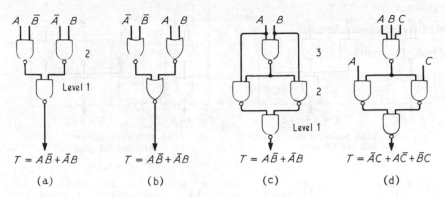

$$T = A\bar{B} + \bar{A}B$$

(a)

$$T = A\bar{B} + \bar{A}B$$

(b)

$$T = A\bar{B} + \bar{A}B$$

(c)

$$T = \bar{A}C + A\bar{C} + \bar{B}C$$

(d)

Fig. 8–14 NOR/NAND implementation

1. NAND implementation: factor the equations to an AND/OR-AND/OR form (always with the OR as the final output), with the complemented variables on odd levels and the uncomplemented variables on even levels. More than two levels will be required in general.
2. NOR implementation: as above, except that final output must be an AND, and the equations should have the form OR/AND-OR/AND.

Once the equations have been factored in this way, the circuit may be drawn in NAND/NOR logic, but the gates should be layed out as if they were in AND/OR logic following the factored equations, and the variables entering the logic at odd levels should be complemented. This transformation process, however, is not easy, since it involves considerable algebraic manipulation and most of the laws and tricks of Boolean algebra are called for. For simpler equations, however, the results can be very effective. Consider our exclusive OR circuit

$$T = (\bar{A} + \bar{B})(A + B)$$

Using partial multiplication of the terms, we have

$$T = A(\bar{A} + \bar{B}) + B(\bar{A} + \bar{B})$$

This is a three-level circuit with the complemented terms occurring on the third and odd level. Direct implementation gives the four-element circuit shown in Fig. 8–14(c). Again, consider the function

$$T = \bar{A}C + A\bar{C} + \bar{B}C$$

This may be factorized, using the Karnaugh map technique described in Chapter 4, keeping the complemented and uncomplemented terms together:

$$T = (A + C)(\bar{A} + \bar{B} + \bar{C})$$

which gives $\qquad T = A(\bar{A} + \bar{B} + \bar{C}) + C(\bar{A} + \bar{B} + \bar{C})$

Table 8–1

NAND implementation of

$T = \bar{A}C + A\bar{C} = \bar{B}C$

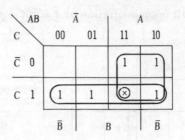

Inhibiting loops are marked with a ⊗

The circuit is shown in Fig. 8–14(d). Note that the equation for T is redundant in the sense that all the prime implicant terms are represented. In many cases this redundancy is essential to achieve the factored form of the equation.

The alternative method, for a small number of variables, is to apply the Karnaugh map to the factoring process. This is preferable to the algebraic method since the technique is easier to apply and, as before, can be used to implement both NAND and NOR elements. Consider the function above, $T = \bar{A}C + A\bar{C} + \bar{B}C$, this is shown plotted on a Karnaugh map in Table 8–1. We can form two loops—A but not ABC, and C but not ABC—from the map; the loop ABC is known as the inhibiting loop. Hence, we can represent the function as

$$T = A(\overline{ABC}) + C(\overline{ABC})$$
$$= A(\bar{A} + \bar{B} + \bar{C}) + C(\bar{A} + \bar{B} + \bar{C})$$

which is identical to the NAND function we arrived at earlier.

Thus we can interpret the main loops (those containing 1's) on the Karnaugh map as representing the inputs to NAND elements at the even circuit levels, and the inhibiting loops as inputs to NAND elements at the odd levels. The choice of loops, however, is restricted to those representing combinations of *uncomplemented* variables, i.e. for three binary variables we have A, B, C, $AB, AC, BC,$ and ABC. As a loop of 1's can be inhibited by a loop of 0's, so the reverse applies—a loop of 0's can be inhibited by a loop of 1's. In practice we can start with loops of either 1's or 0's, but the process must continue taking alternate loops in order to account for the sequence of odd and even levels. In this way multi-level circuits may be designed which contain many levels of factored gating. Quite often in complex circuits, the first loops to be formed are those whose outputs will be needed later, as inhibitors, in order to produce the required factored circut.

In the example above we started with a 1's loop and inhibited with a 0's loop, which gave all the 1's entries. We must now account for the 0 entries,

Table 8–2 NAND implementation of $T = \bar{A}\bar{B}C + ABC + A\bar{B}\bar{C}$

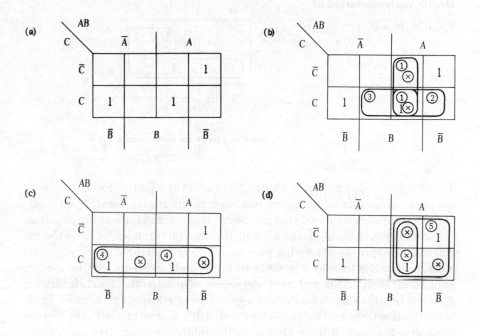

since all entries, both 1 and 0, must be included in the final circuit. Thus if we take the unity loop (the loop comprising the whole map) and inhibit this with the outputs representing the 1's entries (which were obtained earlier) we shall get the final result. In practice this simply means putting all the 1's outputs as inputs to a single gate, representing in this case the final OR gate.

To illustrate these ideas further let us consider a more complicated function:

$$Z = \bar{A}\bar{B}C + ABC + A\bar{B}\bar{C}$$

To implement this function in straightforward two-level logic would require, with invertors, seven NAND elements. Table 8–2 shows the Karnaugh maps for the factoring process. The first step is to form loops which may be useful later in obtaining the final output function. In this case we take the loops BC and AC and inhibit with loop AB, this gives the outputs ② and ③ [see Table 8–2(b)] representing the 0's $A\bar{B}C$ and $\bar{A}BC$ respectively. We next take the loop C and inhibit this with the outputs ② and ③ [Table 8–2(c)] which yields the 1's, output ④, $\bar{A}\bar{B}C$ and ABC; we now have to find the remaining 1, $A\bar{B}\bar{C}$. We do this by taking loop A and inhibiting with AB and output ②, to give $A\bar{B}\bar{C}$. We now have all the 1's represented by outputs ④ and ⑤, and to obtain the final output we have only to account for the 0's in the final gate.

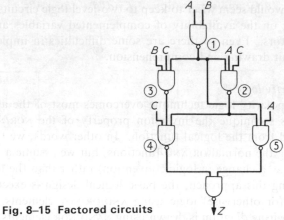

Fig. 8–15 Factored circuits

The complete circuit is shown in Fig. 8–15; it uses a total of six NAND elements, a saving of one unit.

Both the algebraic and map techniques need considerable practise before one can manipulate the switching equations into the appropriate form with anything like the required skill and ease. Even then, the methods are only practicable for small-variable problems. In point of fact there are several disadvantages to using this factoring technique:

1. The method of factoring means, in most cases, that different length signal paths exist for the same variable because of increased redundancy. Figure 8–15 is an example of this, where the logic signal A comes in at three different levels. We have seen in the last chapter that this can give rise to dynamic hazards in both combinational and sequential circuits.
2. The number of interconnecting paths is increased, and in high speed systems this can cause cross-talk problems, as well as an increase in the cost of system wiring.
3. In a number of cases the saving in logic-units is not great, and in any case the cost of logic units is rapidly becoming of secondary importance in integrated circuit systems.
4. In many practical systems the complement of the variables will be readily available, as alternative outputs from bistable registers and counters, etc., making the normal two-level circuit a much better proposition.
5. The logical function of the circuit is often masked by the factoring, and this can be a handicap to the service technician. In fact it has often been suggested that logic design should be kept simple to allow for easy and rapid fault-finding. Furthermore, the logic diagram and connection diagrams are quite different, bearing little relationship to one another. This again can lead to production and commissioning difficulties.

Thus it would seem wiser to keep to two-level logic circuits where possible, depending on the availability of complemented variables and large enough fan-in factors. Even so there are some difficulties in implementation, and logic circuit drawing and comprehension.

Dual-polarity logic[26]
The dual-polarity logic technique overcomes most of the above difficulties. Using this technique the inversion property of the NOR/NAND element is dissociated from the logical function. In other words, we treat the units as performing the normal OR/AND functions, but we assume a change of signal polarity (i.e. a change in logic convention) rather than the logical NOT function. Using this approach, the basic logical design is executed in terms of two-level (or otherwise) logic using AND/OR/NOT elements. Then the final logic *and* wiring diagram is drawn using NAND/NOR elements bearing in mind that

(i) the NAND element acts as an AND gate for positive logic and as an OR gate for negative logic, with a change of logic convention at the output in both cases;
(ii) the NOR element acts as an AND gate for negative logic and as an OR gate for positive logic, again with a change of logic convention at the output.

This is shown in Fig. 8–16, where the negative logic (logic 1, being represented by a voltage level more negative than logic 0) is represented by dotted lines, and the positive logic by full lines. Note that NAND/NOR elements used as invertors do not change the signal convention (by definition) but logically

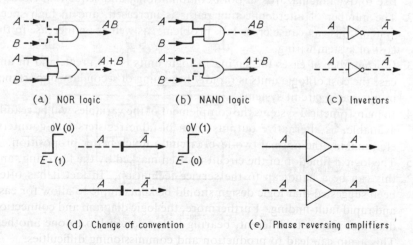

(a) NOR logic   (b) NAND logic   (c) Invertors

(d) Change of convention   (e) Phase reversing amplifiers

Fig. 8–16 Dual polarity logic

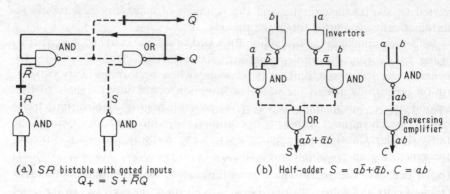

(a) SR bistable with gated inputs
$$Q_+ = S + \bar{R}Q$$

(b) Half-adder $S = a\bar{b}+\bar{a}b$, $C = ab$

Fig. 8–17 Implementation using dual polarity logic

invert the appropriate logic signal, whatever the convention. This must not be confused with the phase reversing amplifier (still, of course, a basic NOR/NAND unit) which is defined as a logic convention changer. The circuit operation is identical in both cases, it is purely a matter of logic convention and definition. In the same way, we can change the convention of a signal, and hence perform the logical inversion, at any point in the circuit [see Fig. 8–16(d)].

The use of this method allows logic diagrams (Fig. 8–17) to be used directly as wiring diagrams with complete understanding of the signal polarities at any point in the circuit. Furthermore, theoretical circuits may be directly con-

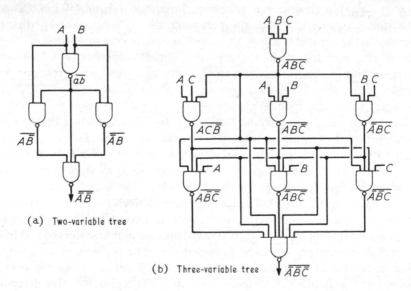

(a) Two-variable tree

(b) Three-variable tree

Fig. 8–18 NAND tree circuits

verted to NAND/NOR circuits, and the problem of complemented inputs is automatically accounted for in the process.

Before we conclude the discussion on NAND/NOR logic systems, it is worthwhile considering the implementation of one further class of circuit. In general, the NAND/NOR unit is at its worst when performing AND-AND or OR-OR operations due to the need for inversion of the input signals to the second stages. Surprisingly, however, when implementing an electronic tree-circuit, which requires AND-AND operations, the equivalent NAND circuit is fairly simple. Consider the circuit shown in Fig. 8–18(a), this is a NAND tree for generating all possible combinations of two variables. It is very similar to the exclusive OR circuit which gives three of the four combinations ($\overline{AB}$, $\overline{A}\overline{B}$ and $\overline{A}\overline{B}$), the fourth is obtained by taking these three to an output gate which gives $\overline{A}\overline{B}$. Since the circuit has a systematic structure (easily apparent on a close examination) it may be extended to any number of variables. Figure 8–18(b) shows the three-variable tree, and an algorithm for generating n-variable tree-circuits is described by Maley and Earle.[25]

8–8 Software-hardware approach to logic systems

In many large digital control systems, a real-time digital computer is often incorporated as the main controlling element. As a consequence of this, a considerable amount of logical equipment is required to act as an interface for the input/output devices, which may be either digital or analogue in nature. As an example of this, consider a digital computer system which receives digital input data over telephone lines at a 50-baud (50 bits/second) data rate. Assume also that the computer has a 20-bit word-length and operates in the parallel mode, with an average order execution time of 20 μs. The data are encoded into a serial message format comprising (say, 16 five-bit groups) which incorporates some form of error detection and correction. The simplest technique, as we have seen in Chapter 1, is to use a simple parity check on both the individual groups and the overall message.

The systems designer may be faced with the problem of designing logic circuitry both to encode and decode the message form. This will involve, on the encoding side, parallel-to-serial conversion of the computer words, the insertion of the parity bits, and the assembly into message groups. The decoding process requires a check of the serial message for errors (with correction where necessary), a serial-to-parallel conversion, and the assembly into computer words. Furthermore, the necessary control logic, including the generation and recognition of start signals, and the data transfers to and from the computer store must also be provided for. The problem may be solved using conventional logic design techniques, by breaking down the overall system into suitable sub-systems such as shift-registers, error-detecting circuits, control circuits, etc., and then applying the design theory. Before this, and as a preliminary to drawing the system block-diagram, it is very profitable to prepare some form of flow-diagram showing the sequence of operations required in the system. Implementation of the theoretical design would proceed in the usual way, possibly using some type of integrated circuit module.

But is this necessarily the best approach? Suppose the system requirements on message length were changed; unless this was allowed for in the original design and extra (redundant in the first instance) equipment included, it could mean a complete redesign of the system. Moreover, the logical system is quite complex, and the development and production costs could be very high. Is there, in fact, an alternative way to tackle the design of this logical system, which could overcome many of these attendant drawbacks? There is, of course, and the answer lies with the digital computer. The process of programming a digital computer,[27] i.e. preparing the list of instructions in machine code or some higher level language which the computer then obeys in sequence (see Appendix), is a completely analogous process to that of logical design. In fact, since the computer is itself a logic complex, the computer program instructions are merely a means of selecting particular logical paths through the machine. Thus, there exists a direct relationship between logic hardware and computer software, or program. Glaser[28] has also made the point that software and hardware are almost functionally indistinguishable, and that a close relationship exists between computing languages, machine design and logic design. In fact it is highly probable that the theory of computer programming (at the moment there is very little theory, only expert practitioners) lies somewhere in switching theory. In fact, many of the ideas of switching theory can readily be adopted to programming techniques; for example in the field of linear programming problems.[29][30] When computers are present in a system, this means of implementation should always be considered, but the possible economic and technical trade-offs (i.e. the cost of producing the software/cost of designing and producing hardware), ease of modifying system specifications, availability of computer time, effect on maintenance and servicing, etc., should be borne in mind. In fact some of the most difficult decisions the computer systems engineer has to face are concerned with the question of hardware versus software implementation.

In the data-link example above, it is possible to start with the same block and flow-diagrams prepared for the logical design and to write a computer program to fulfil the requirements. In general, because we are more concerned with bit, rather than number, manipulation, the programs would be written in basic machine code language. Since in this case as the input is very slow (50 bits/s or 20 ms/bit), it would be possible to have a direct serial input/output to an external one-bit buffer register (or possibly the computer input/output register), and to allow the computer to perform all the encoding and decoding operations. A small amount of external control logic would also be needed to tell the computer when the data were available, and also to synchronize the computer output with the link equipment. The amount of external hardware required is heavily dependent on the time available in the computer for computation and the other external loads. Note that, in this case, with 20 μs orders and 20 ms input data rate, it is possible to perform about 1000 computer instructions between inputs.

Clearly, if the logical designer is to fulfil his function completely, he must have an intimate knowledge of digital computer design and programming, as well as a complete understanding of switching theory. This will become even more apparent when we consider the ideas discussed in the next chapter.

References and bibliography

(1) HARRIS, J. N., GRAY, P. E., and SEARLE, C. L. *Digital transistor circuits* (Semiconductor Electronics Education Committee, Vol. 6). Wiley, New York, 1966.

(2) ATKINS, J. B. Worst-case circuit design. *I.E.E.E. Spectrum*, 1965, **2**, 152–161.

(3) HELLERMAN, L. A computer application to reliable circuit design. *I.R.E. Trans. Reliab. Qual. Control*, 1962, **RQC11**, 5–18.

(4) KEONJIAN, E. *Microelectronics*. McGraw-Hill, New York, 1963.

(5) KHAMBATA, A. J. *Introduction to large scale integration*. Wiley, New York, 1969.

(6) TODD, C. R. An annotated bibliography on NOR and NAND logic. *I.E.E.E. Trans. electron. comput.*, 1963, **EC12**, 462–464.

(7) MARCOVITZ, M. W. and SEIF, E. Analytical design of resistance coupled logical circuits. *I.R.E. Trans. electron. comput.*, 1958, **EC7**, 109–119.

(8) EVANS, G. Tolerancing the transistor NOR circuit. *Electron. Engng*, 1963, **35**, 659–663.

(9) ROUSE, H. *Advanced mechanics of fluids*. Chapman and Hall, London, 1959.

(10) METRAL, A. Description of Coanda's ideas. *Proc. 5th Int. Congr. appl. Mech.*, 1938, p. 256.

(11) GLAETTLI, H. H. Digital fluid logic elements. From *Advances in computers*, F. L. Alt and M. Rubinoff (Eds). Academic Press, New York, 1963, pp. 169–243.

(12) BOWLES, R. E. State of the art of pure fluid systems. *Proc. Am. Soc. mech. Engrs Sym. Fluid Jet Control Devices, New York, 1962*, 7–12.

(13) KEISTER, W., RITCHIE, A. E., and WASHBURN, S. H. *The design of switching circuits*. Van Nostrand, Princeton, N.J., 1951.

(14) APPELS, J. and GEELS, B. *Handbook of relay switching technique*. Macmillan, New York, 1966.

(15) KNOOP, A. R. *Fundamentals of relay circuit design*. Chapman and Hall, London, 1964.

(16) KARNAUGH, M. Pulse switching circuits using magnetic cores. *Proc. Inst. Radio Engrs*, 1955, **43**, 570–584.

(17) BENNION, D. R. and CRANE, H. D. All magnetic circuit techniques. From *Advances in computers*, F. L. Alt and M. Rubinoff (Eds). Academic Press, New York, 1963, pp 53–133.

(18) QUARTLEY, C. J. *Square loop ferrite circuitry*. Iliffe, London, 1962.

(19) TORNG, H. C. *Introduction to the logical design of switching systems*. Addison-Wesley, Reading, Mass., 1964. Chap. 8.

(20) *Guide to integrated circuits available in U.K.*, Parts 1 and 2 logic systems. Design Electronics D.E. Data No. 2. See also
D.E. Supplement on integrated circuits. Heywood-Temple Tech. Publication, 1967, **4.**

(21) MITCHELL, M. M. and AHRONS, R. W. MOS micropower complementary transistor logic. *Computer Design*, 1966, **5**, 28.

(22) LEWIS, P. M. and COATES, C. L. *Threshold logic*. Wiley, New York, 1967.

(23) GRISAMORE, N. T., ROTOLO, L. S., and UYEHARA, G. Y. Logical design using the stroke function. *I.R.E. Trans. electron. comput.*, 1958, **EC7**, 181–183.

(24) EARLE, J. Synthesizing minimal stroke and dagger functions. I.R.E. Conv., 1960, Part II. *I.R.E. Trans. Circuit Theory*, 1960, **CT7**, 144–154.

(25) MALEY, G. A. and EARLE, J. *The logic design of transistor digital computers*. Prentice-Hall, Englewood Cliffs, N.J., 1963. Chap. 6.

(26) KINTNER, P. M. Dual-polarity logic as a design tool. *I.R.E. Trans. electron. comput.*, 1959, **EC8**, 227–228.

(27) MCCRACKEN, D. D. *Digital computer programming*. Wiley, New York, 1957.

(28) GLASER, E. L. Hardware/software interaction. *First Congress of the Information Sciences*, Homestead, Va., 1962.

(29) ROOT, J. G. An application of symbolic logic to a selection problem. *Operations Research*, 1964, **12**, 519–526.

(30) BURSTALL, R. M. Heuristic method for a job-scheduling problem. *Operations Research Quarterly*, 1966, **17** (3), 291–304.

(31) HELLERMAN, A. A catalogue of three variable OR-invert and AND-invert logical circuits. *I.E.E.E. Trans. electron. comput.*, 1963, **EC12**, 198–223.

(32) ELLIS, D. T. A synthesis of combinational logic with NAND or NOR elements. *I.E.E.E. Trans. electron. comput.*, 1965, **EC14**, 701–705.

(33) JARVIS, D. B. The effect of interconnections on high speed logic circuits. *I.E.E.E. Trans. electron. comput.*, 1963, **EC12**, 476–487.

(34) HAWKINS, J. K. *Circuit design of digital computers*. Wiley, New York, 1968.

(35) PEATMAN, J. B. *Design of digital systems*. McGraw-Hill, New York, 1972.

9 Automatic design of logical systems

9–1 Introduction

We have seen in many of the switching examples discussed in this book, how the amount of computation required to deal with even small-variable problems soon becomes excessively tedious and time consuming, and thus prone to considerable error. The minimization of combinational circuits, the reduction of unspecified state-tables, and the state-assignment problem, for example, all require considerable computation. Furthermore, due to the lack of a suitable theory, many problems involve the determination of a large number of solutions in order to arrive at an optimum design, i.e. a trial and error approach. It is highly probable that this is one of the chief reasons why logical designers fight shy of using switching theory. The simple problems can be solved with the aid of past experience and intuition, while the more difficult, large-variable problems, involve far too much work to be really practicable. One solution to this quandary would be to devise completely automatic design algorithms, programmed for a digital computer, which would allow the logical designer to input the system specification, so that the computer would design the logic circuits and produce wiring schedules or actual logic diagrams. Those areas of design which as yet remain intractable could be 'solved' using heuristic problem solving methods,[1][2] or a simple iterative trial and error approach. Externally introduced criteria, such as logic type, fan-in/fan-out factor, etc., would enable the designer to control and reduce the amount of computation required.

This is a feasible but very ambitious and naive project, as can be seen from Fig. 9–1; the amount of software development required would be considerable and the computer would need to be very fast, and possess extensive storage capability. Moreover, even if such a computer were available, it is very doubtful if the average designer would be allowed access to it. It is also likely that, for large-variable systems, a trial and error approach to, say, the state-assignment problem, would be beyond even the largest computer. Hartmanis[3] has, in fact, suggested that sequential circuits with as few as twenty internal states would prove intractable using a computer iterative routine.

In a large number of cases, though, the designer is more concerned with obtaining a feasible and error free logic circuit than with the search for the design nearest the optimum. This is particularly so now that integrated circuits have become so cheap and readily available. Thus, an alternative

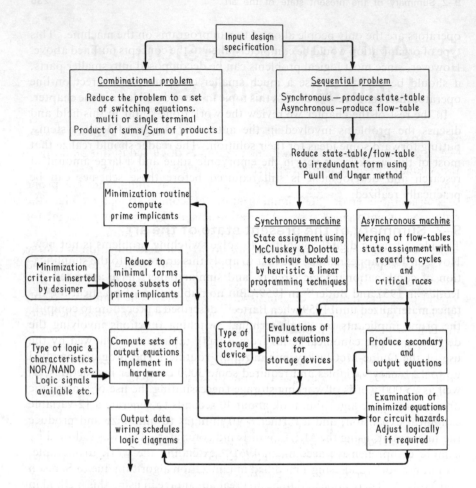

Fig. 9–1 Flow diagram of automatic logic design procedure

approach would be a computer aided design scheme in which individual routines, say for minimization, state reduction and assignment, etc., would be available for use by the design team when required. Operator participation would be an essential feature of the method, since facilities must be available for the designer to inspect intermediate results and suggest possible alternative problem-solving methods and criteria to the computer. Furthermore, the decision to stop the computation when an acceptable solution has been reached must be left to the designer. In other words, we have to include the logic designer as an essential part of the computer system, to provide the necessary overall control and inductive abilities.

This broaches an entirely different philosophy for computer usage. At the present time we tend to have large computer installations where the staff operators are the only people allowed to run programs on the machine. This type of organization would be completely alien to the concepts outlined above. However, since most logical problems can be decomposed into smaller parts, it should be possible to use a much smaller computer with direct on-line operator intervention. We discuss this topic in more detail later in the chapter.

In the rest of the chapter we review the work done so far in this field and discuss the problems involved in the automatic design of logic systems, putting forward some ideas for their solution. The reader should realize that most of this work is, as yet, in the embryonic stage and a large amount of research and development is still required before these schemes can be practically realized.

9–2 Summary of the present state of the art

The idea of using digital computers to solve switching problems is not new. Hoy[4] in 1955 appears to be the first to apply this approach to the simplification of combinational logic circuits, and similar papers have appeared, by Roth[5] in 1957 and Butler[6] in 1959. But no publication of practical importance materialized until 1959 when Bartee[7] described a procedure to compute the prime implicants for single terminal switching functions involving the derivation of the canonical terms from a truth-table input, followed by the use of the Quine-McCluskey minimization routine. The program handled up to 12 binary variables and required some 3000 computer instructions, as well as 25,000 words of working storage (necessitating the use of a magnetic drum store). The algorithm took about 40 seconds to generate a 12-variable canonical expansion, and a further 8–10 minutes to minimize and produce the final result, using the M.I.T. Whirlwind computer. This was followed by a more comprehensive account in 1961[8] extending the work to multiple-output networks and using a modified minimization algorithm due to Samson and Mills.[9] There appeared to be no great advantage in using this method in place of the Quine-McCluskey, except perhaps a claim that it is easier to program. A further improvement was the handling of 'don't care' conditions and the inclusion of various constraints for minimality, plus the actual listing of minimal functions. Work has also been done by Karp *et al.*[10] in 1961 on the synthesis of combinational circuits using a minimization method similar to that of Roth.[11] The same technique has also been used by Bernard and Holman in 1967[12] who minimized an eight-variable function in 1·9 seconds using a KDF9 computer, this is one of the few British papers[13] on this topic. The Pyne-McCluskey[14] algorithm for solving prime implicant tables has also been successfully programmed, but as far as the Author is aware it has not been included in a complete design program. An alternative technique, and perhaps a better method for large-variable problems, of solving prime implicant tables has also been suggested by Gimpel[15] in 1965. Various algorithms have been developed for factoring NOR/NAND logic, but that due to Dietmeyer and Schneider[16] in 1965, is orientated towards computer design and has been successfully programmed using the I.B.M. 1620 for an eight-variable six-term problem.

A comparable amount of work has been done on the computer design of sequential systems. The work published by Stearns and Hartmanis[17] in 1961 on state-assignment has not been programmed for a computer, and it has been suggested that it would prove difficult to do so because of the amount of 'hand-tailoring' involved. Schneider[18] in 1962 reported a state-assignment algorithm, as did Armstrong[19] in the same year. This last paper, based on the work of Humphrey,[20] described a computer program for the I.B.M. 7090 machine solving problems with up to 100 internal states, and 30 input variables, in about 120 seconds. However, the most important paper to date on state-assignment was published by Dolotta and McCluskey[21] in 1964. Though still not producing optimum results, the amount of computation required was considerably less than other methods, and easily programmed for a digital computer. Moreover, the choice of assignment code is determined by using 'scoring' factors (Section 6–8) which could if required be altered to suit particular design cases or modified in the light of previous design experiences. Thus, we have the beginnings of a heuristic or 'rule of thumb' algorithm which could be programmed for a digital computer. Further work on the state assignment problem using the Stearns and Hartmanis technique has also been described by Kohavi[22] in 1964, and Karp[23] in the same year.

The efficacy of the Armstrong method to produce anything like optimum results was questioned in a paper by Elsey[24] in 1963. This paper is the only one known to the Author which attempts the complete design of an asynchronous system. It draws heavily on the work of Huffman,[25] and a major part of the algorithm is concerned with the hazard-free assignment of the internal states. The input took the form of a primative flow-table, and the output consisted of the required secondary and excitation equations. The results obtained, however, were non-optimum, in that the circuits did not have the minimum number of states or logic, and in the example chosen did not compare favourably with the normal Huffman design procedure. Elsey suggests that optimum design is impossible for large-variable problems due to the impracticability (restricted by computer speed) of trying all possible coding assignments. The reason for this could be due to the dangers involved in taking a simple design procedure, and programming it directly for a conventional digital computer.

Another paper published by De Francesco and LaCrosse[26] in 1963 used the methods, now somewhat outdated, due to Phister,[27] to design synchronous sequential circuits. In this approach, the input equations for a particular storage element were obtained using the characteristic equations for the device, and the application equation as derived from the original circuit specification, expressed as a transition table. There appears to be no particular advantage in trying to program this technique. The work of Paull and Ungar[28] in 1959 on the reduction of internal states in incompletely specified switching functions would appear to be very well suited for computer implementation, but does not appear to have been utilized. An extension to these methods by Grasselli[29] in 1965 has evolved a technique which requires considerably less computation, and provides a source for a good computer algorithm.

An alternative approach to the problem of automatic design, which is particularly orientated towards the description and analysis of logic systems, is that due to Schlaeppi[30] in 1964. This paper discussed the development of a computer language called LOTIS (LOgic TIming Sequencing), which can be used to describe and simulate a logic system, including its timing, thereby assisting the designer in the engineering and evaluation of his circuits. This would be useful, for example, when designing high speed circuits using integrated logic with strip transmission line connections and multilayer boards, comprising a large logic sub-system. Fast systems of this nature have the disadvantage that once the circuit is built, it is virtually impossible to rectify logical errors by changing the logic assembly, without wrecking the entire system. Thus it is economic prudence to simulate and check-out the design before actual constructional work proceeds. A similar technique is due to Proctor[31] who described a logic design translator (LDT). Here the logical machine is described, using a special block diagram type of computer language, by specifying registers and the necessary interconnections and transfers between them. The translator produces a set of logic equations for the machine, including a timing analysis and the selection of a suitable micro-programming control sequence. Schorr[32] has proceeded along similar lines and has attempted to design and simulate logic systems by automating the heuristic methods normally used today in digital systems design. Again the system is specified in a block diagram, using a specially developed register language, and produces a set of Boolean equations as its output.

Neither of these last two methods treat the digital system as an integrated whole (i.e. as a large sequential machine) or consider any practical implications such as economics or hardware type. Furthermore, the major part of the design needs to be performed first so that the machine can be specified in the register languages. However, the work shows that computer techniques can and should be used in the design of logic systems, and also emphasizes the fact that hardware and software descriptions of digital machines are virtually indistinguishable.

Another approach to the design of logic systems which could well repay further investigation is that due to Hartmanis,[33] whereby large sequential machines are decomposed into smaller ones, and an attempt made to achieve an optimum design for these smaller machines. This method of synthesis has also been investigated by Ablow and Yoeli.[34] It is apparent from this review that many of the problems found in logical design have been at least partially solved using computer methods. As yet, however, no serious attempt has been made to coordinate these techniques into a complete automatic design procedure. The main reason for this would appear to be the technical difficulties associated with the implementation, combined with the inadequacy of present day computer systems. In the next section we look at some of these problems and suggest how they might be solved in the future.

9–3 Automatic design—methods and problems

The incorporation of a switching algorithm, such as the McCluskey minimization routine, into a computer program is not as easy as it might at first appear. In writing these programs we are essentially concerned with the examination and manipulation of bits, and bit patterns, rather than numbers. Although the computer is of course a logical machine, its main operational languages such as ALGOL, FORTRAN, etc.,[35] are undoubtedly orientated towards the processing of numerical data. Moreover, some computers are organized on a decimal basis which makes them quite useless for this type of work; it is imperative to use a binary machine if anything like the required efficiency is to be achieved. Thus, when programming switching problems, it is necessary to use the basic machine code language, or some form of symbolic assembly program (see Appendix) in order to perform the required bit operations, and also to exercise control over the storage and efficiency (running time) of the programs. In some cases, a higher level language, such as ALGOL, can be used for program organization, with machine code program inserts performing the actual bit and pattern processing. Even so, the basic order code of many computers is still inadequate for the purpose. For example very few computers (except some real-time process control machines) include logical operations, except for the AND or collate functions, in their order repertoire. Consequently, it is necessary to resort to writing sub-routines for the logical operations which are both time consuming and wasteful of storage space.

Let us consider a typical operation, say the comparison of two switching terms, to detect if they differ in one variable only; this will be recognized as a standard procedure required in most minimization routines. The switching terms would be represented in the computer store as two binary words. There are various ways of performing this operation, but the simplest is to combine the two terms using the logical exclusive OR function, and if the terms differ in one variable only the result will contain a single 1, i.e.

$$\text{Term } a = 1 \quad 1 \quad 0 \quad 1 \quad 0 \quad 1 \quad 1 \quad 1 \quad 0 \quad 1$$
$$\text{Term } b = 1 \quad 1 \quad 1 \quad 1 \quad 0 \quad 1 \quad 1 \quad 1 \quad 0 \quad 1$$
$$a \oplus b = 0 \quad 0 \quad 1 \quad 0 \quad 0 \quad 0 \quad 0 \quad 0 \quad 0 \quad 0$$

This is a good technique to use, since the position of the 1 also indicates the identity of the eliminated variable.

If the computer possessed a machine code order which performed the exclusive OR operation, the comparison would be simply a question of programming two instructions, i.e.

> fetch term a to accumulator
> combine accumulator exclusive OR with term b

Unfortunately if this instruction is not available, we are forced to write a sub-routine using the AND function, and a logical inversion operation obtained by extracting the 2's complement and subtracting 1. In this way we have the essential requirements for a logic system—the AND/NOT or NAND function. As we have seen, the exclusive OR function can be represented logically by

$$F = a\bar{b} + \bar{a}b = \overline{(a \cdot \overline{ab})(b \cdot \overline{ab})}$$

These logic equations may be converted directly to computer machine code instructions (see Table 9–1). The exclusive OR may be programmed in terms of NAND's [Table 9–1(a)], but in *this particular case* the procedure may be shortened by forming $\bar{a}b$ and $a\bar{b}$, and using the normal binary addition order in place of the OR function, since no carries can occur on addition [see Table 9–1(b)].

It is clear from this example that the exclusive OR sub-routine uses many instructions and hence increases the storage requirements and running time of the program. This is particularly true in a minimization problem where many such comparisons must be made to achieve the final result. It is worth while at this stage to emphasize once again the close similarity between logical design and computer programming, and the point we made in the last chapter on software-hardware equivalence.

Another area in which the computer is rather inadequate is that of data storage and extraction. The switching terms are normally stored in binary notation using a positional marker representation, e.g. $\bar{a}\bar{b}\bar{c}d$ would be stored as 0001 in a certain part of the computer word. In most problems, however, it is also necessary to store other information; for instance, in the minimization of multi-terminal functions, we also need to store the function numbers and the eliminated variables, for example,

$$Z_1 Z_2 \qquad 1, 5/9, 13 \text{ — — } 01$$

It is not strictly necessary to store the combining switching terms (1, 5/9, 13), since they can be obtained from the resulting prime implicants by a canonical expansion. All this information can be packed into a computer word, or words, but it must be extracted to allow comparison and modification to take place. The standard procedure for this is the collating procedure (i.e. the AND operation) with constants of all 1's in the relevant bit positions.

Table 9–1 Computer programming of exclusive OR

$$a = 1\ 1\ 0\ 1\ 0\ 1\ 1\ 1\ 0\ 1 \qquad b = 1\ 1\ 1\ 1\ 0\ 1\ 1\ 1\ 0\ 1$$

(a)

Machine code instruction	Accumulator contents	Logical function
Fetch a to accumulator	1 1 0 1 0 1 1 1 0 1	a
Collate accumulator with b	1 1 0 1 0 1 1 1 0 1	$a.b$
Take 2's complement of accumulator	0 0 1 0 1 0 0 0 1 1	
Subtract +1 from accumulator	0 0 1 0 1 0 0 0 1 0	$\overline{a.b}$
Store $\overline{ab}$ leaving accumulator unchanged		
Collate accumulator with a	0 0 0 0 0 0 0 0 0 0	$a.\overline{ab}$
Take 2's complement of accumulator	0 0 0 0 0 0 0 0 0 0	
Subtract +1 from accumulator	1 1 1 1 1 1 1 1 1 1	$\overline{a.\overline{ab}}$
Store $a.\overline{ab}$ leaving accumulator unchanged		
Fetch $\overline{ab}$ to accumulator	0 0 1 0 1 0 0 0 1 0	$\overline{ab}$
Collate accumulator with b	0 0 1 0 0 0 0 0 0 0	$b.\overline{ab}$
Take 2's complement of accumulator	1 1 1 0 0 0 0 0 0 0	
Subtract +1 from accumulator	1 1 0 1 1 1 1 1 1 1	$\overline{b.\overline{ab}}$
Collate accumulator with $\overline{a.\overline{ab}}$	1 1 0 1 1 1 1 1 1 1	$(b.\overline{ab})(a.\overline{ab})$
Take 2's complement of accumulator	0 0 1 0 0 0 0 0 0 1	
Subtract +1 from accumulator	0 0 1 0 0 0 0 0 0 0	$\overline{(b.\overline{ab})(a.\overline{ab})}$

(b)

Machine code instruction	Accumulator contents	Logical function
Fetch a to accumulator	1 1 0 1 0 1 1 1 0 1	a
Take 2's complement	0 0 1 0 1 0 0 0 1 1	
Subtract +1 from accumulator	0 0 1 0 1 0 0 0 1 0	$\overline{a}$
Collate accumulator with b	0 0 1 0 0 0 0 0 0 0	$\overline{a}b$
Store $\overline{a}b$ leaving accumulator unchanged		
Fetch b to accumulator	1 1 1 1 0 1 1 1 0 1	b
Take 2's complement	0 0 0 0 1 0 0 0 1 1	
Subtract +1 from accumulator	0 0 0 0 1 0 0 0 1 0	$\overline{b}$
Collate accumulator with a	0 0 0 0 0 0 0 0 0 0	$a\overline{b}$
Add $a\overline{b}$ to accumulator	0 0 1 0 0 0 0 0 0 0	$a\overline{b} + \overline{a}b$

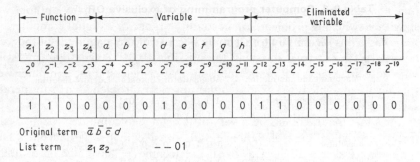

Original term $\bar{a}\,\bar{b}\,\bar{c}\,d$

List term $z_1\,z_2$ — — 01

Fig. 9–2 Computer representation of switching variables

Suppose, for example, we had a 20-bit computer word packed to represent the expression above (Fig. 9–2). To extract the variable part of the word, we must collate the computer word with a constant of 00001111111100000000, and then shift the result to the position required for comparison, say the least significant end of the accumulator; Table 9–2 shows the program operations required. In addition to these operations there are frequent requirements for the sorting and classification of data,[36] for example, the initial assembly of the switching terms into single digit groups before comparison in minimization operations. It is also necessary to keep track of store layout and allocation, and the extraction and modification of appropriate data in sequence, i.e. loop facilities, sub-routine entries and general program organization. These are the so called 'red-tape' or 'housekeeping' requirements associated with any programming problem, but the difficulties are much greater in non-numerical applications.

It is apparent that in its present form, the basic structure and language of the digital computer is not altogether well suited for logical or non-numerical problems; it could also be argued that it is inconveniently designed for the efficient running of numerical programs! This means that programming switching problems in particular, leads to very inefficient programs using vast amounts of storage space and requiring excessively long running times. Moreover, the writing of machine code programs is itself a very difficult and

Table 9–2 Extraction of data

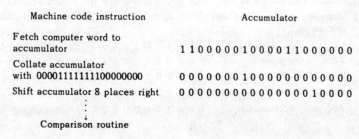

Machine code instruction	Accumulator
Fetch computer word to accumulator	1 1 0 0 0 0 0 1 0 0 0 0 1 1 0 0 0 0 0 0
Collate accumulator with 00001111111100000000	0 0 0 0 0 0 0 1 0 0 0 0 0 0 0 0 0 0 0 0
Shift accumulator 8 places right	0 0 0 0 0 0 0 0 0 0 0 0 0 0 0 1 0 0 0 0
⋮	
Comparison routine	

time-consuming process. Hence, perhaps, the views of many authors who state that switching problems are beyond the range of a digital computer. In some cases this is certainly true, simply because of the magnitude of the work involved; for example, to try all the possible 10,810,800 assignments for a nine-state machine is out of the question. Nevertheless, if the computer were specifically designed to handle non-numerical problems, a considerable saving in time and storage could be achieved.

It is a fact that there has been very little change in computer system design since the original ideas of Babbage and Von Neuman—the machines have simply got faster and bigger as hardware techniques have advanced. In the past, machines were developed by engineers, generally without regard to the way in which they would be used, and with little or no cooperation with programmers. An exception, perhaps, is the I.B.M. Stretch machine[37] which seemed to go to the other extreme, with programmers defining a system structure without considering the engineering difficulties involved. Consequently, we have the development of high level computer languages such as FORTRAN, ALGOL, etc., which facilitate the problems involved in program preparation and machine usage. These languages are really a software simulation, involving many thousands of machine code instructions, of some advanced structured special purpose computer. In other words, the programmers have taken the engineers' embryonic machine and produced a sophisticated adult designed to solve a particular problem, in most cases a numerical one.

Unfortunately, the efficiency, measured in terms of program running time, has deteriorated in the process, hence the need to resort to basic machine code in real-time problems, in which time is at a premium. The reason for this is that the initial (source) program is written in some form of basic English (or in mathematical symbolism) and the computer itself (via the medium of a compiler) decides how best to implement these statements in basic machine code instructions (i.e. the object program). In general, this process is less efficient (uses more instructions) than that in which the problem is programmed directly in machine code.

Up to now the computer engineers' main argument in favour of this situation is one of flexibility—the computer is a general purpose machine, and any attempt to implement in hardware a machine working in ALGOL, say, would seriously restrict the range of applications. There are a number of points which should be considered here. First, computer applications divide into two well-defined areas:

1. Scientific, i.e. numerical calculations such as matrix algebra, linear programming, solution of differential equations, etc.
2. Non-numerical problems, i.e. the examination, collation and presentation of data, such as in information retrieval, learning and games

playing, critical path (PERT) techniques, automated design, and the control of complex processes, both commercial and technical.

It is, in fact, in the realm of non-numerical applications that computers will be increasingly used in the future. A second point to consider is that in any programming task there are a number of similar organizational problems to be overcome—the 'housekeeping' routines mentioned earlier.

Thus, we can make out a case for two quite different types of digital computer. This has already been acknowledged in some degree by the design of special computers for real-time (i.e. process control) data-handling applications, but again these modifications are mainly hardware innovations such as interrupt facilities for peripheral devices. The internal organization and order code (except in some cases where logical orders are included) still remains very much the same as that for the scientific and commercial machine.

Barron and Hartley[38] have stated, and the present author fully supports this view, that the correct approach to computer system design is to start with the problem-orientated language and to attempt to implement these requirements in terms of hardware when this is feasible from an engineering point of view. Before this, however, we need to develop two distinct types of computer languages, one for numerical computation and the other for non-numerical applications. ALGOL, FORTRAN, or some such relative, would appear to be an ideal choice for the first, but no satisfactory non-numerical language seems to exist, though some work has been done in defining languages for real-time working (e.g. JOVIAL[39] and CORAL, a subset designed for radar data-handling) and for list processing (e.g. LISP[40]). Both the numerical and non-numerical languages could have a common core of organizational procedures, which might perhaps be based on the present ALGOL routines. With these languages as the starting point, work could then proceed on the design of a suitable hardware implementation.

In the next section we consider some of the work done so far to achieve these ends, and the basic requirements for non-numerical data processing.

9–4 Requirements for a non-numerical computer

Non-numerical programming is primarily concerned with bit and symbol manipulation and in particular the sorting, examination, modification, etc., of large lists or tables of symbols. The main characteristics of such a program are[41]

1. Manipulation of symbols that have no numerical meaning.
2. Storage requirements cannot be specified in advance—for example, in a logical design problem it is impossible to say how many store locations will be required for the minimization procedure from an examination of the input equations.

3. The storage organization and data relationships are continually changing as the program proceeds.
4. Frequent modification of the data and program is required.

Many of these problems, in particular that of storage organization, can be overcome by using a list processing language.[42] In a normal computer program, the allocation of storage space is done in sequence, thus we would store the terms of a switching problem, say, in a block of consecutive stores [see Fig. 9–3(a)]. This means that we must know beforehand exactly how much storage will be required and, if this is not known, an estimate must be made which is based on the worst possible conditions that could arise in the program. Furthermore, additional blocks of storage must be reserved for data generated in the program. It is obvious that in a complex problem, the estimation of the storage requirement is very difficult, and often results in uneconomical store utilization due to the use of too generous safety factors. Thus, we need some means of allowing extra storage to be automatically allocated when required (while the program is running) according to problem size. This facility, sometimes known as *dynamic storage allocation*, is available to a certain extent in some versions of the ALGOL compiler.

The concept of a list memory, the basis of all list processing languages, was developed to alleviate the store allocation problem. In a list, each symbol is stored in a separate computer store, not necessarily consecutively, together with a *link* or *'tag' address*. Thus, each store location contains two items of information: (a) the actual list symbol, and (b) the address of the next symbol on the list, i.e. the link. The final word on the list must contain an 'end' symbol, in place of the link address. Thus it is only necessary to know the address of the first symbol, or 'head' of the list, in order to gain access to the stored information. Furthermore, the list may easily be extended, using any

Fig. 9–3 List processing

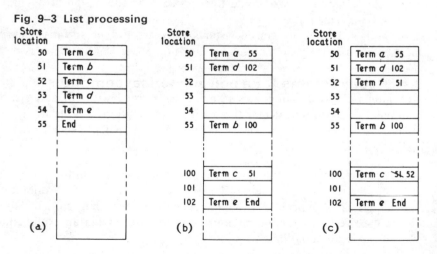

available storage space, by modifying the link part of the word. This technique is illustrated in Fig. 9–3(b); the five members of the list, a, b, c, d, and e, are stored in locations 50, 55, 100, 51, and 102. Note that term a, for example, indicates that the next symbol on the list is held in store location 55. The last symbol is stored in location 102, and contains an 'end' symbol in place of the link. To modify the list so that a new symbol, f, may be inserted between symbols c and d, the link of symbol c must be altered to the address of the new symbol f, and the word containing f must have a link address to symbol d [Fig. 9–3(c)]. In order to operate this list structure it is also necessary to have an 'available space' list, recording the free storage in the computer.

It is possible for list structures to have many levels of sub-lists, that is, the main list link will name the head of another sub-list and so on. Furthermore, in many cases, the routine being performed on the main list (for example, symbol comparison and modification) may also have to be executed on a sub-list should one be encountered during the routine. In this case the routine itself is then used as a sub-routine, the process being known as *recursion*. This facility is not usually available in conventional computer order codes, though some versions of the ALGOL compiler have recursion procedures. The reason for this is that sub-routines are conventionally stored in a set of locations which include the actual program, input variables, intermediate results, and a link address back to the main program. Consequently, each time the sub-routine is executed, the previous results are either destroyed or lost, thereby preventing any recursive action. Thus, if the recursive facility is required, special provisions must be made to prevent this happening and the most common technique is the '*push-down*' *store*. This is achieved by replacing every store location which holds intermediate results, or link addresses, etc., by a 'push-down' store, in which data are always added to, or taken from, the top of a list. Thus the data may be 'stacked' and used as and when required. This technique was used by Dijkstra in developing the ALGOL language, as a means of implementing operations, e.g. arithmetical functions, expressed in a Polish string notation.[43]

There is also a need for extracting and performing comparisons between parts of a computer word (bit selection). These operations would be facilitated if the computer word was organized on a 'field' basis. Using this method, sections of a word could be specified by indicating the first and last digit positions, and this could be further extended by allowing variable word-lengths, or bytes, of declarable length. Also with this scheme it should be possible to specify operations between bytes, or sections of a word. Thus, the comparison of symbols packed in a computer word would involve one simple instruction, replacing the succession of collate, shift, subtract, etc., orders required in most machines.

The basic order code of the machine must have provisions for logical operations such as the exclusive and inclusive OR, AND, and inversion functions. Also the requirements for shifting digits in a word must be extended to a pure logical shift in either direction, and possibly an end-around shift. Special bit-group conditional comparison orders could also be included, these would jump to, or skip, locations if bit-groups were identical. Arithmetic facilities are also required by the non-numerical computer but these need be only of the most elementary nature, i.e. fixed-point addition and subtraction. Multiplication and division, and especially floating-point working, is not required. The usual conditional jumps, input/output, counting, and sub-routine link instructions would obviously also be necessary. Many of these facilities are already available, in some form or other, in special high level languages, such as list processing or real-time control languages. However, these are still written in basic machine code for a conventional computer and consequently are still very inefficient, although convenient to use. Some work has been done on defining a logical language computer for non-numerical processing,[44][45][46] but as yet no hardware realizations have materialized. Computers have however been designed to implement the basic structure of an ALGOL type language.[47][48][49]

The most important hardware advances to date have been in the concepts of computer storage. In the conventional computer, storage locations are addressed by allocating a number to each storage position, and reference must eventually be made to this absolute address in order to extract the data stored there—a sort of numbered 'pigeon-hole' technique. Recent work on associative stores,[50] where the store is addressed by contents rather than by location, makes feasible the idea of multiple-address and bulk processing schemes.[51][52] This would enable information to be stored anywhere, and it would be retrieved by specifying a 'tag' which is stored with the computer word. Thus, most of the programming problems associated with list processing and sorting techniques could easily be overcome[53] without resorting to expensive (in the sense of running time and storage space) software procedures.

9–5 Consideration of a contemporary system

It is the Author's contention that, if a non-numerical computer were presently available which possessed most of the qualities discussed above, many of the hitherto intractable problems of logical circuit design could be solved. In particular, the development of a complete computer-aided logical design program would become a practical proposition. However, we are, in reality, faced with the necessity of using the facilities that are available at the present time, to provide the solution to our problem. What then is the best method to employ, to achieve a present day solution?

There is no reason why the design problem cannot be broken down into a number of discrete steps, such as minimization, state-reduction, state assignment, etc., and the circuits designed using a step-by-step procedure, with the logical designer providing the overall control. Intermediate results could be inspected, and the computer programs varied accordingly, using some form of on-line input/output device. In the simplest case this could be a teleprinter working in the 'conversational mode', or a cathode ray tube display complete with 'light-pen' facilities as used in the M.I.T. MAC system.[54][55] In order to alleviate many of the difficulties associated with programming the problem in basic machine code, some form of list processing language could be used. In practice though, due to the large amount of software involved in the compiler, this would probably involve the use of a large, fast computer system to prepare the programs, which could then be converted for use on a much smaller (and more readily available) computer.

Alternatively, the programs could be prepared directly on a small real-time process control computer with a logical order-code and some form of bulk storage, say a disk file. Due to the limited amount of storage and the inefficiency of most high level languages, it would probably be necessary to work in basic machine code.

9–6 Other aspects of design automation

Considerable work has been done in the computer industry on the use of computer techniques in the development and production of new computers.[56] Computer programs have been evolved which determine the best inter-connection paths for logic boards (cabinet back wiring), the placement of logic boards in the cabinet assemblies, and the initial positioning of logic elements on the boards.[57] In this way many of the tedious and error-prone data-processing operations associated with the 'engineering' of a computer system have been entirely automated. The logical designer simply feeds his design, generally in a tabular or block diagram form detailing type of logic unit and connections, etc., into the computer which then proceeds to prepare a complete placement and wiring schedule. The I.B.M. 360 design automation system[57] also has additional facilities for a complete software simulation of the logical design, permitting the investigation and checking of delay times and electrical circuit properties such as logic levels, fan-out, etc. The logical design may also be modified during the course of the simulation to account for design errors and their subsequent rectification. Furthermore, data concerning wiring and design errors found during the commissioning period can also be fed into the computer, allowing modification to the production schedules for subsequent machines. As a result of using this system, maintenance data, in the form of logic diagrams complete with voltage and current check-points, are produced automatically by the computer using digital-plotter or line-printer output equipment. One technique that has been used in the evaluation of critical delaying paths in these design automation systems is PERT[58] (Programme Evaluation and Review Technique). It has been successfully applied to the determination of critical timing paths, the timing slack between various inputs and the probability of achieving an output by a certain time.

Another approach which is currently being investigated is that of automated maintenance.[59] Finding logical faults in a large computer system, or any digital system for that matter, can be a difficult and time wasting task. The normal technique is to write 'trouble-shooting' programs for the system which localize the fault to a section of the logic hardware, which can then be investigated using standard test-procedures. If, however, the maintenance requirements are taken into consideration during the initial system and logical design phase (and included in any subsequent design automation) it becomes possible to prepare diagnostic programs which pinpoint the particular faulty logic element, or sub-system. The computer itself, using those sections which are working correctly, prints out a list of faulty elements which may then be exchanged for spare units.

As well as this particular computer application, computer-aided design techniques are being increasingly applied to all branches of engineering. For example, electronic circuit design and analysis, micro-circuit design and manufacture, electricity distribution problems, etc.[60][61][62]

References and bibliography

(1) LEDLEY, R. S. *Programming and utilizing digital computers.* McGraw-Hill, New York, 1962. Chap. 8.

(2) MINSKEY, M. A selected descriptor-indexed bibliography to the literature on artificial intelligence. *I.R.E. Trans. hum. Factors Electron.*, 1961, March, 39–55.

(3) HARTMANIS, J. On the state assignment problem for sequential machines, 1. *I.R.E. Trans. electron. comput.*, 1961, **EC10**, 157–165.

(4) HOY, E. C. Simplifying switching functions using a general purpose digital computer. Dissertation Elect. Engng Dept. M.I.T., Cambridge, Mass., 1955.

(5) ROTH, C. H. Digital computer solution of switching circuit problems. Dissertation Elect. Engng Dept. M.I.T. Cambridge, Mass., 1957.

(6) BUTLER, K. J. and WARFIELD, J. N. A digital computer program for reducing logical statements to a minimal form. *Proc. Nat. Electronics Conf.*, 1959, **15**, 456–466.

(7) BARTEE, T. C. Automatic design of logical networks. *Proc. Western Joint Computer Conf.* San Francisco, 1959, pp 103–107.

(8) BARTEE, T. C. Computer design of multiple-output logical networks. *I.R.E. Trans. electron. comput.*, 1961, **EC10**, 21–30.

(9) SAMSON, E. W. and MILLS, B. E. Circuit minimization: algebra and algorithm for new Boolean canonical expansion. Air Force Cambridge Research Center Report, AFCRC TR-54-21, Bedford, Mass., 1954.

(10) KARP, R. N., MCFARLIN, F. E., ROTH, J. P., and WILTS, J. R. A computer program for the synthesis of combinational switching circuits. *Proc. A.I.E.E. Annual Symp. Switching Circuit Theory*, 1961, p. 181.

(11) ROTH, J. P. Minimization over Boolean trees. *I.B.M. Jl Res. Dev.*, 1960, **5**, 543–558.

(12) BERNARD, D. F. and HOLMAN, D. F. The use of Roth's decomposition algorithm in the multi-level design of circuits. *British Computer Society Symp. Logic Design.* University of Reading, July, 1967.

(13) LEWIN, D. W. Automatic design of switching systems. Dissertation for Masters Degree, Elect. Engng Dept., University of Surrey, 1965.

(14) PYNE, I. B. and MCCLUSKEY, E. J. The reduction of redundancy in solving prime implicant tables. *I.R.E. Trans. electron. comput.*, 1962, **EC11**, 473–482.

(15) GIMPEL, J. F. A reduction technique for prime implicant tables. *I.E.E.E. Trans. electron. comput.*, 1965, **EC14**, 535–541.

(16) DIETMEYER, D. L. and SCHNEIDER, P. R. A computer orientated factoring algorithm for NOR logic design. *I.E.E.E. Trans. electron. comput.*, 1965, **EC14**, 868–874.

(17) STEARNS, R. E. and HARTMANIS, J. On the state assignment problem for sequential machines II. *I.R.E. Trans. electron. comput.*, 1961, **EC10**, 593–603.

(18) SCHNEIDER, M. I. *State assignment algorithm for clocked sequential machines.* Lincoln Lab. Tech. Report No. 270, May, 1962.

(19) ARMSTRONG, D. B. A programmed algorithm for assigning internal codes to sequential machines. *I.R.E. Trans. electron. comput.*, 1962, **EC11**, 466–472.

(20) HUMPHREY, W. S. *Switching circuits with computer applications.* McGraw-Hill, New York, 1958. Chap. 10.

(21) DOLOTTA, T. A. and MCCLUSKEY, E. J. The coding of internal states of sequential circuits. *I.E.E.E. Trans. electron. comput.*, 1964, **EC13**, 549–562.

(22) KOHAVI, Z. Secondary state assignment for sequential machines. *I.E.E.E. Trans. electron. comput.*, 1964, **EC13**, 193–203.

(23) KARP, R. M. Some techniques of state assignment for synchronous sequential machines. *I.E.E.E. Trans. electron. comput.*, 1964, **EC13**, 507–518.

(24) ELSEY, J. *An algorithm for the synthesis of large sequential switching circuits.* Coordinated Science Lab. University of Illinois Report No. R-169, 1963, May.

(25) HUFFMAN, D. A. The synthesis of sequential switching circuits. *J. Franklin Inst.*, 1954, **257**, 161–190 (March), 275–303 (April).

(26) DE FRANCESCO, H. F. and LACROSSE, T. R. Automated logical design. *I.E.E.E. Int. Conv. Rec.*, 1963, **11**(4), 94–101.

(27) PHISTER, M. *Logical design of digital computers.* Wiley, New York, 1963.

(28) PAULL, M. C. and UNGAR, S. H. Minimizing the number of states in incompletely specified switching functions. *I.R.E. Trans. electron. comput.*, 1959, **EC8**, 356–367.

(29) GRASSELLI, A. A method for minimizing the number of internal states in

incompletely specified sequential networks. *I.E.E.E. Trans. electron. comput.*, 1965, **EC14**, 350–359.

(30) SCHLAEPPI, H. P. A formal language for describing machine logic timing and sequencing (LOTIS). *I.E.E.E. Trans. electron. comput.*, 1964, **EC13**, 439–448.

(31) PROCTOR, R. M. A logic design translator experiment demonstrating relationship of language to systems and logic design. *I.E.E.E. Trans. electron. comput.*, 1964, **EC13**, 422–430.

(32) SCHORR, H. Computer-aided digital system design and analysis using a register transfer language. *I.E.E.E. Trans. electron. comput.*, 1964, **EC13**, 730–737.

(33) HARTMANIS, J. Loop free structure of sequential machines. *Inf. Control*, 1962, **5**, 25–43.

(34) ABLOW, C. M. and YOELI, M. *Synthesis of automata by decomposition techniques.* Stanford Res. Inst. Contract AF 19(628)5092, 1966, Sept.

(35) ROSEN, S. (Ed). *Programming systems and languages.* McGraw-Hill, New York, 1967.

(36) **KNUTH, D. E. *The art of computer programming*, Vol. 3: *Sorting and searching.* Addison-Wesley, Reading, Mass., 1973.**

(37) BUCHHOLZ, W. *Planning a computer system.* McGraw-Hill, New York, 1963.

(38) BARRON, D. W. and HARTLEY, D. F. The influence of automatic programming on machine design. *British Computer Society Conf. The impact of users' needs on the design of data processing systems.* Edinburgh, 1964, April.

(39) SHAW, C. J. JOVIAL—a programming system for real-time command systems. From *Annual review of automatic programming*, R. Goodman (Ed). Pergamon Press, London, 1963. Vol. 3, pp 53–119.

(40) MCCARTHY, J. Recursive functions of symbolic expressions and their computation by machine I. *Communs Ass. comput. Mach.*, 1960, **3**, 184–195.

(41) GREEN, B. F. Computer languages for symbol manipulation. *I.R.E. Trans. electron. comput.*, 1961, **EC10**, 729–735.

(42) FOSTER, J. M. *List processing.* Macdonald, London, 1967.

(43) **WEGNER, P. *Programming languages, information structures and machine organization.* McGraw-Hill, New York, 1968.**

(44) OVERHEU, D. L. An abstract machine for symbolic computation. *J. Ass. comput. Mach.*, 1966, **13**, 444–468.

(45) BROWN, R. M. *et al.* The CSX-1 computer. *I.E.E.E. Trans. electron. comput.*, 1964, **EC13**, 247–250.

(46) WIGINGTON, R. L. A machine organization for a general purpose list processor. *I.E.E.E. Trans. electron. comput.*, 1963, **EC12**, 707–714.

(47) *The B5000 concept.* Burroughs Corporation, 1963.

(48) GRAM, C. *et al.* GIER—A Danish computer of medium size. *I.E.E.E. Trans. electron. comput.*, 1963, **EC12**, 629–650.

(49) MULLERY, A. P. A procedure-orientated machine language. *I.E.E.E. Trans. electron. comput.*, 1964, **EC13**, 449–445.

(50) HANLON, A. G. Content addressable and associative memory systems—a survey. *I.E.E.E. Trans. electron. comput.*, 1966, **EC15**, 509–521.

(51) HELLERMAN, H. Parallel processing. *I.E.E.E. Trans. electron. comput.*, 1966, **EC15**, 82–91.

(52) CRANE, B. A. and GITHENS, J. A. Bulk processing in distributed logic memory. *I.E.E.E. Trans. electron. comput.*, 1965, **EC14**, 186–196.

(53) MUTH, V. O. and SCIDMORE, A. K. A memory organization for an elementary list processing computer. *I.E.E.E. Trans. electron. comput.*, 1963, **EC12**, 262–268.

(54) LEWIN, M. H. An Introduction to Computer Graphics Terminals. *Proc. Inst. elect. electron. Engrs*, 1967, **55**, 1544–1552.

(55) PRINCE, M. D. Man-computer graphics for computer-aided design. *Proc. Inst. elect. electron. Engrs*, 1966, **54**, 1698–1708.

(56) GILL, S. The use of computers in designing computers. *Ind. Research (London)*, 1962, **15**, 159–163.

(57) CASE, P. W. *et al.* Solid logic design automation. *I.B.M. Jl Res. Dev.*, 1964, **8**, 127–140.

(58) KIRKPATRICK, T. I. and CLARK, N. R. PERT as an aid to logic design. *I.B.M. Jl Res. Dev.*, 1966, **10**, 135–141.

(59) MALING, K. A computer organization and programming system for automated maintenance. *I.E.E.E. Trans. electron. comput.*, 1963, **EC12**, 887–895.

(60) HARP, W. W. Computer aided design in the U.S.A. *Design Electronics*, 1967, **4**, 42–44.

(61) BREUER, M. A. General survey of design automation of digital computers. *Proc. Inst. elect. electron. Engrs*, 1966, **54**, 1708–1721.

(62) BREUER, M. A. Recent Developments in the Automated Design and Analysis of Digital Systems. *Proc. Inst. elect. electron. Engrs*, 1972, **60**, 12–27.

(63) BREUER, M. A. (Ed.). *Design automation of digital systems.* Vol. 1: *Theory and techniques.* Prentice-Hall, Englewood Cliffs, N.J., 1972.

10 Logic design with complex integrated circuits

10–1 Introduction

Many of the design techniques described in earlier chapters have tacitly assumed that the final logic networks will be realized using basic NAND/NOR gates and bistables. This has resulted in an emphasis on theoretical algorithms for economical implementation based on the minimal number of gates and bistables required by the circuit. This approach originates from the early days of digital circuits when all logic networks were realized with discrete modules and is of course still fundamentally sound. However, the recent advances that have been made in integrated circuit technology are rapidly making this philosophy obsolete.

Medium scale integrated (MSI) circuits providing complex logic functions such as counters, shift registers, decoders, multiplexers, read only memory (ROM), etc., are now available very cheaply in standard dual-in-line packages. These devices enable many standard logic operations, such as the binary decoding tree of Section 3–10, to be implemented directly using a single module. The availability of MSI modules, with up to a hundred gates per chip, is inevitably beginning to influence the techniques of logic system design. Many of the established methods are rapidly becoming superfluous, for example, the emphasis on combinational logic minimization in terms of gates, state-reduction, etc. In many cases it is better practice to utilize standard MSI packages, even if this introduces redundant, or even unused, gates, than design optimized logic to be implemented at the gate level. Thus the criteria for economical implementation have now been raised to a higher level, and must take into account the number of packages and the cost of printed circuit boards and back wiring.

Another and more important change is that designers are using these complex elements as sub-system components and modifying their design techniques accordingly. For instance, to implement the pattern recognition circuit described in Example 3 of Section 5–4, the serial input would be clocked into a 4-bit shift register and the outputs compared with the required pattern using a 4-bit magnitude comparator, both modules being available as MSI circuits.

Logic design is thus being elevated to a higher, sub-system, level where complex elements, rather than basic gates, are being interconnected to give the required system function. Moreover, we have a situation where the component manufacturers are providing modules (based on conventional logic functions) which are being imposed on the designers, rather than the systems designers dictating what modules should be available. Consequently, designers are being forced of necessity to work at an intuitive level with little or no theoretical basis. The reason for this is obvious; theory has not kept pace with practice. What is needed is a new theory of switching circuits at the sub-system level rather than as we have it at present the logic gate level.

In this chapter we shall attempt to describe some of the techniques that are emerging for designing at the sub-system level, and also indicate those theoretical concepts which could pave the way for a new theory of switching circuits.

10–2 MSI sub-systems

There are a considerable number of MSI circuits which are commercially available, Table 10–1 shows some typical units. The circuits are normally monolithic integrated devices employing Schottky, bipolar, or MOS technology in conjunction with CML or TTL mode logic.[1] In the majority of cases the devices are supplied in flat-pack and dual-in-line packages with up to 24 pins, and are directly compatible with standard TTL logic systems. As can be seen from Table 10–1, many of these circuits are conventional and frequently use

Table 10—1 Typical MSI circuits

MSI module	*Comments*
Decade counter 4-bit binary counter	Synchronous and asynchronous versions, also up/down counters
4 and 8-bit shift registers	Parallel in/parallel out, parallel in/serial out, serial in/parallel out and serial in/serial out versions
4 and 8-bit bistable latches	D-type bistables, used as buffer registers.
BCD to binary converter Binary to BCD converter BCD to decimal decoder 4 line to 16 line (1 of 16) 4, 8 and 16-bit data selectors	Also called a demultiplexer Selects 1 out of n lines, also called a multiplexer
2 to 4-bit binary full adder 4-bit magnitude comparitor 8-bit odd/even parity generator 4-bit complement element	Performs $A > B, A < B$ and $A = B$ Gates either true or complement form
4-bit arithmetic logic unit (ALU)	Performs 16 binary arithmetic and logic operations controlled by four function select lines
16 to 64-bit random-access memories	Used as fast scratch-pad and buffer stores
256–1024 bit read-only memories	Used as read-only stores and decoders, arranged as 32, 8-bit words and 256, 4-bit words respectively.

logic circuits which we have already considered in the text but implemented as a single device. The more unusual circuit from our point of view is the read-only memory (ROM) module. A read-only memory is a circuit that accepts a binary code (called an *address*) at its input terminals and delivers a unique binary code (or *word*) at its output terminals for each of the input combinations. The functional relationship existing between the input and output codes is fixed, usually at the time of manufacture and as specified by the customer using a truth-table format. The ROM shown in Fig. 10–1 is analogous to a combina-

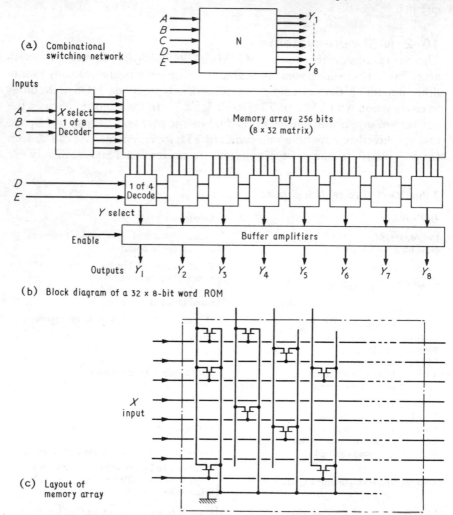

(a) Combinational switching network

(b) Block diagram of a 32 × 8-bit word ROM

(c) Layout of memory array

Fig. 10—1   Read-only memory

tional switching network and in fact the diode switching matrix is an early example of a read-only memory. In this case, however, the ROM is implemented in integrated circuit from generally using MOS or bipolar technology,[2][3] and has a switching time (called *access time*) of some 25–750 ns.

The basic storage element of the MOS read-only memory is the MOS transistor, which is used in an analogous way to the diode–resistor combination in the conventional diode matrix. Thus, a logical 1 is represented in the memory array by the physical presence of a transistor in that position; to specify a logical zero, the transistor is omitted. Insertion or deletion of a transistor in the matrix can be accomplished by changing a simple photomask in the MOS production process. Alternatively, each bit may be represented by a bipolar transistor and the coding performed by connecting or disconnecting the emitter lead of the transistor. In order to keep the number of circuit connections to a minimum the address decoding logic and sense amplifiers are produced on the same substrate as the memory matrix.

In the block diagram shown in Fig. 10–1 (b) the inputs A, B, and C are used to select 1 out of 8 input lines into the memory array, while D and E selects 1 out of 4 lines; note that there are 8 identical Y decoders, one for each bit of the 8-bit word, and that they are accessed simultaneously. The read-out of a particular bit location in the array is accomplished by sensing for current flow at the intersection of the selected X and Y lines.

An alternative form of read-only memory (PROM) is electrically programmable after manufacture by storing a charge in selected bit positions, this is achieved by connecting voltage pulses to the required locations which are then addressed in the usual way.

The random-access memory (RAM) is a similar device except that in this case the stored words may be addressed and written directly using logical inputs, as well as being read. Standard static bistable circuits are usually employed in this form of memory, again being implemented in either MOS or bipolar technology. The writing operation is accomplished by applying the word to be written to separate data inputs, addressing the store in the usual way, and then enabling the write control waveform. Note that the RAM, though still possessing the characteristics of a combinational circuit, is a true storage device in that it possesses a clocked delay time determined by the write-enable waveform. Like most bistable devices the RAM is *volatile*, in the sense that the stored data is lost when the power supply is removed; this does not, of course, apply to the read-only memory. For many applications this can be a severe disadvantage, however, it is possible to make special provisions (such as providing a separate battery power supply) which render the memory effectively non-volatile.

Typical of the more conventional MSI circuits is the data selector or multiplexer unit, shown in Fig. 10–2. This is a combinational switching circuit which generates the output function:

$$Z = \bar{x}\bar{y}\bar{z}A + \bar{x}\bar{y}zB + \bar{x}y\bar{z}C + \bar{x}yzD + x\bar{y}\bar{z}E + x\bar{y}zF \\ + xy\bar{z}G + xyzH$$

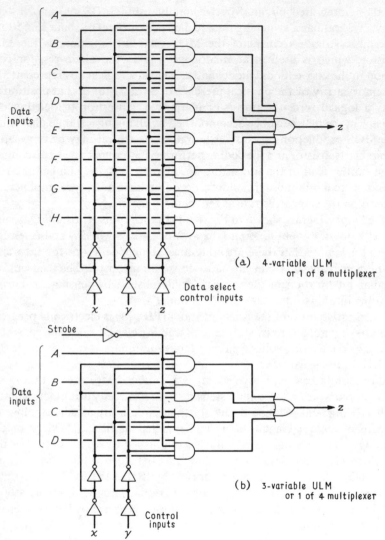

(a) 4-variable ULM
     or 1 of 8 multiplexer

Data select
control inputs

(b) 3-variable ULM
     or 1 of 4 multiplexer

Control
inputs

Fig. 10—2 Multiplexer circuits

where xy and z are the control waveforms and A,B,C,D,E,F,G and H the
input lines which are required to be switched to the output. Thus, the logical
operation of the circuit is to select 1 out of 8 possible inputs and present it at
the output. Other versions of this circuit are also available, for instance a
dual 1-out-of-4 data selector, implemented in one package, with two common
control inputs. It is also possible to obtain the converse of this function, that
is, a demultiplexer circuit which performs the operation of decoding a binary
input code to separate (and mutually exclusive) output lines, for example, a
4-line to 16-line decoder.

Another general purpose unit which is obtainable in MSI in various forms is the shift register; some typical circuits are shown in Fig. 10–3. Shift registers are used in general to store and manipulate serial data, for example, they may be made to shift their contents left or right by the application of a shift (or clock) pulse. The operation of the shift register has already been discussed to some extent in Problem 7–3, where a design for a single asynchronous shift register stage was derived from first principles.

Storage and shift registers may be either static, consisting of bistable elements, or dynamic using MOS devices with 2 or 4 phase clocking.[4] Dynamic registers operate in the serial mode only but static registers, usually employing SR bistables, may have either parallel or serial access of data. Dynamic MOS storage may also be used for RAM modules, but in this case a periodic refresh signal is required to conserve the stored data.

Various other specialist functions can be obtained in MSI (see Table 10–1) which enable many standard logic systems, such as a fast parallel adder, to be assembled from a small number of packages. Moreover, technology has already reached the stage when LSI (large scale integration) can be used to fabricate major sub-systems with hundreds of gates on a single micro-circuit chip. For example, it is now possible to obtain complete register structures, control and decoding units, arithmetic and logic units, etc., on single chips which may be interconnected to form small mini-computer systems.[5]

10–3 Implementation using MSI sub-systems

As we have stated in the Introduction, the appearance of complex MSI circuits has had a marked effect on the implementation of logic equations. In many cases the need to apply standard combinational minimization techniques no longer exists, and the designer can work with canonical minterm (or maxterm) expressions derived directly from a truth-table. In particular, the use of ROM modules allows both combinational and sequential circuits to be economically implemented without recourse to conventional design techniques.

10–3–1 Multiplexer modules

Multiplexer circuits, as described in Section 10–2, are capable of generating Boolean equations and may consequently be used to implement combinational switching circuits.[6] For example, a four-way multiplexer with four data input lines (A, B, C, and D) and two control lines x and y can produce any Boolean function of three variables. This can be achieved by connecting two of the binary variables to the control inputs and the other variable (or variables) to the data input lines. Now, using each of the four possible combinations of the control lines, the required output terms may be generated by applying either logic 1, logic 0, the variable or the inverse of the variable to the input lines.

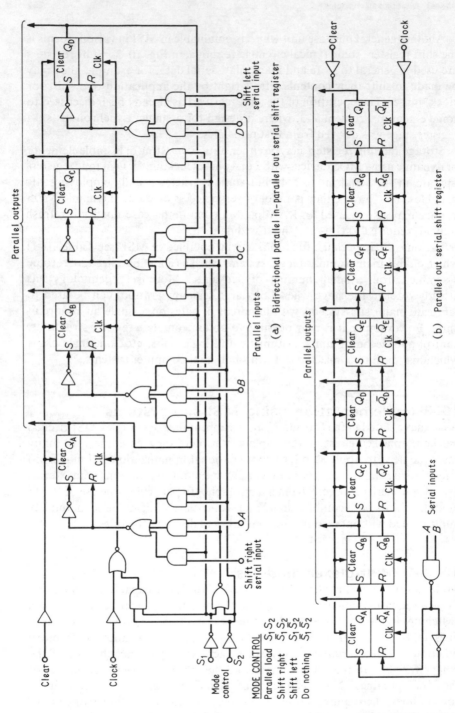

Parallel outputs

Clear

Clock

S_1
Mode control
S_2

MODE CONTROL
Parallel load $S_1 S_2$
Shift right $\bar{S_1} S_2$
Shift left $S_1 \bar{S_2}$
Do nothing $\bar{S_1} \bar{S_2}$

Shift right serial input

Parallel inputs

A B C D

Shift left serial input

(a) Bidirectional parallel in-parallel out serial shift register

Clear

Clock

Parallel outputs

A
B Serial inputs

(b) Parallel out serial shift register

Fig. 10—3 Typical shift register circuits

The technique is illustrated in Figs 10–4 (a) and (b), where the output functions

$$Z = \bar{x}_1\bar{x}_2\bar{y}_1 + \bar{x}_1 x_2 + x_1\bar{x}_2\bar{y}_1$$

and

$$Z = \bar{x}_1\bar{x}_2 y_3 + x_1 x_2 y_4$$

are generated using a four-way multiplexer unit. The operation of the circuit shown in Fig. 10–4(a) is such that when $\bar{x}_1\bar{x}_2$ is 1 the output signal should be 1 or 0 according to whether y_1 is 1 or 0, corresponding to the term $\bar{x}_1\bar{x}_2 y_1$, therefore y_1 is connected to the A input line. Similarly, since the output should

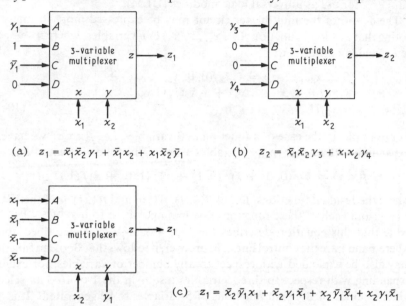

(a) $z_1 = \bar{x}_1\bar{x}_2\, y_1 + \bar{x}_1 x_2 + x_1\bar{x}_2\,\bar{y}_1$

(b) $z_2 = \bar{x}_1\bar{x}_2\, y_3 + x_1 x_2\, y_4$

(c) $z_1 = \bar{x}_2\,\bar{y}_1 x_1 + \bar{x}_2\, y_1\bar{x}_1 + x_2\,\bar{y}_1\bar{x}_1 + x_2\, y_1\bar{x}_1$

Fig. 10—4   Implementation using multiplexers

always be 1 when $\bar{x}_1 x_2$ is 1, the B input is connected permanently to logic 1. In the case of the term $x_1\bar{x}_2\bar{y}_1$, the inverse of y_1 is connected to the C input line. Finally, since there are no terms which require $x_1 x_2$, input D is put to logic 0.

Note that in the above examples the variables x_1 and x_2 appear in each term of the required expressions and are therefore the obvious candidates for connection to the control lines of the multiplexer. However, the choice of variables for the control inputs is generally not unique, though in many cases it can be rather critical. Consider implementing function Z_1 above, with the variables $x_2 y_1$ going to the control input. The first step is to expand the function to its full canonical form, giving the expression:

$$Z_1 = \bar{x}_1\bar{x}_2 y_1 + \bar{x}_1 x_2\bar{y}_1 + \bar{x}_1 x_2 y_1 + x_1\bar{x}_2\bar{y}_{1/}$$

which can then be implemented directly as shown in Fig. 10–4(c). Note, however, that if we had chosen $x_1 y_1$ as the control inputs it would have been impossible to generate the output equations.

In the general case, any one of the four signals 0, 1, y_1 and $\bar{y}_1$ (shown in Fig. 10–4(a)) could have been connected to any one of the four multiplexed input lines, giving $4^4 = 256$ different input combinations. Since this corresponds exactly to the number of different Boolean functions of 3 variables (that is 2^{2^n} where n is the number of variables), it follows that multiplexer circuits can be used to generate any 'random' switching function. In fact the multiplexer modules described above are identical to the circuits proposed by Yau and Tang[7][8] for use as universal logic modules (ULM).

The action of the multiplexer circuit may be expressed more formally by noting that any logic function $f(x_1, x_2, \ldots x_n)$ of n variables, where $n \geqslant 3$, can be expanded to the form:

$$f(x_1, x_2, \ldots x_n) = \bar{x}_1 \bar{x}_2 f(0, 0, x_3, \ldots x_n) +$$
$$\bar{x}_1 x_2 f(0, 1, x_3, \ldots x_n) + x_1 \bar{x}_2 f(1, 0, x_3, \ldots x_n) +$$
$$x_1 x_2 f(1, 1, x_3, \ldots x_n) \tag{10–1}$$

For example, in the case of a function of 3 variables, i.e., $f(x,y,z)$, we have, by expanding with respect to the variables x and y, the following equation:

$$f(x, y) = \bar{x} \bar{y} f(0, 0) + \bar{x} y f(0, 1) + x \bar{y} f(1, 0) + x y f(1,1)$$

where the residual functions, $f(0, 0), f(0, 1), f(1, 0)$ and $f(1, 1)$ are functions of z only, and each of these functions assumes one of the four values $0\ 1, z$ or $\bar{z}$. Note that this equation describes the 1 of 4 data-selector described above, where x and y are the control lines. Moreover, it follows that Boolean functions may also be expanded with respect to any number of variables, for example expanding with respect to three variables results in the 1 of 16 data selector which enables all Boolean functions of 5 variables to be generated. It is also possible to expand about a single variable, for instance:

$$f(x_1, x_2, \ldots x_n) = \bar{x}_1 f(0, x_2, \ldots x_n) + x_1 f(1, x_2, \ldots x_n)$$

which can be realized using a 3-variable multiplexer by connecting both control lines together and only using the A and D input lines, i.e., the input lines corresponding to the control terms $\bar{x} \bar{y}$ and xy.

Though it will be obvious from above that ULM's handling any number of variables can be produced, the complexity of the circuits increases rapidly and from economical and maintenance considerations it is better to implement logic functions using a number of identical small variable ULM's. This is possible by connecting multiplexers in arrays or two or more levels, corresponding to repeated expansion of the residue functions in equation (10–1) above until they are functions of the variable x_n only.

As an example of this process we shall consider the implementation of the 5-variable switching function discussed in Section 3–6 using only 3-variable multiplexer circuits. The canonical form of the function is given by:

$$T = \bar{V}\bar{W}\bar{X}\bar{Y}Z + \bar{V}\bar{W}\bar{X}YZ + \bar{V}\bar{W}\bar{X}Y\bar{Z} + \bar{V}\bar{W}X\bar{Y}\bar{Z} + \bar{V}\bar{W}X\bar{Y}Z +$$
$$\bar{V}\bar{W}XY\bar{Z} + \bar{V}\bar{W}XYZ + \bar{V}W\bar{X}Y\bar{Z} + \bar{V}WXYZ + V\bar{W}X\bar{Y}Z +$$
$$V\bar{W}XYZ + VWX\bar{Y}Z$$

which can be implemented directly using a 5-variable ULM, that is, a 1 to 16 multiplexer unit. To do this the variable $WXYZ$ would be used as the control inputs and the data inputs would be $\bar{V}$, V, 0 or 1. Note that the terms $V\bar{W}X\bar{Y}Z$ and $V\bar{W}XYZ$ must be accommodated by simplifying with $\bar{V}\bar{W}X\bar{Y}Z$ and $\bar{V}\bar{W}XYZ$ respectively and applying logic 1 to the corresponding inputs of the multiplexer. To implement using 3-variable multiplexers the process is similar. First, we expand the function about the variables Y and Z, simplifying where necessary, i.e.,

$$T = \bar{Y}\bar{Z}(\bar{W}X + VWX) + \bar{Y}Z(\bar{V}\bar{W}\bar{X} + \bar{V}\bar{W}X) + YZ(\bar{V}\bar{W}\bar{X}$$
$$+ \bar{W}X + \bar{V}W\bar{X} + \bar{V}WX) + YZ(\bar{V}\bar{W}\bar{X}$$
$$+ \bar{V}\bar{W}X)$$

This gives the first level of implementation. The residue terms can now be expanded further to obtain the second level, this may be done by inspection using WX as the control inputs. From the equations above it is obvious that the residue terms for $\bar{Y}Z$ and YZ are identical and consequently only one multiplexer is required to generate the output function; the output can of course be shared at the input to the first level multiplexer. The final circuit is shown implemented using 3-variable multiplexers in Fig. 10–5(b).

An alternative, and perhaps simpler, design technique involves the use of Karnaugh maps to determine the input variables. After deciding the type of multiplexer to be used (i.e., 3 or 4-variable ULM) and the control input variables, an ON term listing is made for the switching function, see Table 10–2(a). In this table only those input combinations which generate an output are listed and the ordering of the table is given by the choice of control variables. Note that the same control variables have been chosen as before (YZ) and that the entries in the input column refer to the first level multiplexer. The next step in the procedure is to plot the input and control variables (VWX) on Karnaugh maps for each of the 3-variable multiplexers in the second level, this is shown in Table 10–2(b). Note that it is again obvious that the inputs B' and D' to the first level multiplexer are identical and D' can thus be ignored.

The Karnaugh maps are interpreted in terms of the control inputs WX and the data inputs $ABCD$; for instance, the column $\bar{W}\bar{X}$ corresponds to input A, $\bar{W}X$ to input B, and so on. To determine the value of the input variable V we note that if a column has two zeros the data input must be $V = 0$, similarly for two ones, $V = 1$. The other values are obtained by noting the position of the minterm and reading the corresponding value of the input variable V. For instance, from Table 10–2(b) for M_0 we have $A = 0$ (all zeros), $B = 1$ (all

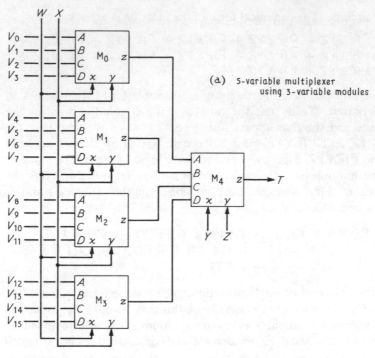

(a) 5-variable multiplexer
using 3-variable modules

Fig. 10—5   Multilevel implementation using multiplexers

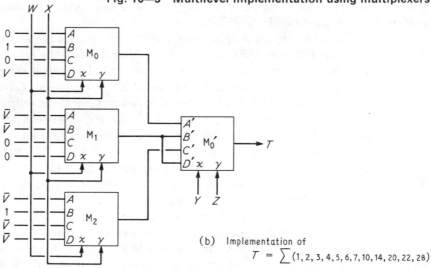

(b) Implementation of
$$T = \sum(1, 2, 3, 4, 5, 6, 7, 10, 14, 20, 22, 28)$$

ones), $C = 0$ (all zeros) and $D = V$. Note that the results obtained are identical with those found using the algebraic technique, but in this case automatic minimization has been performed on the map (for example, multiplexer M_2

Table 10–2 Multiplexer circuit design using Karnaugh maps

VWX	Input	YZ
001		00
101	A'	00
111		00
000	B'	01
001		01
000		10
001		10
010	C'	10
011		10
101		10
000	D'	11
001		11

(a) ON terms listing

M_0

V \ WX	00	01	11	10
0		1		
1		1	1	

A B D C

$A = 0$
$B = 1$
$C = 0$
$D = V$

M_1

V \ WX	00	01	11	10
0	1	1		
1				

A B D C

$A = \bar{V}$
$B = \bar{V}$
$C = 0$
$D = 0$

M_2

V \ WX	00	01	11	10
0	1	1	1	1
1		1		

A B D C

$A = \bar{V}$
$B = 1$
$C = \bar{V}$
$D = \bar{V}$

(b) K-maps for second level multiplexers

term). The mapping technique can of course be used for single level circuits and may easily be extended to 4- and 5-variable ULM's.

It is advantageous to contrast the implementation of this function using multiplexers with that obtained earlier in Section 3–6. In this case, after performing the standard minimization routines the reduced form of the equation was found to be:

$$T = VX\bar{Y}\bar{Z} + \bar{V}\bar{W}Z + \bar{V}Y\bar{Z} + \bar{W}X\bar{Z}$$

which requires two packages for its implementation, i.e., one dual 4-input NAND unit and a triple 3-input NAND unit. If a 1 of 16 multiplexer had been used only one package would have been required; using 1 of 4 multiplexers four packages (all identical) are needed. This could be reduced to three if a dual 1 of 4 package with common control lines is used.

Though the cost of multiplexer units is some five times higher at the present time than basic gate packages there is nevertheless considerable advantage to be gained from this method of implementation. The obvious gain if one 1 of 16 multiplexer is used is the reduced cost of wiring and layout of printed circuit boards. Other considerations include the reduced number of spare packages that will be required and the ease of testing and maintenance. An obvious disadvantage in the case of cascaded modules is the increased propagation time through the circuits. Multiplexer units are, on average, some two or three times slower than corresponding TTL NAND/NOR units. This difference balances itself out with single package multiplexer implementation since most conventional logic circuits involve at least two gate levels.

It will be apparent that switching functions can be implemented using multiplexers in a variety of ways, the example given above is by no means a unique solution. Note, moreover, that in this case the canonical equation was used as the starting point for the factorization procedure. This in general seems to be a better approach; using the reduced form of equation can often lead to difficulties—the reader is invited to try this for himself! In fact this is an important practical advantage of the technique, in that it is no longer necessary to find the minimal sum or product of a function in order to effect an economical realization.

In multi-level implementation the selection of suitable control inputs at the first level is very important, since this can affect the number of multiplexers required in the second and subsequent levels. If possible the choice must be made so as to optimize the number of 0, 1, and common inputs (that is, inputs which can be shared at the data inputs of the multiplexer, see Fig. 10–5(b). An alternative approach is to select variables for higher order levels that are either identical or the inverse of one another; this latter characteristic is only applicable when the multiplexer has both true and complemented outputs. In all cases the objective is to reduce the number of multiplexers required in the higher order levels. The problem is further complicated since there is no reason why the control inputs at higher order levels should all be the same (though in practice they often are); the use of individual control inputs can often lead to a reduction in the number of modules required in the preceding levels.

Unfortunately there is no formal design theory, as yet, which considers implementation at the sub-system level, for example, the systematic minimization of ULM's. Note also that only single-output switching circuits have been discussed. Multiple-output networks present yet another problem; they can, of course, be designed in practice as separate single-output circuits. These aspects of logic design are ideal topics for further research but ones which seem to have claimed little attention, perhaps because it is difficult to decide on the ideal form of ULM. However, the multiplexer circuit seems able to perform this function and, since it is commercially available, work could profitably proceed using this device as the basic element.

10–3–2 Read-only memory modules(9)(10)(11)(12)

Using ROM's, the design and implementation of combinational and sequential switching circuits becomes a rather trivial operation. There is no need to employ any of the conventional minimization techniques (indeed to do so could lead to pitfalls in the design) and the designer can work directly from a truth or assigned state-table.

As an illustration of the technique Table 10–3 shows the layout of a ROM (containing 32 words each of 8-bits) to perform the switching function discussed in the last section. The format is identical to the initial truth-table, the five input variables (minterms) correspond to the ROM address, and the contents of the words (one bit in each) to the output function. Thus, to implement the switching circuit, the designer simply specifies the position in the ROM of the 1's in the required output function. To use the ROM, the unit is addressed with the input variables which causes the corresponding word containing the required output bit to be read down.

Note that only one bit is used in each output word of the ROM; with this vertical layout the bits in a word may be totally unrelated for a given input address. Consequently, multiple output switching functions can easily be programmed, and in fact the ROM shown in Table 10–2 represents what is essentially a multiple output circuit with up to 8 output functions, one for each bit of the word.

When designing with ROM's there is no need to consider 'don't-care' conditions since the devices are only available in standard modules and hence no savings are possible. The choice of ROM is determined solely by the number of variables involved and the size of ROM which will accommodate them; in our example we have 5 variables, therefore a ROM with at least 2^5 words will be required. If the number of minterms for a given function of n variables is greater than 2^{n-1} it is sometimes more convenient to program the complement of the function (equivalent to using maxterms) and invert the output of the ROM.

Contrasting this form of implementation with conventional NAND gate logic is it obviously uneconomic for a single-output circuit, since the cost of a ROM package is some ten times greater. However, when used as a multiple output circuit, for example in a microprogram control unit for a computer or when translating from one code to another, the economic gains are considerable. This is particularly true when wiring and testing costs are considered.

For large-variable problems direct implementation using a single ROM soon becomes impractical since every additional switching variable doubles the number of words required in the memory. This limitation may be overcome in the majority of cases by employing smaller ROM's in cascaded or multi-level circuits. Since it is always possible to connect ROM's together to produce a larger sized store, for example two 32 × 8-bit word modules can be connected together to give a 64 × 8-bit word store, the techniques of cascading are effectively those of minimization at the sub-system (i.e., ROM) level.

Table 10—3 Read-only memory formats

Address input variables $A_0 A_1 A_2 A_3 A_4$	Output word output functions $Z_0 Z_1 Z_2 Z_3 Z_4 Z_5 Z_6 Z_7$
0 0 0 0 0	0 0 0 0 0 0 0 0
0 0 0 0 1	1 0 0 0 0 0 0 0
0 0 0 1 0	1 0 0 0 0 0 0 0
0 0 0 1 1	1 0 0 0 0 0 0 0
0 0 1 0 0	1 0 0 0 0 0 0 0
0 0 1 0 1	1 0 0 0 0 0 0 0
0 0 1 1 0	1 0 0 0 0 0 0 0
0 0 1 1 1	1 0 0 0 0 0 0 0
0 1 0 0 0	0 0 0 0 0 0 0 0
0 1 0 0 1	0 0 0 0 0 0 0 0
0 1 0 1 0	1 0 0 0 0 0 0 0
0 1 0 1 1	0 0 0 0 0 0 0 0
0 1 1 0 0	0 0 0 0 0 0 0 0
0 1 1 0 1	0 0 0 0 0 0 0 0
0 1 1 1 0	1 0 0 0 0 0 0 0
0 1 1 1 1	0 0 0 0 0 0 0 0
1 0 0 0 0	0 0 0 0 0 0 0 0
1 0 0 0 1	0 0 0 0 0 0 0 0
1 0 0 1 0	0 0 0 0 0 0 0 0
1 0 0 1 1	0 0 0 0 0 0 0 0
1 0 1 0 0	1 0 0 0 0 0 0 0
1 0 1 0 1	0 0 0 0 0 0 0 0
1 0 1 1 0	1 0 0 0 0 0 0 0
1 0 1 1 1	0 0 0 0 0 0 0 0
1 1 0 0 0	0 0 0 0 0 0 0 0
1 1 0 0 1	0 0 0 0 0 0 0 0
1 1 0 1 0	0 0 0 0 0 0 0 0
1 1 0 1 1	0 0 0 0 0 0 0 0
1 1 1 0 0	1 0 0 0 0 0 0 0
1 1 1 0 1	0 0 0 0 0 0 0 0
1 1 1 1 0	0 0 0 0 0 0 0 0
1 1 1 1 1	0 0 0 0 0 0 0 0

We will now consider a simple example of cascaded ROM circuits using the 6-variable switching function previously discussed in Section 3–9, that is:

$$T = \Sigma \, (5, 15, 20, 29, 41, 42, 45, 47, 53, 58, 61, 63)$$

The circuit can of course be implemented directly using a ROM with $2^6 = 64$ words which would be obtained by connecting together four 16×4-bit word stores. However, we shall show that it is possible to implement this function using two ROM's connected in cascade with the output of one feeding directly into the other.

Table 10—4 Cascaded ROMs

Decimal form	Variables AB	CDEF		Variables CDEF	Coded form $Z_1 Z_2 Z_3$
5	00	0101		0100	0 0 0
15	00	1111		0101	0 0 1
20	01	0100		1001	0 1 0
29	01	1101		1010	0 1 1
41	10	1001		1101	1 0 0
42	10	1010		1111	1 0 1
45	10	1101			
47	10	1111		(b) Shared terms and coding	
53	11	0101			
58	11	1010			
61	11	1101			
63	11	1111			

(a) ON terms listing

Input variables AB	$Z_1 Z_2 Z_3$	Outputs $T_1 T_2 T_3 T_4$
00	0 0 1	1 0 0 0
00	1 0 1	1 0 0 0
01	0 0 0	1 0 0 0
01	1 0 0	1 0 0 0
10	0 1 0	1 0 0 0
10	0 1 1	1 0 0 0
10	1 0 0	1 0 0 0
10	1 0 1	1 0 0 0
11	0 0 1	1 0 0 0
11	0 1 1	1 0 0 0
11	1 0 0	1 0 0 0
11	1 0 1	1 0 0 0

(c) Layout of first-level ROM

In the cascaded technique the variables are partitioned and recoded in order to achieve data-compression. This is possible since, in general, most switching functions contain terms with common variables or minterms, for example, the terms $\bar{A}\bar{B}CDEF$ and $ABCDEF$ share the variables $CDEF$. Table 10–4 shows the ON terms listing for the original function (which has been partitioned into blocks containing variables AB and $CDEF$) and the shared terms in $CDEF$. Any other permutation or combination of variables may be used, but the best choice is that set (or sets) of variables which gives rise to the smallest number of shared terms. From Table 10–4(b) it is apparent that 3 bits are necessary to code the shared $CDEF$ terms, thus a ROM with 16 words of 3 bits will be required to generate the coded outputs; variables AB assume all possible values and a more economic coding is impossible. The cascaded circuit takes the form shown in Fig. 10–6 in which the variables $CDEF$ go to ROM 2, which

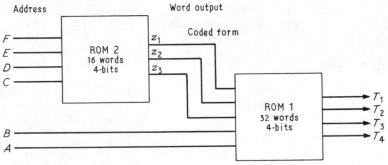

Fig. 10—6   Cascaded ROM network

generates the coded output $Z_1 Z_2 Z_3$, and this output together with the variables AB go to ROM 1 which generates the final switching function. The layout of ROM 1 is shown in Table 10–4(c); note that only those input terms which generate an output are shown, all the other words in the ROM will contain zeros.

Thus, using cascaded implementation the number of 16 4-bit word ROM's has been reduced from four to three, assuming that ROM 1 consists of two such ROM's connected together. The technique produces even greater savings when large variable functions are to be implemented. Unfortunately, no formal design algorithms exist for this technique and consequently the method is essentially heuristic in nature. However, some work has been done by the semiconductor manufacturers who have devised computer programs to determine the best partitioning and coding of the truth-table for the design of specialized ROM networks.

As we would suspect, read-only memories are also ideal devices for the realization of synchronous and asynchronous sequential circuits. Let us commence our discussion of this topic by considering the implementation of the asynchronous Gray-code counter designed earlier in Problem 7–2. Using

ROM's, the conventional design procedure remains unchanged and the starting point for the ROM implementation is the assigned flow-table, reproduced for convenience in Table 10–5(a), which is simply rearranged to the

Table 10–5 Implementation of asynchronous circuit using ROM's

(a) Assigned flow table

y_2y_3 \ xy_1	00	01	11	10
00	① 000	1 000	⑧ 100	2 001
01	3 011	⑦ 101	8 100	② 001
11	③ 011	7 101	⑥ 111	4 010
10	5 110	⑤ 110	6 111	④ 010

Address $x\,y_1\,y_2\,y_3$	Output word $y_1\,y_2\,y_3\,y_4$
0 0 0 0	0 0 0 0
1 0 0 0	0 0 1 0
0 0 0 1	0 1 1 0
1 0 0 1	0 0 1 0
0 0 1 1	0 1 1 0
1 0 1 1	0 1 0 0
0 0 1 0	1 1 0 0
1 0 1 0	0 1 0 0
0 1 1 0	1 1 0 0
1 1 1 0	1 1 1 0
0 1 1 1	1 0 1 0
1 1 1 1	1 1 1 0
0 1 0 1	1 0 1 0
1 1 0 1	1 0 0 0
0 1 0 0	0 0 0 0
1 1 0 0	1 0 0 0

(b) Transition table

transition-table form to give the store layout directly. The transition-table, shown in Table 10–5(b), shows the required transitions from present to next states of the counter when the external input is applied. The circuit is shown implemented in Fig. 10–7 using a 16 word 4-bit ROM; note that the $y_1y_2y_3$ outputs (the counter is, in fact, a Moore machine) are fed directly back to the

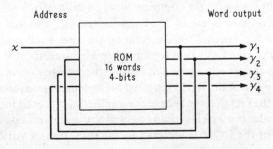

Fig. 10—7   Grey-code asynchronous counter using ROM

address inputs of the ROM to give the required sequential (i.e., feedback) action. In the case of the more general Meely machine, output functions can easily be accommodated by allocating appropriate bits in the ROM word which generate the output functions directly.

An implementation of this form is possible because the integrated circuit ROM is constructed from active devices, which give the necessary gain round the feedback loop. The equivalent in the ROM to an asynchronous stable state condition is when the output word is used to address its own location—a form of dynamic loop. Thus, the ROM circuit is directly analogous to the conventional NAND/NOR implementation of the excitation equations. However, in this case there is an added advantage in that there is no longer any need to examine and correct for static hazards. The occurrence of static hazards arises during the minimization procedures and since, when using ROM's, all the basic switching terms are effectively used, hazards of this type are eliminated.

Synchronous machines may be implemented using ROM's in a similar manner, though in this case there is a timing problem to be considered. In some cases the ROM is provided with an enable or strobe line which can be used like a system clock; for instance, the outputs can be disabled until all the transients on the input lines have died away. However, the required delay round the loop must be obtained by using external bistable devices (for example, a MSI 4-bit D-type bistable latch unit) to register (that is, delay) the outputs before returning them to the address inputs.

To illustrate the procedure we will implement the synchronous sequence detector discussed in Problem 6–3. The starting point is, as before, the conversion of the assigned state-table (shown in Table S–48(c)) into a transition table (shown in Table 10–6) which can then be used to program the contents of the ROM. Figure 10–8 shows the basic method of incorporating timing control; note that D-type bistables, controlled by the system clock, are used to ensure synchronous operation. This form of implementation is, in fact, equivalent to the general model for a sequential circuit, where the application equations (page 100) are used to realize the circuit.

It is interesting to consider the effect that implementing sequential machines with ROM's has on conventional logic design theory. It will be obvious that the need for minimization of the combinational circuitry (for instance, bistable input equations) no longer exists. For similar reasons minimal state-assignment procedures for synchronous machines are also irrelevant. However, state reduction and row reduction (merging) procedures are still of moderate importance since these techniques can reduce the number of words required in the ROM. The size of the ROM required to implement a sequential machine is determined by the fact that the sum of the number of bits used for the external input and state codes must be less than or equal to the address bits of the ROM. The wordlength of the ROM is dictated by the total number of bits required for the state code and output functions.

Table 10—6 ROM layout for synchronous sequence detector

Address $y_1 y_2 y_3$	$x_1 x_2$	Output word $y_1 y_2 y_3$	$F1$
0 0 0	0 0	0 0 0	0
0 0 0	0 1	0 0 0	0
0 0 0	1 1	0 1 0	0
0 0 0	1 0	0 1 0	0
0 1 0	0 0	0 0 0	0
0 1 0	0 1	1 1 0	0
0 1 0	1 1	0 1 0	0
0 1 0	1 0	0 1 0	0
1 1 0	0 0	1 0 0	0
1 1 0	0 1	0 0 0	0
1 1 0	1 1	0 1 0	0
1 1 0	1 0	0 1 0	0
1 0 0	0 0	0 0 0	0
1 0 0	0 1	0 1 1	0
1 0 0	1 1	0 1 0	0
1 0 0	1 0	0 1 0	0
0 1 1	0 0	0 0 0	0
0 1 1	0 1	0 0 0	0
0 1 1	1 1	0 0 1	1
0 1 1	1 0	0 0 1	1
0 0 1	0 0	0 0 1	1
0 0 1	0 1	0 0 0	0
0 0 1	1 1	0 1 0	0
0 0 1	1 0	0 0 1	1

One theoretical concept which could prove useful in the design of ROM systems is that concerned with the decomposition of large sequential machines into smaller machines, which can then be connected in serial–parallel configurations to give the same characteristics.[13] This work could be extended to ROM's in order to reduce the amount of storage required for a given machine.

The economic advantage of ROM's is not obviously apparent; for example, in the case of the two sequential circuits discussed above the cost of the ROM far exceeds the cost of the logic packages in the original designs. However, if we consider not only the reduced cost of engineering a single package, but also the costs involved in design, testing, maintenance, etc., there are considerable advantages. Nevertheless, at the present time one must consider carefully whether or not to use ROM's (or for that matter MSI in general). For small one-off systems logic packages are still the most economic method of realiza-

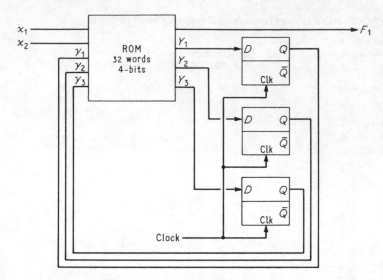

Fig. 10—8   ROM interpretation of synchronous sequence detector

tion, but for large quantity-produced systems MSI is far superior. One advantage of using ROM's is that many different functions can be obtained by simply reprogramming the ROM. Thus, it is possible to have a basic circuit configuration, say for a sequential encoding circuit, in which the type of code can be changed by plugging in a new ROM unit; this characteristic is sometimes referred to as a 'loadable personality'.

Perhaps the greatest benefit, however, to be obtained by using ROM's is the comparative ease with which the resultant circuits can be checked. The testing of random logic circuit boards, with some 100–200 gates, imposes severe problems for the digital systems manufacturer. Every logic connection in the circuit must be checked for correct operation and the presence of possible faults, and the obvious method of applying all possible inputs and monitoring the output soon becomes impracticable. Deriving suitable test-schedules to detect and diagnose faults, usually the responsibility of the logic designer, is a time consuming and expensive process. This can be a particularly difficult task when the boards contain sequential logic. In fact no completely satisfactory procedure for evolving test schedules has of yet been devised. Moreover, even if the tests are derived automatically using formal methods[14] it is still necessary to use a complex general purpose tester to check out the circuit boards. Using ROM's a standard test schedule (and tester) can easily be produced, based on the combinational logic and electrical properties of the ROM, which can then be used to rapidly check out ROM's whatever their application. This philosophy, of course, is completely general, and applies to any basic sub-system component, but it is particularly relevant to ROM devices.

10–4 Modular realization of digital systems

Numerous attempts have been made to partition digital systems (in particular computers) into suitable basic modules which can take full advantage of LSI technology. From the technology point of view the following properties are desirable for a logic systems module made in LSI:

   (a) high circuit density; that is a large number of gates
   (b) regular structure and interconnection pattern
   (c) high circuit to edge connector ratio
   (d) versatility in use
   (e) easily testable

Though many of the modules suggested have been well suited for the technology, unfortunately, due to a lack of a suitable system theory, they did not possess the universality required of such a device. In this section we shall survey some of the more important sub-systems that have been proposed for systems realization.

One approach that has often been adopted is to use a standard circuit to perform different logical operations, for instance the programmable arithmetic and logic unit. In this respect the basic accumulator circuit can be used to generate many useful functions. The accumulator consists of a binary full-adder and clocked buffer register, and its operation is to add a binary number presented at its inputs to the contents of the register. Figure 10–9(a) shows a typical circuit using standard MSI modules. By making suitable connections to the input of the accumulator the circuit can be made to perform a variety of functions. For example, an up-counter may be produced by simply connecting the binary number 0001 to the inputs $A_1A_2A_3A_4$, similarly for a down-counter the number 1111 would be used; the action of the accumulator under these conditions is shown in Table 10–7. The principle may be extended to design incremental counters of any value; in the case of down-counters the 2's complement of the number must be used.

Accumulators can also be wired to giving shifting operations (performed on the contents of the buffer register). In this application (shown in Figs 10–9(b) and (c)) the outputs of the register ($B_1B_2B_3B_4$) are fed back to the inputs of the accumulator. The left shift is obtained very easily by adding the contents of the register to itself, thereby doubling the number; an end-around shift may be obtained by connecting C_{out} to C_{in} (the carry input and output). For a right shift the 1's complement of the number in the register is added one digit place to the right; that is, half the number is subtracted from itself. The correction for 2's complement notation is performed by connecting the $\bar{B}_4$ output to C_{in}; it is also necessary to put input A_4 to logic 1.

Another useful application of the accumulator is that it can be wired as a binary rate multiplier. To achieve this all that is needed is to connect the required binary rate M to the input terminals of the accumulator and take the output from C_{out}. Used in this way the output generates M pulses for each

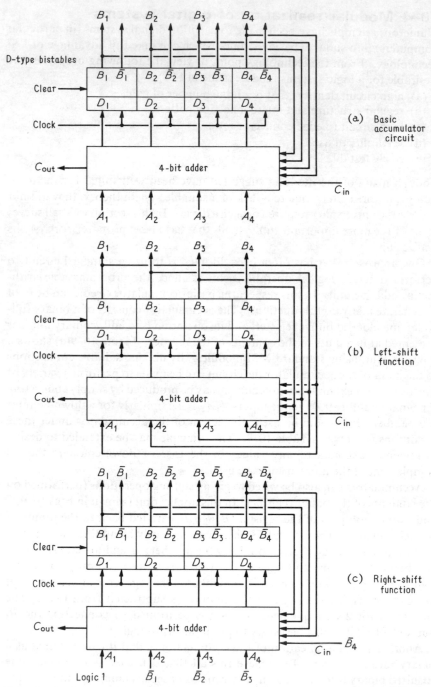

Fig. 10—9 Accumulator circuits

Table 10–7 Dual purpose accumulator circuit

Function	Clock pulse	$A_1 A_2 A_3 A_4 C_{in}$	$B_1 B_2 B_3 B_4$	$C_0 D_1 D_2 D_3 D_4$	Decimal
Up	0	0 0 0 1 0	0 0 0 0	0 0 0 0 1	0
Counter	1	0 0 0 1 0	0 0 0 1	0 0 0 1 0	1
	2	0 0 0 1 0	0 0 1 0	0 0 0 1 1	2
	3	0 0 0 1 0	0 0 1 1	0 0 1 0 0	3
	4	0 0 0 1 0	0 1 0 0	0 0 1 0 1	4
			etc		
Down	0	1 1 1 1 0	0 0 0 0	0 1 1 1 1	0
Counter	1	1 1 1 1 0	1 1 1 1	1 1 1 1 0	15
	2	1 1 1 1 0	1 1 1 0	1 1 1 0 1	14
	3	1 1 1 1 0	1 1 0 1	1 1 1 0 0	13
	4	1 1 1 1 0	1 1 0 0	1 1 0 1 1	12
			etc.		
Left	0	0 1 0 1 0	0 1 0 1	0 1 0 1 0	5
Shift	1	1 0 1 0 0	1 0 1 0	1 0 1 0 0	10
	2	0 1 0 0 0	0 1 0 0	0 1 0 0 0	Overflows
	3	1 0 0 0 0	1 0 0 0	1 0 0 0 0	
			etc.		
Right	0	1 0 1 1 1	1 0 0 0	1 0 1 0 0	8
Shift	1	1 1 0 1 1	0 1 0 0	1 0 0 1 0	4
	2	1 1 1 0 1	0 0 1 0	1 0 0 0 1	2
	3	1 1 1 1 0	0 0 0 1	1 0 0 0 0	1
			etc.		

input cycle of 2^n, where n is the number of stages in the register; Table 10–8 illustrates this operation for $M=5$.

The obvious extension of this method is to arrange for the various input connections to be switched automatically using a coded input, that is to program the accumulator. Though this technique has many advantages, particularly in small special purpose digital systems, the concept is too confined to be of general use in digital systems.

As suggested above, most of the work on digital sub-system components has been orientated towards the design of computers. One such system, described by Podraza, Gregg, and Slager[15] uses four MSI functional building blocks (FBB) which are generally applicable to the design of parallel data-processing structures. The main considerations in partitioning the system in order to derive these modules were based on component technology arguments rather than systems theory. The four basic sub-systems used in the approach are:

Table 10—8 Binary rate multiplier

Clock pulse	$A_1 A_2 A_3 A_4 C_{in}$	$B_1 B_2 B_3 B_4$	$C_0 D_1 D_2 D_3 D_4$
0	0 1 0 1 0	0 0 0 0	0 0 1 0 1
1	0 1 0 1 0	0 1 0 1	0 1 0 1 0
2	0 1 0 1 0	1 0 1 0	0 1 1 1 1
3	0 1 0 1 0	1 1 1 1	1 0 1 0 0
4	0 1 0 1 0	0 1 0 0	0 1 0 0 1
5	0 1 0 1 0	1 0 0 1	0 1 1 1 0
6	0 1 0 1 0	1 1 1 0	1 0 0 1 1
7	0 1 0 1 0	0 0 1 1	0 1 0 0 0
8	0 1 0 1 0	1 0 0 0	0 1 1 0 1
9	0 1 0 1 0	1 1 0 1	1 0 0 1 0
10	0 1 0 1 0	0 0 1 0	0 0 1 1 1
11	0 1 0 1 0	0 1 1 1	0 1 1 0 0
12	0 1 0 1 0	1 1 0 0	1 0 0 0 1
13	0 1 0 1 0	0 0 0 1	0 0 1 1 0
14	0 1 0 1 0	0 1 1 0	0 1 0 1 1
15	0 1 0 1 0	1 0 1 1	1 0 0 0 0
0	0 1 0 1 0	0 0 0 0	0 0 1 0 1

(a) *universal logic FBB*—similar to the 3-variable ULM's described in Section 10–3–1 but modified to incorporate binary addition and subtraction operations.

(b) *register FBB*—rather than implement a complete register assembly the approach here was to use a 'bit-slice' technique whereby one bit position of all registers is implemented on the same chip. Since a minimal central processor for a computer requires five registers (see Fig. A–3) the chip was designed with five gated bistable circuits. Note that this technique enables computer words of any length to be assembled.

(c) *carry FBB*—this unit comprises a nine-stage carry look-ahead[16] circuit which can be used with a universal logic FBB to give a full-adder unit.

(d) *control FBB*—this unit provides selection control inputs for the register and universal logic FBB's and consists of AND/OR gates. The module is also used to control instruction decoding and execution.

In this system the control unit of the computer (see Section A–3) can be implemented using either a ROM containing stored micro-program, or a sequential network employing register FBB's as the control bistables, the latter being the preferred method.

Another way of attacking the problem has been to use cellular logic arrays, and considerable work has been done in this field.[17] Cellular logic is basically an iterative network (see Section 4–3) comprising a number of identical cells interconnected in a regular array. The cells may be either sequential or combinational logic networks, normally operating in asynchronous mode. Each cell has a primary input (x), which serves as an external input to the network. There are also a number of intercell leads that carry signals between adjacent cells, and a primary output (z); a typical cellular logic structure is shown in Fig. 10–10. The logic behaviour of the cells in an array is defined in terms of

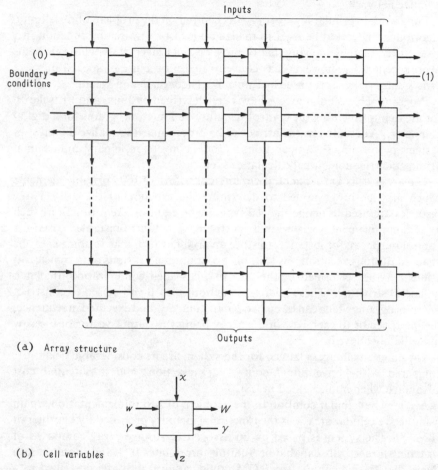

(a)   Array structure

(b)   Cell variables

Fig. 10—10   Cellular logic design

their truth or state-table (also called a cell-table). It is also necessary to specify the signals that are applied to the intercell leads entering the edges of the network, these are called *boundary conditions*. The state of a cell in an iterative array is the property described by the value of all the inputs to the cell plus the internal state variables, if any.

It is interesting to note the close analogy that exists between unilateral iterative networks and synchronous sequential machines. For example, the boundary conditions correspond to the initial state of a sequential machine. It is always possible to convert from a synchronous circuit to an iterative one, or vice versa, by performing a space–time transformation.[18][10] This simply means arranging that the serial (time) input is converted to a parallel (space) input which is then used as the external inputs to the individual cells in the iterative network.

Early work in cellular logic arrays was centred on the problem of developing algorithms that could be used to realize an arbitrary switching function in a given array, thereby showing that the array was a universal switching element. More recent work, however, has concentrated on the use of special purpose arrays, such as those proposed by Kautz[20], Nicoud[21], and Dean.[22]

Programmable cellular arrays have been described by Jump and Fritsche[23] for use in implementing the control structure and microprograms for a digital computer. Alternatively, the array can be programmed to realize digital sub-systems performing such operations as radix conversion, binary and decimal arithmetic, trigonometrical calculations, etc.

The array cells are sequential circuits consisting of four bistable elements which may be programmed to determine the function of the cell. Three bistables are used to define the cell type giving eight different functions such as add, complement, register, null, shift, etc. The fourth bistable is used for control purposes, for instance, to store a variable which may in some cases be changed during execution. By suitable programming, various data transform-ations may be performed by the cells in a cascaded configuration, that is a unilateral structure. These micro-instructions may then be used to construct micro-programs which can be embedded in the array, and executed in sequence, the input vector to each row in the array being the output vector of the row immediately above it.

The main advantages claimed for the system are its considerable flexibility, compared with conventional control organization, and a potential cost advantage when implemented in LSI.

A somewhat similar solution to the problem of LSI implementation, again using active cellular arrays, is the functional memory proposed by Gardner of IBM.[24] The system is based on an associative storage array composed of writable storage cells capable of holding three states 0, 1 and 'don't-cares'. (Note that in this context the ROM could, quite rightly, be described as a cellular array.)

An associative store is accessed by simultaneously comparing the contents of all the memory locations with a tag or descriptor word. The tag-bits are normally held in a selected field of the stored words, the remaining bits being used for data. When a match is found the contents of the corresponding word, or its absolute address, appear at the output of the store. In the functional memory, 0's and 1's are matched in the usual way, but cells containing 'don't-care' entries match to inputs of both 0 and 1. It is possible in an associative store to have more than one word containing the same tag-bits and output accordingly; this is known as the *multiple response* problem. This characteristic is utilized in the functional memory by arranging that the internal store outputs are OR'ed together to give the final output.

As we have seen earlier, a major problem when using memory arrays is the rapid increase of store size for large variable systems; one of the chief advantages of functional memory is that it considerably reduces the size of array required for a given application. For example, using a ROM to generate the logic functions $Z_1 = A_1 + B_1$ and $Z_2 = A_2 + B_2$ would necessitate sixteen words of memory; however, using an associatively addressed functional memory only four words of storage are required. How this is achieved may be seen from Table 10–9, using the input $A_1\bar{B}_1A_2B_1$ the required output is 11,

Table 10—9 Table look-up techniques

Address $A_1B_1A_2B_2$	Word output Z_1Z_2	Search input $A_1B_1A_2B_2$	Read output Z_1Z_2
0 0 0 0	0 0	1 X X X	1 0
0 0 0 1	0 1	X 1 X X	1 0
0 0 1 0	0 1	X X 1 X	0 1
0 0 1 1	0 1	X X X 1	0 1
0 1 0 0	1 0		
0 1 0 1	1 1		
0 1 1 0	1 1	1 0 1 1	1 1
0 1 1 1	1 1		
1 0 0 0	1 0		
1 0 0 1	1 1	(b) Functional memory	
1 0 1 0	1 1		
1 0 1 1	1 1		
1 1 0 0	1 0		
1 1 0 1	1 1		
1 1 1 0	1 1		
1 1 1 1	1 1		

(a) Conventional ROM

which is obtained by direct addressing in the case of the ROM. In the functional memory the same input causes the stored words IXXX, XXIX and XXXI to respond simultaneously (due to the 'don't-care' entries) and the OR'ed output is 11 as before. The stored combinations in the functional memory are essentially the prime implicant terms of the switching functions, with the eliminated variables represented by X's, i.e., 'don't-cares'. For example, the functions Z_1 and Z_2 shown in Table 10–9 reduce to the following set of PI's:

$$Z_1 = A_1 + B_2 = \text{XXIX} + \text{XXXI and}$$
$$Z_2 = A_2 + B_2 = \text{IXXX} + \text{XIXX}$$

Thus functional memory can give significant table compression over conventional two-state arrays, typically n to n^2 words instead of 2^n, where n is the number of variables. Moreover, it can be programmed to perform complex logical operations by associative table-look-up within the store, with all the attendant advantages of ROM. In addition it has the useful ability that the contents of the store can be written during processing, thereby allowing the functional memory to be used for local storage, working registers, etc.

The LSI modules described above are not commercially available to the logic designer but were discussed in order to indicate current trends in system design. Moreover, the majority of these systems have emanated from the computer industry and are orientated towards the specific problems (for example, control unit design) encountered in that field. At the present time no general purpose sub-system modules, excluding the ROM and multiplexer which are really at a much lower system level, exist. What is the reason for this state of affairs? Is it possible in fact to devise a universal systems module? The answer to these questions has been hinted at throughout this chapter—that is, there is a need for a formal systems theory. In order to evolve and use a specific module, a theoretical background must exist in order to generate a sound design procedure. The starting point for such a theory must be the specification and description of the system, leading to evaluation and design. In the final section of this chapter we will consider the current state of systems design theory and the possible implications on LSI implementation.

10–5 Design at the systems level

One of the most important proposals to formalize logic systems design was made by Wilkes and Stringer[25] in 1953 who postulated a *micro-program* method for designing the control unit of a computer. Since then the technique has been widely extended and adopted generally for the design of complex control units.[26] In the control of any logic process, for example a binary multiplication algorithm, the operation can be broken down into a sequence of gating and clocking signals which must occur at specific places in the circuit at the right time. Let us consider as an example a 4-bit serial binary multiplier performing the following simple algorithm:

(a) The least significant digit (LSD) of the multiplier is examined. If it is a 1 the multiplicand is added to the product register; no action is taken if the LSD of the multiplier is zero.

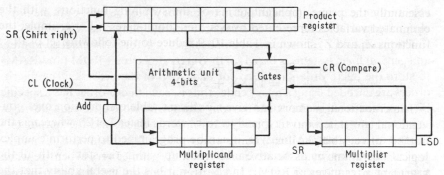

Fig. 10—11   Serial multiplier

(b) The contents of the product and multiplier registers are shifted one place right.

(c) A check is made for the end of the operation. If it is complete, the process stops, otherwise step (a) is repeated.

Figure 10–11 shows a schematic diagram of the circuit (which could easily be constructed from standard MSI modules) required to perform this operation. Note that the multiplication of two 4-bit binary numbers yields an 8-bit product, and that four clock pulses are required to perform each addition. Though the circuit shown is a synchronous sequential machine, and could indeed be represented as such, the usual design practice would be to implement the algorithm directly in terms of registers, etc.

Control of the multiplier circuit is effected by arranging that the shift-right, add, compare signals, etc., are generated in the correct sequence; the location of these signals is, of course, hard-wired into the circuit. The usual way of deriving these signals, or *micro-orders*, would be to use a gated counter circuit (or programmer) controlled by the system clock. A sequence of such micro-orders to execute a specified process is called a micro-program.

The problem is considerably more complicated when designing the control unit for a digital computer, since the multiplication order would be only one of many in the instruction set of the machine (see Section A2). Consequently it is necessary to initially decode the instruction, and to optimize the large number of micro-orders required by the individual micro-programs. In the early machines the decoding and control processes were performed using hardwired AND/OR networks or diode matrices, in conjunction with a timing circuit, which were evolved using what was essentially an intuitive design procedure. Wilkes' work showed how the design process could be formalized (and hence simplified) by considering the micro-orders as instructions in a normal computer program, including such facilities as conditional jumps, looping, etc. Consequently, control algorithms could be derived (and documented) using standard programming procedures and then implemented directly in hardware. The original micro-program circuits of Wilkes were very similar in concept (though not in technology!) to the read-only memory, operating in a feedback mode to give a conditional jump characteristic.

The present approach to control unit design[27][28] for both small computers and general logic systems is based on the integrated circuit ROM (and RAM) to store the micro-orders required for each step of the process. The micro-orders are encoded using a unary code; that is, each micro-order has a specific bit allocated to it in the ROM word. The ROM words are read down in sequence, unless a jump to a new location is specified, and the output bits applied directly to the logic being controlled. This technique of micro-programming, known as the *horizontal* technique, can be very expensive when a large number of micro-orders (and hence large wordlengths) are required, and other more economic methods have been devised. In this simple account of micro-programming many questions have been left unanswered, particularly the question of conditional loops and addressing and the problems of encoding and optimizing the micro-instruction words; the reader is referred to more specialized books on the subject for a treatment of these topics.[29][30]

Computer systems have evolved into a fairly regular parallel structure consisting of registers, arithmetic and logic units, control units, data and control highways, etc. (for example, see Fig. A–3). The intuitive design procedures used in computer systems engineering, which are centred around this register structure and their interconnections have been semi-automated using *register transfer languages* (see also page 237). Many different types of logic design languages have emerged[31][32][33][34] but they are all based on the use of a problem-orientated computer language to specify a proposed register structure and the required logical operations between them.

Using this technique the micro-programs for a particular machine code instruction set may be specified as operational statements using software procedures, for example:

$$|C| : T \leftarrow R + S \qquad\qquad (10\text{--}2)$$

indicates that when $C = 1$ the contents of register R are added to the contents of register S and the result placed in register T. In these procedures the contents of a register (the name and size of which must be initially declared in the program) is treated as a vector with n components; individual elements may be referred to by, for example, using subscripts of the form: $T_{(5)} \leftarrow R_{(3)} \oplus S_{(2)}$. Various logical connectives, such as $+, \ldots \oplus$, etc., are allowed in the language, being applied component by component in the register transfer operations. Essentially, register transfer languages are used to describe the data paths and processing operations between registers (normally parallel operation is assumed). The control operations are implicitly specified by the sequential ordering of the program statements (for synchronous systems) and by the use of various conditional relationships. For example, in (10–2) above $|C|$ could either be a simple clock input (specified as $|t_1|$, $|t_2|$, etc.) or a compound conditional of the form $|\bar{A}_1B_2\bar{C}_3 = 1|$. Timing and control in register transfer languages, particularly for asynchronous and parallel operations, can be a difficult problem. Microprograms (or logic systems in general) expressed in the form of a register transfer language may be translated using software procedures into a set of Boolean logic equations representing a hardware implementation of the system. Moreover, similar techniques may be used for the simulation and evaluation of logic circuits.

Thus, using register transfer languages design equations may be generated automatically from an algorithmic specification of the data transfers within the system. Unfortunately, from the viewpoint of LSI, these equations are generally implemented in the conventional way using NAND/NOR gates. The register operations may, however, be regarded as a primitive set of circuit functions in the same way as we think of bistables and NAND/NOR gates. The register transfer module (RTM) concept of Bell et al.[35][36] is based on this principle and postulates a basic set of modules for high-level digital systems design.

The RTM system (manufactured by the Digital Equipment Corporation under the name PDP16) consists of about 20 different modules and a method of interconnecting modules via a common bus that carries data and timing signals for the register transfers. The modules are based on the primitive structure types defined by Bell and Newell[36] in the PMS and ISP descriptive system. This is a notational system used to describe computer structures at the information flow level (*Processor-Memory-Switch*) and the register transfer level (*Instruction Set Processor*) these ideas have been successively used for the design of the DEC PDP11 computer system. Using these concepts logical algorithms may be represented by a conventional flow-chart to specify the control flow, coupled to a data structure that holds the data and carries out processing operations; the ISP register transfer language is used to define the required transfer operations.

The four main module types are as follows:

(a) *DM-type* (data operations combined with memory). These units comprise registers and transfer gates, plus processing logic. Typical operations would be: $\leftarrow A + B$, $\leftarrow A \oplus B$, etc.; that is, an evaluation of the right-hand side of a transfer equation.

(b) *M-type* (memory). These units consist of bistable registers, flag-bistables (single bit stores), ROM and conventional random access stores.

(c) *K-type* (control). These modules control the transfer of data between registers by initiating operations in DM and M types, they are analogous to the control structure of a program. Various K-types are available, the two most important being:

    K (evoke)—used to initiate a function consisting of a date operation and register transfer. When a Ke is evoked it in turn evokes an operation in a DM unit, say, and when that function is complete (deter-

mined by a line back from the evoked unit) the Ke unit then evokes
the next K-type in the control sequence. This procedure is generally
referred to as the '*handshaking*' principle and is widely used in asynchronous operation; Fig. 10–12(a) shows the flow-chart diagram for

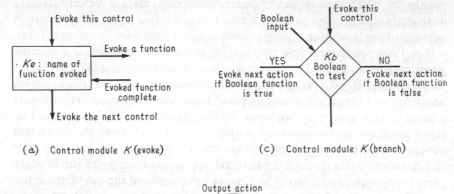

(a) Control module K (evoke)   (c) Control module K (branch)

**Fig. 10—12 Register
transfer modules**   (b) State diagram representation

the module. The action is basically that of a finite-state machine (see
Fig. 10–12(b)); that is, Ke represents an internal state with the ability
to initiate an output action (on receipt of an evoke signal) and then
make a transition to another state.

K(*branch*)—this unit provides for the routing of control flow based on
the condition of a Boolean variable; the equivalent flow-chart is
shown in Fig. 10–12(c).

(d) *T-type* (transducers). These units provide an interface to peripheral
equipment such as teletypes, paper tape readers, etc.

Thus, using these techniques the designer can flow-chart a logic process or
algorithm using standard programming methodology, which can then be
implemented directly into RTM hardware. Note the similarity between this
approach and that using register transfer languages. In both cases the system
structure is decided beforehand (in terms of register, etc.) and the control and
data paths are separated in the design process.

At the present time RTM modules are implemented in terms of standard
boards containing TTL and MSI packages, however, there is no reason why
LSI technology should not be used. The concept of RTM is obviously not a
complete solution to the general problem of design at the sub-system level,
since the designs produced tend to be rather constrained (based on conventional
computer structures) and somewhat uneconomic. However, the ideas represent
a step in the right direction, allowing designers with very little experience of

logic circuitry (but some knowledge of register operations and flow-charting) to produce sound designs.

A more generalized approach to the problem of system specification and realization is based on the idea of Petri nets[38][39], and the use of occurrence graphs.[40] The LOGOS system[41] under development at Case Western Reserve University is an attempt to utilize these ideas to develop a specification system capable of implementing logic processes in either hardware or software form.

The Petri net, in principle very similar to the state-diagram, is a directed graph which may be used to represent control structures in digital systems. As illustrated in Fig. 10–1(a), the Petri net has two kinds of nodes: *places* drawn as circles, and *transitions* drawn as bars. Each directed line, or arc, connects a place to a transition, or vice versa. In the former case the place is called an input place and in the latter, an output place of the transition. Note that concurrent, or parallel, operations are easily represented on the Petri net.

The various paths through the Petri net can be simulated by a form of party game (first suggested by Holt (38)) involving tokens and the use of these for marking places in the net. A Petri net *marking* is an assignment of tokens to each place int he net. Progress through the net, from one marking to another, is determined by the *firing* of transitions according to the following rules:

(a) A transition is enabled if all of its input places holds a token.
(b) Any enabled transition may be fired.
(c) A transition is fired by transferring tokens from input places to output places.

When Petri nets are used to represent the control structures of digital systems, asynchronous operation is assumed and control signals must be sent to and from the control and data structures. A 'ready' signal is sent from the control structure to initiate operations in the data structure (such as addition, multiplication, etc.), the data processing unit replying with an acknowledge signal when the operation has been completed. The transition firing procedure for the Petri net is consequently modified to involve four basic steps:

(a) Remove tokens from input places.
(b) Send a ready signal to the processing unit.
(c) Wait for acknowledge signal.
(d) Put tokens in output places.

Figure 10–13 shows the control and data structures for evaluating the expression $(x + y)(x^2 + y)/z^2$. The process is initiated by placing a token in place Q (equivalent to generating a 'ready' signal), the data structure responding with an acknowledge signal when the registers x, y, and z are loaded. Then, applying the transition firing rules as stated above to transitions a, b, and c, the next stages of the process are initiated; this procedure is continued until the evaluation is complete, as indicated by a token in place z.

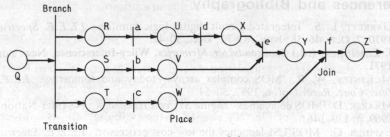

(a) Petri Net control structure

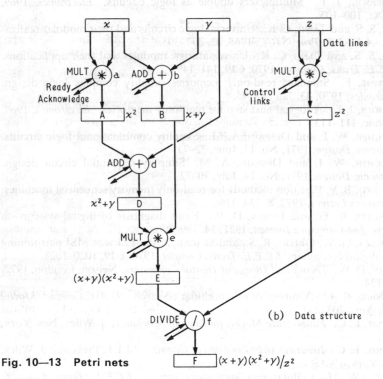

(b) Data structure

Fig. 10—13   Petri nets

It is possible to represent the individual functions of a control network (for example, a place containing a token, branches, joins, etc.) by a hardware circuit. Using these components a direct translation from a Petri net into control logic may easily be accomplished. It is interesting to note the similarity between this method and the RTM design procedure described earlier.

Though the above methods have allowed considerable insight into systems design theory, and in some cases generated potential design techniques, they all fall short of providing a general solution to the problems of system specification evaluation and implementation. It is essential for the future development of complex digital systems that such a theory be developed.

References and Bibliography

(1) GARRETT, L. S. Integrated circuit digital logic families. *I.E.E.E. Spectrum*, 1970, **7**, Oct., 46–58; Nov., 63–72; Dec., 30–42.

(2) J. EIMBINDER, (ed.) *Semiconductor Memories*. Wiley-Interscience, New York, 1971.

(3) McKINTEY, W. R. MOS complex arrays—today and tomorrow. *I.E.E.E. Inter-Conv. Record*, pt. 6, 1967, 50–54.

(4) MRAZEK, D. MOS delay lines. *Digital Systems Handbook*. NS Inter-National, 1969, p. 139–146.

(5) LAPIDUS, G. MOS/LSI launches the low-cost processor. *I.E.E.E. Spectrum*, 1972, **9**, 33–40.

(6) ANDERSON, J. L. Multiplexers double as logic circuits. *Electronics*, 1969, **42**, Oct, 100–105.

(7) YAU, S. S. and TANG, C. K. Universal logic circuits and their modular realization. *A.F.I.P.S. Proc. SJCC*, 1968, **32**, 297–305.

(8) YAU, S. S. and TANG, C. K. Universal logic modules and their applications. *I.E.E.E. Trans. Comput.*, 1970, **C19**, 141–149.

(9) KRAMME, F. Standard read-only memories simplify complex logic design. *Electronics*, 1970, **43**, Jan., 88–95.

(10) NICHOLS, J. L. A logical next step for read-only memories. *Electronics*, 1967, **40**, June, 111–113.

(11) FLETCHER, W. I. and DESPAIN, A. M. Simplify combinational logic circuits. *Electronic Design*, 1971, No. 13, June, 72–73.

(12) FLETCHER, W. I. and DESPAIN, A. M. Simplify sequential circuit design. *Electronic Design*, 1971, No. 14, July, 70–72.

(13) HOWARD, B. V. Partition methods for read-only memory sequential machines. *Electronics Letters*, 1972, **8**, 334–336.

(14) BENNETTS, R. G. and LEWIN, D. W. Fault diagnosis of digital systems—a review, *The Computer Journal*, 1971, **14**, 199–206.

(15) PODRAZA, G. V., GREGG, R. S., and SLAGER, J. R. Efficient MSI partitioning for a digital computer. *I.E.E.E. Trans. Comput.* 1970, **C19**, 1020–1028.

(16) LEWIN, D. W. *Theory and Design of Digital Computers*. Nelson, London, 1972, 131–134.

(17) MINNICK, R. C. A survey of microcellular research. *J. Ass. Comput. Mach.*, 1967, Apr., 203–241.

(18) HENNIE, F. C. *Finite-State Models for Logical Machines*. J. Wiley, New York, 1968.

(19) HENNIE, F. C. *Iterative Arrays of Logical Circuits*. M.I.T. Press and J. Wiley, New York, 1961.

(20) KAUTZ, W. H. Cellular-logic-in-memory arrays. *I.E.E.E. Trans. Comput.*, 1969, **C18**, 719–727.

(21) NICOUD, J. D. Iterative arrays for radix conversion. *I.E.E.E. Trans. Comput.*, 1971, **C20**, 1479–1489.

(22) DEAN, K. J. Conversion between binary code and some binary decimal codes. *Radio and Electronic Engineer*, 1968, **35**, 49–53.

(23) JUMP, J. R. and FRITSCHE, D. R. Microprogrammed arrays. *I.E.E.E. Trans Comput.*, 1972, **C21**, 974–984.

(24) GARDNER, P. L. Functional memory and its microprogramming implications. *I.E.E.E. Trans. Comput.*, 1971, **C20**, 764–775.

(25) WILKES, M. and STRINGER, C. Micro-programming and the design of control circuits in an electronic digital computer. *Proc. Camb. Phil. Soc.*, 1953, **49**, 230–238.

(26) ROSIN, R. Contemporary concepts of micro-programming and emulation. *Computing Surveys*, 1969, **1**, 197–212.

(27) LANGLEY, F. J. Small computer design using microprogramming and multi-function LSI arrays. *Computer Design*, 1970, **9**, April, 151–157.

(28) DAVIDOW, W. H. General purpose microcontrollers: part I economic considerations; part II design and applications. *Computer Design*, 1972, July, 75–79; August, 69–75.

(29) LEWIN, D. W. *Theory and Design of Digital Computers*. Nelson, London, 1792, Chapter 4.

(30) HUSSON, S. *Microprogramming: Principles and Practice*. Prentice Hall, Englewood Cliffs, N.J., 1970.

(31) FRIEDMAN, T. D. and YANG, S. C. Methods used in an automatic logic design generator (ALERT). *I.E.E.E. Trans. Comput.*, 1969, **C18**, 593–614.

(32) DULEY, J. R. and DIETMEYER, D. L. A digital system design language (DDL). *I.E.E.E. Trans. Comput.*, 1968, **C17**, 850–861.

(33) DULEY, J. R. and DIETMEYER, D. L. Translation of a DDL digital system specification to Boolean equations. *I.E.E.E. Trans. Comput.*, 1969, **C18**, 305–313.

(34) IVERSON, K. E. A common language for hardware, software and applications. *A.F.I.P.S. Proc. FJCC*, 1962, **21**, 345–351.

(35) BELL, C. G., EGGERT, J. L., GRASON, J., and WILLIAMS, P. The description and use of register transfer modules (RTM's). *I.E.E.E. Trans. Comput.*, 1972, **C22**, 495–500.

(36) BELL, C. G. and GRASON, J. The register transfer module design concept. *Computer Design*, 1971, May, 87–94.

(37) BELL, C. G. and NEWELL, A. *The PMS and ISP descriptive system for computer structures*. *A.F.I.P.S. Proc. SJCC*, 1970, **36**, 351–374.

(38) HOLT, A. W. *Information System Theory Project*. Applied Data Research Tech. Report No. RADC-TR-68-305, Sept. 1968.

(39) PATEL, S. S. and DENNIS, J. B. The description and realization of digital systems. *Proc. Comp. Con. 72 Sixth Annual I.E.E.E. Computer Society International Conference*, 1972, pp. 223–226.

(40) HOLT, A. W. *Introduction to occurrence system*. *Associative Information Techniques*, E. L. Jacks (ed.) Elsevier, New York, 1971, 175–203.

(41) HEATH, F. G. The LOGOS system. *I.E.E. Conference, CAD*, I.E.E. Conf. Pubn No. 86, 1972, 225–230.

(42) TANG, C. K. A storage cell reduction technique for ROS design. *A.F.I.P.S. Proc. FJCC*, 1971, **39**, 163–169.

(43) THURBER, K. J. and BERG, R. O. *Universal logic modules implemented using LSI memory techniques*. *A.F.I.P.S. Procs. FJCC*, 1971, **39**, 177–194.

(44) SCHMID, H. and BUSCH, D. Generate functions for discrete data. *Electronic Design*, 1970, Sept., 42–47.

(45) TOY, W. N. Modular LSI control logic design with error detection. *I.E.E.E Trans. Comput.*, 1971, **C20**, 161–166.

(46) DENNIS, S. F. and SMITH, M. G. LSI implications for future design and architecture. *A.F.I.P.S. Proc. SJCC*, 1972, **40**, 343–351.

(47) DAVIDOW, W. H. The rationale for logic from semiconductor memory. *A.F.I.P.S. Proc. SJCC*, 1972, **40**, 353–358.

Appendix—Introduction to computers and computer programming

A-1 Introduction

The fundamental principles of organizing a digital computer were set forth by Babbage[1] in the early part of the nineteenth century. As a result of building calculating machines to compute mathematical tables, Babbage conceived the idea of an *analytical engine* and, though it was never built, laid the foundation for modern automatic computing machines. These ideas were later extended, though not changed in principle, by Von Neuman[2] who applied them to the design of an actual machine. A digital computer consists of the following functional elements:

1. A *store* or memory for numbers and instructions.
2. An *arithmetic unit*, where arithmetical operations are performed on the numbers.
3. A *control unit* for controlling the operations of the machine, and ensuring that they take place in the correct sequence.
4. An *input/output* unit, used to transfer data into, and out of, the computer store.

Figure A-1 shows a block schematic diagram for the digital computer.

In general, a numerical problem is solved using a digital computer by first breaking down the calculation into a number of discrete arithmetic operations, such as add, subtract, etc. These operations, together with any necessary organizing functions such as input, output, register transfers, etc., are then arranged to form a *program* of instructions for the computer. This

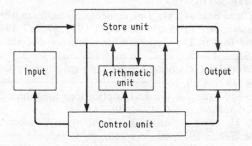

Fig. A-1 Computer block diagram

program, suitably coded in a binary form, is then written into the computer store using the input and control units.

Instructions are read down from the store in sequence and obeyed, again under the action of the control unit, using the arithmetic unit as and when required. The store contains both program and data, plus 'working-space' and storage for results. The final operation is to output the results of the calculation via the output unit. Note the similarity between machine and manual computation. In the latter, a desk calculating machine could be regarded as the arithmetic unit, books of tables, computing procedure and note-pads as the store, and the control unit, of course, is the human computor.

A–2 Instruction and number representation

In a digital computer, the program instructions and numbers (operands) are stored together in the store unit. Each location of the store contains a fixed number of bits (called a *computer word*) and is allocated an absolute store address. The computer words, the length of which can vary from 18–40 bits for practical machines, are used to represent *both* computer instructions and data [see Fig. A–2(a)]. The *instruction* word is divided up into an *order*, and an *address* section. The order part has sufficient bits to allocate a binary or octal code to all the *machine code orders;* likewise, the range of the address section is such as to enable all the store locations to be specified directly. Thus in our example, assuming an 18-bit wordlength, we can address 4096 (2^{12}) store locations, and represent up to 32 (2^5) machine code orders. The function of the remaining bit, called a *modifier*, will be explained later. Numbers

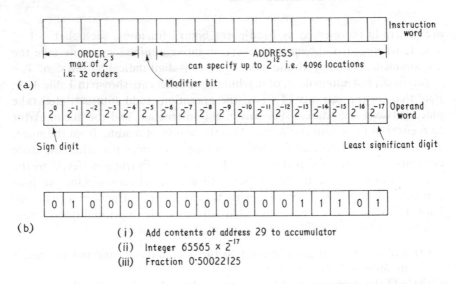

(a)

    |←   ORDER$_5$ →| |←————————— ADDRESS ———————————→|
       max. of 2^5 can specify up to 2^{12} i.e. 4096 locations
       i.e. 32 orders

(b)

(i)   Add contents of address 29 to accumulator
(ii)   Integer 65565×2^{-17}
(iii)   Fraction 0.50022125

Fig. A–2 Computer word format

Table A–1 Machine code orders

Order code in octal	Mnemonic	Description of order
00	IN	Input character from paper tape to accumulator
01	OUT	Output character from accumulator to paper tape
02		
03		
04		
05		
06		
07		
10	ADD	Add contents of address specified in instruction to accumulator. Location specified is unchanged
11	SUB	Subtract contents of address specified in instruction from accumulator, location specified is unchanged
12	FET	Fetch contents of address specified in instruction to accumulator, location specified is unchanged
13	STR	Store contents of accumulator in address specified in instruction, accumulator remains unchanged
14	COM	Take 2's complement of accumulator contents
15	SHFL	Shift accumulator left N places (N specified by address digits)
16	SHFR	Shift accumulator right N places (N specified by address digits)

are generally represented as fixed-point binary fractions, such that $-1 \leq x < 1$, where x is the binary number; negative numbers normally take the 2's complement form with the most significant digit indicating the sign.

A typical, but minimal set, of machine code orders are shown in Table A–1; note that, in the majority of cases, the operations (add subtract, etc.) take place between the address specified in the instruction and the accumulator (a register in the arithmetic unit). Also the action of reading from the store, i.e. in the orders fetch, add, subtract, collate, etc., does not affect the store contents, which remain unchanged. However, the instruction 'fetch' to the accumulator (or 'store' in the computer store) always overwrites the previous contents. Computers operating with this type of instruction format are known as *single-address* machines. It is also possible to get multiple-address machines, where two addresses are specified, for example:

(a) add the contents of address 1 to the accumulator, and put the result in address 2, or

(b) add the contents of address 1 *and* address 2 to the accumulator.

Table A–1 continued

17	COL	Collate accumulator with contents of the address specified in instruction, location unchanged
20	ADDM	Add + 1 to modifier register
21	FETM	Fetch contents of modifier to accumulator modifier unchanged
22	STRM	Store contents of accumulator in modifier, accumulator unchanged
23	LINK	Store contents of instruction register in address specified in instruction and jump to address specified + 1
24		
25		
26		
27		
30	JMP	Jump to address specified in instruction and take next instruction from there
31	JMPN	Jump to address specified in instruction if accumulator negative, otherwise take next instruction in sequence
32	JMPP	Jump to address specified in instruction if accumulator positive, otherwise take next instruction in sequence
33	JMPO	Jump to address specified in instruction if accumulator zero, otherwise take next instruction in sequence
34	STOP	Stop
35	JMPM	Jump to address specified in instruction if modifier
36		zero, otherwise take next instruction in sequence
37		

The instruction and operand words are stored in the computer as simple binary patterns and, as we shall see later, their interpretation depends on what part of the computer they are routed to. Figure A–2(b) shows the computer representation of the instruction 'add the contents of address 29 to the accumulator', note that it can also represent the binary integer 65565×2^{-17}, and the binary fraction 0·50022125.

We can now make use of these ideas to understand how a simple computer program is written. Suppose we wish to write a program to add two numbers together, say x_1 and x_2; the program is shown in Table A–2. The program instructions are stored in the computer in locations 1000–1003 (octal notation), and the data in locations 1004 and 1005; the answer should be stored away in location 0022. Note that we must specify exactly where the instructions and data are held in the computer store. Furthermore, it is the binary equivalent of the machine code instructions, represented in Table A–2 in octal code, that would actually be stored in the computer. At this stage it is best to ignore the obvious question of how the program got into the computer

Table A–2 Simple computer program

	Store location	Instruction		Description
Block address	1000	12	1004	Fetch x_1 to accumulator
	1001	10	1005	Add x_2 to accumulator
	1002	13	0022	Store accumulator
	1003	34	0000	Stop
	1004	x_1		
	1005	x_2		

store in the first place, and simply assume that it is there. The execution of the program is apparent from Table A–2: the first instruction brings x_1 (the contents of store location 1004) to the accumulator, the next instruction adds x_2 (the contents of location 1005), the result, $x_1 + x_2$, is stored away in location 0022 and the computer comes to a halt. We now describe in some detail how the computer performs these operations.

A–3 Digital computer operation

The block diagram of a parallel digital computer is shown in Fig. A–3. The instructions and data forming the computer program are initially placed in the computer store in the locations specified by the programmer. The selection and reading of a store location is performed by the store address unit, which takes the address either from the control register or the instruction register and, after decoding, initiates a store read/write cycle (on receipt of an appropriate control waveform), and places the contents of the selected location into the memory register. Information may be read into the store by transferring the data to the memory register, and, after addressing the store address unit with the store location, initiating a 'write' cycle only.

Arithmetic operations are performed by the arithmetic unit (parallel full-adder stages) in conjunction with the accumulator and/or the auxiliary register X. Shifting operations are executed by means of shifting gates incorporated in the common highway. This device is peculiar to parallel computers, and consists simply of all the common interconnections of the input and output terminals associated with the register gates. All the registers in the computer would be of the set-reset d.c. bistable variety, and, except for the instruction register, would be capable of storing a computer word (18 bits in this case). The instruction register, or sequence control register, is equal in length to the address part of the instruction word. To effect a transfer between one register and another, say the memory register and the accumulator, the output and input gates of the respective registers would be opened simultaneously, and the data allowed to flow round the common highway. The process of shifting is really one of re-routing the data on the common highway, by gating up or down the register input connections. Note that it is not possible to do this without using an intermediate buffer register (say the X register), as it is physically impossible to open both input and output gates of a register at the same time.

The program control unit governs the sequential operation and decoding of instructions, and provides overall machine control. The clock pulse generator (normally a crystal controlled oscillator and a pulse-squarer circuit) produces a succession of timing (clock) pulses, which are counted by the operations counter and used to provide signals which control the operations necessary to obey a particular instruction, as decoded by the order decoding matrix.

In order to execute the program, the computer must read down and obey each instruction in the correct sequence. The internal sequence of the machine alternates between a '*read*' *cycle*, when the instruction is read down from store and transferred to the control register, and an '*obey*' *cycle*, when the order is decoded and obeyed. A computer operating in this way is generally referred to as a *two-beat* machine.

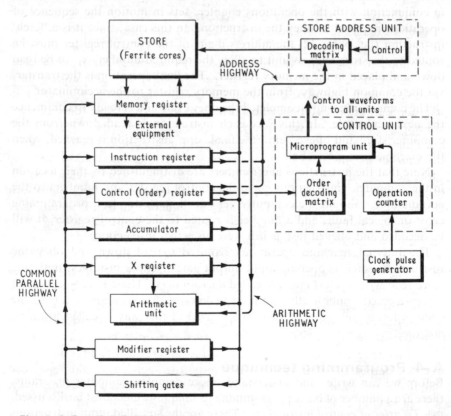

Fig. A–3 Parallel digital computer

Let us now explain how the simple program described in the last section would be performed. The first step is to place the address of the location in which the first instruction is stored (i.e. 1000) in the instruction register; we will assume that this may be done manually using a keyboard. The machine is now started and it immediately goes into the 'read' cycle, this has the effect of transferring the contents of the instruction register to the store address unit (via the address highway) where it is decoded. This results in the contents of the location (i.e. the first instruction) being placed in the memory register, and then transferred via the common highway to the order register. During the time it takes to read down the instruction (the read/write time of the store is approximately 1–10 μs) the contents of the instruction register are passed through the arithmetic unit and +1 added in to the least significant digit position. This ensures that the next instruction will be taken from location 1001 in the following read cycle, thus ensuring the sequential read-out of the instructions. The computer is now ready to enter the obey cycle, and the first step is to transfer the order digits of the control register to the order decoding matrix in the control unit. Here the order is decoded and, in conjunction with the operations counter, sets in motion the sequence of operations required to obey the instruction. In this case, since it is a 'fetch' instruction (i.e. order 12) the address digits of the control register must be routed to the store address unit to allow the required number, x_1, to be read down and placed in the memory register. The final operation is the transfer, via the common highway, from the memory register to the accumulator.

The computer has now completed the obey cycle and is ready to commence the next read cycle. In this way each instruction is read down from the computer store and obeyed until the final 'stop' instruction is reached, when the machine comes to a halt.

Note that the instructions and numbers are distinguished by their location in the computer—instructions go to the control register and numbers to the accumulator. Should the computer get out of step, due to a programming error or logical fault, and a number is routed to the control register, it will be decoded and obeyed just as if it were an actual instruction.

The internal machine operations required to read down and obey the instructions, such as opening input/output gates, setting bistables, initiating store read/write cycles, etc., are called *micro-orders*. These micro-orders can be represented symbolically and used to describe the execution of a machine code order, a collection of such orders used in this way is called a *micro-program*.[3]

A–4 Programming technique

Before we can write, and understand, more complex computer programs, there are a number of basic programming techniques which must be discussed.
(a) *Transfer of control instructions*. These are the so called jump instructions

(see Table A–1) and they enable the normal sequential operation of the computer to be bypassed. The action of obeying the instruction replaces the contents of the instruction register with the address part of the jump instruction. Consequently, the next instruction is not taken in sequence, but from the new address specified in the jump instruction. This is how the computer program may be started, by manually obeying a jump instruction to the start of the program.

There are a number of such instructions—the one described above is called an unconditional jump. Others depend on the state of the accumulator (or modifier) registers, whether zero, positive or negative, etc. This is the conditional transfer of control operation, which allows the computer to discriminate between various courses of action.

(b) *Order modification.* One of the most powerful concepts of digital computer programming is the fact that a computer can modify its own instructions. This may be done very simply by fetching an instruction to the accumulator, where all the normal computer orders may be performed on it. One of the main reasons for requiring order modification is to save storage space in the computer. For example, suppose we wish to add ten numbers together, this may be done by simply extending the program of Table A–2 in a linear fashion by adding nine extra add instructions, giving a total of 12 instructions for the program.

An alternative way of doing this is shown in Table A–3(a). In this case, after each number has been added to the sum store (location 2020), the actual 'add' instruction in location 1001 (i.e. 10 2021) is brought to the accumulator. A constant is then subtracted, which is in fact equivalent to the last order to be obeyed (i.e. 10 2031), and if the result is zero, as determined by the jump instruction, we know the program has been completed. If it is not zero, however, we must add back what we subtracted, plus an additional 1 to ensure that the next number in sequence is added to the sum store. The modified instruction is then returned to its correct place in the program, and the process is repeated. The reader is advised to work carefully through all these program examples, as this is the only way of becoming completely familiar with the ideas involved. The reader is also warned that all the instructions, including addresses and constants are in the *octal* notation.

In this program we have established the idea of a loop, that is, a number of instructions (in this case nine) which are performed many times during the execution of a program. The *loop constant* determines the number of times this repetition actually happens, and it is necessary to perform a *loop test* each time the set of instructions is obeyed.

The number of program instructions required still totals 12 as before, but the program may be extended to add together any number of variables simply by changing the program constants. However, the running time of

Table A–3

(a)   Add together ten numbers – direct order modification

Store location		Instruction		Comment
→1000	12	2020		Fetch x_1 to accumulator
1001	10	2021		Add $x_2, x_3, ..., x_{10}$ to accumulator
loop 1002	13	2020		Store $(x_1 + x_2)$, $(x_1 + x_2 + x_3)$, etc.
1003	12	1001		Fetch add instruction to accumulator
1004	11	1012	Loop test	Subtract constant (10 2031)
1005	33	1011		Jump if accumulator zero
1006	10	1013		Add constant (10 2032)
1007	13	1001	Modifi- cation	Replace instruction back into program
1010	30	1000		Jump back to start of program
1011	34			Stop
1012	10	2031		Loop constants
1013	10	2032		
⋮				
2020	x_1			Numbers to be added
2021	x_2			
⋮				
2031	x_{10}			

(b)   Add together ten numbers – modifier registers

Store location		Instruction		Comment
1001	12	1011		Fetch constant – 10 octal to accumulator
1002	22			Store accumulator in modifier
1003	12	2020		Fetch x_1 to accumulator
loop →1004	10	2031/M		Add $x_2, x_3, ..., x_{10}$
1005	35	1010		Jump if modifier zero, (loop test)
1006	20			Add + 1 to modifier register (count)
1007	30	1004		Jump back to start of program
→1010	34			Stop
1011	37	7770/M		10 octal as pseudo-order (loop constant)
⋮				
2020	x_1			Numbers to be added
2021	x_2			
⋮				
2031	x_{10}			

the program has been considerably altered. In the simple linear program there are only 12 instructions to be performed, but if the modification program is used, the loop instructions will be repeated nine times, giving a total of 82 instructions. Thus it is essential to keep the loop as small as possible, and in some cases where time is more important than storage space it may be necessary to resort to a simple linear program. The efficiency of the order modification process can be considerably improved if modification registers are available. The instruction word described earlier contained a modifier bit, and there is also a modification register included in the computer hardware. The action of the modifier bit, which may be used with any instruction (e.g. written as 10 2031/M), is to indicate to the computer control unit that the contents of the modifier register must be *added* to the instruction *before* it is obeyed. Thus, in this case, before performing the instruction 10 2031/M, the contents of the modifier register, say 24, would be added to the instruction, and obeyed as 10 2055. The instruction itself is left unchanged in the computer store. To facilitate the use of this register, orders for transfers between the accumulator, conditional jumps, and counting (with respect to the modifier register) are included in the machine code (see Table A–1). A good idea of the programming power of a computer can be gained from the number of modification registers it possesses.

If we rewrite our program example of adding together ten numbers, using the modifier register [see Table A–3(b)], we get an immediate improvement in both storage space and running time. The preliminary operations in the program are concerned with setting the loop constant (-10) in the modifier register, and this must be refurnished each time the program is entered. The 'add' instruction, 10 2031/M, is modified each time round the loop; note that the loop count is negative, so that the first 'add' instruction will be obeyed as 10 2021. The next step is the loop test performed on the modifier register and, if non-zero, $+1$ is added to the modifier (thereby setting up a count -10, -7, -6, . . . , 0) and the process repeated.

(c) *Sub-routine links.* During the course of a large program it is often necessary to perform the same set of program instructions many times over, for example in navigational problems for the evaluation of sines and cosines. It is obviously possible to write this set of instructions into the main program each time the operation is required, but this is very wasteful of storage space.

Table A–4 Subroutine link

	Store location	Instruction		Comment
Main program	1000	12	2043	Variable fetched to accumulator
	1001	23	3000	Jump to subroutine (link)
	1002	13	1245	
	1003	30	2000	
	:			
Sub-routine	3000	(	)	Blank location to hold link address
	3001			
	3002			
	3003			
	3004	12	3000	Fetch link address to accumulator
	3005	22		Store accumulator in modifier
	3006	30	1/M	Jump back to main program

A better method is to write the sine/cosine program as a separate program, called a *sub-routine*, and let the main program jump into this sub-routine each time the calculation is required. This means that some method must be devised to ensure that the sub-routine jumps back into the main program at the right point, this is known as the *sub-routine link*. The process is illustrated in Table A–4; the function of the link instruction (order 23) is to place the current contents of the instruction register (in our example, 1001) into the location specified in the instruction address, which is usually the first instruction of the sub-routine (i.e. in this case, location 3000), and then jump to the next instruction (location 3001). When the sub-routine is completed, the link address is placed in the modifier register, and a modified jump instruction back to the main program is performed, i.e. 30 1/M, obeyed as 30 1002. An alternative method, when there are a number of modifier registers available in the machine, is to place the link address directly into one of these registers.

A–5 Input compilers

We now discuss how the program is fed into the computer and stored away. All computers have some form of rudimentary input program, prewired into the main store, or a subsidiary store, which inputs paper tape punched in a pure binary code. The punched paper tape equipment normally uses a 5–8 hole teleprinter code, which is a normal binary-coded alpha-numeric system. Thus a five-bit word, for example, would be allocated to all the numbers, alphabetical characters and control symbols, required in the programming procedure.

Consider the instruction, 12 1004. To convert this to its binary equivalent (as stored in the computer) we simply write down the binary equivalent of the octal numbers:

$$01 \quad 010 \quad 0 \quad 001 \quad 000 \quad 000 \quad 100$$
$$1 \quad\quad 2 \quad\quad 1 \quad\quad 0 \quad\quad 0 \quad\quad 4$$

remembering the modifier bit between the order and address. This 18-bit

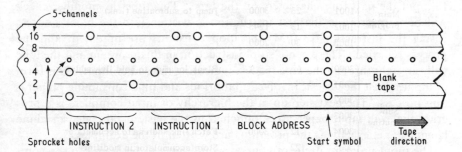

Fig. A–4 Binary input tape

binary word is then divided into four five-bit groups starting from the least significant:

$$00010 \quad 10000 \quad 10000 \quad 00100$$

The telecode character equivalent of each five-bit group is then punched on to the paper tape, most significant group (left-hand side) first.

It is first necessary, however, to tell the computer where to store the program, and this is done by making the first group of four characters on the tape the *block address*, that is, the address where the first instruction is to be stored. Suppose, for example, this was location 1000 (see Table A–2), then the first block would be

$$00 \quad 000 \quad 0 \quad 001 \quad 000 \quad 000 \quad 000$$

that is   00000   00000   10000   00000

Figure A–4 shows the punched paper tape corresponding to the above examples:

block address   1000
                 12   1004
                 10   1005

The very first character on the tape is 11111, and is used to indicate the start of the input tape.

The flow-diagram for the binary input program is shown in Fig. A–5. The paper tape is placed in the tape reader with the blank tape under the reading head, and the program set running. The tape is read, character by character, until the first non-zero character is found—the all 1's group. Then the next four characters on the tape are read into the accumulator one at a time and shifted five places to the left, in this way the complete 18-bit word is assembled in the accumulator. The next step is to check the modifier register (cleared at the start of the program) for zero contents; if it is clear, the contents of the accumulator (which must be the block address) are transferred to the modifier register. The loop counts are reset, and the program jumps back to input the next four characters on the tape. This time the modifier check will be non-zero and the first instruction is written into the block address (using the instruction 13 0/M) the loop constants are up-dated, and the process repeated. There is no 'stop' instruction in this program and the tape will run right through the tape reader, indicating the end of input. This form of input, albeit the fastest, involves a laborious and time-consuming preparation process. The next step up in the hierarchy of input compilers is a program that will input paper tapes punched in the basic octal coded machine language, i.e. exactly as the programs are written in the examples.

The input program itself, of course, would have to be read into the computer using the pure binary input routine. Programming in pure machine

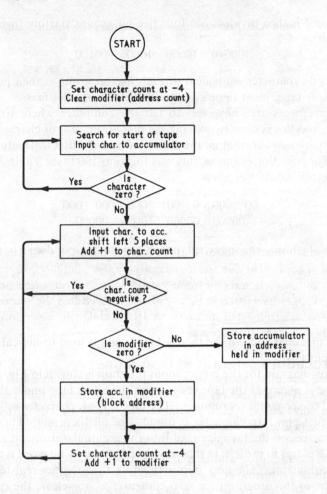

Fig. A–5 Flow diagram of binary input program

code, however, has many disadvantages, but the chief nuisance is that of absolute store addresses. This means that program modifications (e.g. the insertion of additional instructions) require in most cases a complete re-organization of the program. Also, sub-routines have to be placed in any convenient part of the store, and again without some form of relative addressing (with respect, say, to a block address) the program needs to be rewritten each time.

As a result of these inherent handicaps, most present day computers have some form of *symbolic assembly program* as the basic computer language code. In this type of input program, a *mnemonic* code is substituted for the numeric code with a simple one-to-one correspondence to it (see Table A–1). Furthermore, all the store locations are referred to by code words, *identifiers*

Table A–5 Add together ten numbers—symbolic code

Program	Sum of 10 numbers
Data	X1, X2, X3, X4, X5, X6, X7, X8, X9, X10,
	CONS: = – 8
begin	FET CONS
	STRM
START)	FET X1
	ADD X10/MOD
	JMPM
	ADDM
	JMP START
	STOP
end	

or labels, which must be declared at the start of the program. The allocation of storage space is also done automatically by the assembly program, which will print out a dictionary of code words with their absolute addresses if required. Programs written in this symbolic code, called the *source* program (Table A–5), are translated into basic machine code (the *object* program) by an assembly or translator program.

A–6 Procedure orientated languages

Though the use of symbolic assembly programs makes machine code programming very much easier, it is still necessary to program each step in detail. In some cases, e.g. in non-numerical problems, this is necessary if maximum efficiency is desired, but for a large number of mathematical problems (mainly 'one off' calculations) the program running time is not so important as the program preparation time. Moreover, programming mathematical problems in machine-code, in particular using fixed-point arithmetic, can give rise to some nasty scaling problems. Many of these difficulties can be overcome, however, by using floating-point arithmetic, either in hardware or software form.

Another area which often causes trouble is the organization of input and output routines, and the general control of peripheral equipment. In a large program, keeping track of store allocation, up-dating of loop counts, subroutine organization (in short, the general 'housekeeping' procedures) also give rise to many problems.

In order to overcome these difficulties, and in an attempt to make programming easier and available to a larger section of the technical and scientific community, high level computer languages have been developed. These computer languages, called *auto-codes* and *procedure orientated languages* (such as ALGOL, FORTRAN, etc.) allow the program operations to be written in a more easily understood form. The computer itself, or rather the

Table A-6 Example of an ALGOL program

```
comment    Sum of 10 numbers;
begin      Integer x, Sum;
           Integer array  n [1 : 10] ;
           Sum : = 0;
           for  x : = 1  step 1  until  10  do
           begin  Read  n[x];
                    Sum : = Sum + n [x] ;
           end;
           Print  Sum

end
```

software compiler, assembles the necessary machine code instructions required to perform a particular operation. In this way, mathematical problems may be expressed using standard mathematical expressions, including both real and integer numbers. Complete input/output routines may be initiated (called up) by simply writing 'read' or 'print' in the program, and all the necessary 'housekeeping' requirements are organized automatically by the compiler. The description and use of procedure orientated languages is outside the scope of this appendix,[1] but an example of ALGOL programming is shown in Table A-6.

References and bibliography

(1) MORRISON, P. and MORRISON, E. *Charles Babbage and his calculating engines*. Dover Publications, New York, 1961.

(2) TAUB, A. H. (Ed). *John Von Neuman—collected works*. Vol. V. Pergamon Press, Oxford, 1963.

(3) LEWIN, D. *Theory and design of digital computers*. Nelson, London, 1972.

(4) HIGMAN, B. *A comparative study of programming languages*. Macdonald, London, 1968.

(5) EADIE, D. *Introduction to the basic computer*. Prentice-Hall, Englewood Cliffs, N.J., 1968.

(6) NASHELSKY, L. *Introduction to digital computer technology*. Wiley, New York, 1972.

(7) RICHARDS, R. K. *Digital design*. Wiley Interscience, New York, 1971.

(8) KNUTH, D. E. *The art of computer programming*. Vol. 1: *Fundamental algorithms*. Addison-Wesley, Reading, Mass., 1972.

Answers with worked solutions

Chapter 1

1-1 (a) It is best to convert the integral and fractional parts separately. To find the integer equivalent we successively divide by 2, noting the remainder each time, the binary equivalent appears least significant digit first.

	2	2397		
		1198	1	L.S.D.
		599	0	
		299	1	
		149	1	
		74	1	
		37	0	
		18	1	
		9	0	
		4	1	
		2	0	
		1	0	
			1	

Thus, binary number is 100101011101

The fraction is converted by successively multiplying by 2, and noting the integer value each time.

			0·55
M.S.D.	1	1·1	
	0	0·2	
	0	0·4	
	0	0·8	
	1	1·6	
	1	1·2	
	0	0·4	

Thus, binary number is 0·1000110011

Final binary number   100101011101·1000110011 recurring

(b) Proceeding as (a) for binary fractions gives:

			0·79
M.S.D.	1	1·58	
	1	1·16	
	0	0·32	
	0	0·64	
	1	1·28	
	0	0·56	
	1	1·12	
	0	0·24	
	0	0·48	
	0	0·96	

Binary number is   0·11001010001, etc.   1   1·92

(c) Negative numbers are usually represented in either 2's or 1's complement form. First convert 90 to binary equivalent as in (a).

```
Divide by 2 | 90
             45  0
             22  1
             11  0
              5  1
              2  1
              1  0
              1
```

Thus, binary number is 1011010

We must allow one digit position to act as the sign digit. Thus, using eight-bit numbers, we have 01011010. The 1's complement form is the inverse, 10100101, and the 2's complement form is obtained by adding 1 to this at the least significant end, i.e. 10100110.

1-2 (a) As before, convert the binary fractions and integers separately. The decimal integer may be obtained by successively dividing by binary ten, and mentally converting the remainder at each stage to decimal equivalent.

```
            1001
     1010)1011011
          1010
          ────
          1011
          1010
          ────
             1
```

remainder 1 (L.S.D.)

```
     1010)1001
```

remainder 9

Decimal integer is 91

The fraction is converted by successive multiplication by binary ten, and mentally converting the integer at each stage to decimal.

```
      0·101
    1010·
    ─────
      1·01
    101·00
    ──────
    110·01      integer 6 (M.S.D.)
```

```
      0·01
    1010·
    ─────
      0·1
     10·0
    ─────
     10·1      integer 2
```

```
      0·1
    1010·
    ─────
      1·0
    100·0
    ─────
    101·0   integer 5
```

Decimal fraction is 0·625

Thus, decimal number is 91·625

(b) Proceeding as (a) for binary integer
conversion we have:

$$
\begin{array}{r}
10010101 \\
1010\overline{)10111010111} \\
1010 \\
\hline
1101 \\
1010 \\
\hline
1101 \\
1010 \\
\hline
1111 \\
1010 \\
\hline
101
\end{array}
\qquad
\begin{array}{r}
1110 \\
1010\overline{)10010101} \\
1010 \\
\hline
10001 \\
1010 \\
\hline
1110 \\
1010 \\
\hline
1001
\end{array}
$$

remainder 5 (L.S.D.)   remainder 9

$$
\begin{array}{r}
1 \\
1010\overline{)1110} \\
1010 \\
\hline
100
\end{array}
\qquad
1010\overline{)1}
$$

remainder 4   remainder 1

Thus, decimal number is 1495

(c) Converting the binary fraction as in
(a) we have:

$$
\begin{array}{r}
0\cdot111011 \\
1010\cdot \\
\hline
1\cdot11011 \\
111\cdot011 \\
\hline
1001\cdot00111
\end{array}
\qquad
\begin{array}{r}
0\cdot00111 \\
1010\cdot \\
\hline
0\cdot0111 \\
1\cdot11 \\
\hline
10\cdot0011
\end{array}
$$

integer 9 (M.S.D.)   integer 2

$$
\begin{array}{r}
0\cdot0011 \\
1010\cdot \\
\hline
0\cdot011 \\
1\cdot1 \\
\hline
1\cdot111
\end{array}
\qquad
\begin{array}{r}
0\cdot111 \\
1010\cdot \\
\hline
1\cdot11 \\
111\cdot00 \\
\hline
1000\cdot11
\end{array}
$$

integer 1   integer 8

$$
\begin{array}{r}
0\cdot11 \\
1010\cdot \\
\hline
1\cdot1 \\
110\cdot \\
\hline
111\cdot1
\end{array}
\qquad
\begin{array}{r}
0\cdot1 \\
1010\cdot0 \\
\hline
1\cdot0 \\
100\cdot0 \\
\hline
101\cdot0
\end{array}
$$

Decimal fraction is 0·921875   integer 7   integer 5

1-3 (a) The number 149 would be represented as:

$$00001 \quad 00100 \quad 11001$$

(b) To represent 149 in a Hamming code requires 15 bits, thus:

1	2	3	4	5	6	7	8	9	10	11	12	13	14	15
C	C	M	C	M	M	M	C	M	M	M	M	M	M	M

Decimal 149 has the binary equivalent 10010101. The parity checks are

(1) 1, 3, 5, 7, 9, 11, 13, 15;

(2) 2, 3; 6, 7; 10, 11; 14, 15;

(3) 4, 5, 6, 7; 12, 13, 14, 15;

(4) 8, 9, 10, 11, 12, 13, 14, 15;

Inserting the even-parity bits results in

$$010100110010101$$

(c) Diamond $3n + 2$ code representation is

$$00101 \quad 01110 \quad 11101 \quad \text{as binary coded groups}$$
$$or \quad 111000001, \text{ i.e. } 3 \times 149 + 2 = 449$$

(d) 10001   10100   01010

1-4 (a) Error in third group.

(b) Performing parity checks we have

(1) digits 1, 3, 5, 7.	incorrect 1
(2) digits 2, 3; 6, 7.	correct 0
(3) digits 4, 5, 6, 7.	incorrect 1

Message in error and digit 5 should be a 0

(c) Decimal equivalent is 106, subtract 2 gives 104, divide by 3 leaves remainder of 2, therefore error occurred.

Chapter 2

2-1 (a) $F = (A + B + C)(\bar{A} + B + C)(\bar{A} + B + \bar{C})$

$= (A\bar{A} + AB + AC + \bar{A}B + BB + BC + \bar{A}C + BC + CC)(\bar{A} + B + \bar{C})$

$= [C(A + \bar{A} + B + 1) + B(A + 1) + \bar{A}B][\bar{A} + B + \bar{C}]$

$= [C + B(1 + \bar{A})][\bar{A} + B + \bar{C}]$

$= (C + B)(\bar{A} + B + \bar{C})$ \qquad (from $A\bar{A} = 0$, $A + 1 = 1$, $AA = A$,

$\qquad\qquad\qquad\qquad\qquad\qquad\qquad\qquad A + \bar{A} = 1$, $A \cdot 1 + A$.)

Table S–1 Problem 2–1(a)				
A	B	C	$\bar{A}C + B$	F
0	0	0	0	0
0	0	1	1	1
0	1	0	1	1
0	1	1	1	1
1	0	0	0	0
1	0	1	0	0
1	1	0	1	1
1	1	1	1	1

Table S–2 Problem 2–1(b)					
A	B	C	D	$\bar{C}D + A\bar{B} + \bar{A}D$	F
0	0	0	0	0	0
0	0	0	1	1	1
0	0	1	0	0	0
0	0	1	1	1	1
0	1	0	0	0	0
0	1	0	1	1	1
0	1	1	0	0	0
0	1	1	1	1	1
1	0	0	0	1	1
1	0	0	1	1	1
1	0	1	0	1	1
1	0	1	1	1	1
1	1	0	0	0	0
1	1	0	1	1	1
1	1	1	0	0	0
1	1	1	1	0	0

$\qquad F = \bar{A}C + BC + C\bar{C} + \bar{A}B + BB + B\bar{C}$

$\qquad\quad = \bar{A}C + B(C + \bar{C} + 1) + \bar{A}B$

Thus $F = \bar{A}C + B$

The truth-table is shown in Table S–1.

(b) \qquad $F = \bar{A}\bar{C}D + A\bar{C}D + A\bar{B}\bar{C} + A\bar{B}C + \bar{A}CD$

$\qquad\qquad = \bar{C}D(\bar{A} + A) + A\bar{B}(C + \bar{C}) + \bar{A}CD$

$\qquad\qquad = \bar{C}D + A\bar{B} + \bar{A}D(C + \bar{C})$ \qquad (add redundant $\bar{A}\bar{C}D$ term)

$\qquad F = \bar{C}D + A\bar{B} + \bar{A}D$

The truth-table is shown in Table S–2.

(c) $\quad F_1 = D(\bar{A} + B + C + \bar{D})(A + B + \bar{C} + \bar{D})$

$\qquad = D(\bar{A}A + \bar{A}B + \bar{A}\bar{C} + \bar{A}\bar{D} + AB + BB + B\bar{C} + B\bar{D} + AC$
$\qquad\quad + BC + C\bar{C} + C\bar{D} + A\bar{D} + B\bar{D} + \bar{C}\bar{D} + \bar{D}\bar{D})$

$\qquad = D(B + \bar{A}\bar{C} + AC + \bar{D})$ (from $A\bar{A} = 0, A + AB = A$ and $AA = A$)

Thus, $\quad F_1 = DB + \bar{A}\bar{C}D + ACD$

Again, $\quad F_2 = (D + A\bar{C} + \bar{A}C)(\bar{A}\bar{C} + BD + AC)$

$\qquad = \bar{A}\bar{C}D + BDD + ACD + A\bar{C}\bar{A}\bar{C} + A\bar{C}BD + A\bar{C}AC$
$\qquad\quad + \bar{A}C\bar{A}\bar{C} + \bar{A}CBD + \bar{A}CAC$

$\qquad = \bar{A}\bar{C}D + BD + ACD + AB\bar{C}D + \bar{A}BCD$

$\qquad = \bar{A}\bar{C}D + BD(1 + A\bar{C} + \bar{A}C) + ACD$

Thus, $\quad F_2 = \bar{A}\bar{C}D + BD + ACD$

The truth-table for these functions is shown in Table S–3.

2-2 (a) Using De Morgan's theorem we have:

$$T = \overline{[\overline{ab} . a]} . \overline{[\overline{ab} . b]} = (\overline{ab} . a) + (\overline{ab} . b)$$

$$= (\bar{a} + \bar{b})a + (\bar{a} + \bar{b})b$$

$$= a\bar{a} + a\bar{b} + \bar{a}b + b\bar{b}$$

Thus, $\qquad\qquad\qquad T = a\bar{b} + \bar{a}b$

Table S–3
Problem 2–1(c)

A	B	C	D	F_1	F_2
0	0	0	0	0	0
0	0	0	1	1	1
0	0	1	0	0	0
0	0	1	1	0	0
0	1	0	0	0	0
0	1	0	1	1	1
0	1	1	0	0	0
0	1	1	1	1	1
1	0	0	0	0	0
1	0	0	1	0	0
1	0	1	0	0	0
1	0	1	1	1	1
1	1	0	0	0	0
1	1	0	1	1	1
1	1	1	0	0	0
1	1	1	1	1	1

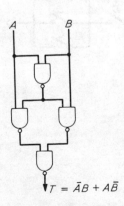

$T = \bar{A}B + A\bar{B}$

Fig. S–1 Problem 2–2

It is interesting to note that the original equation represents the NAND configuration for the exclusive OR circuit, see Fig. S–1.

(b) $\qquad T = \overline{(a + b + \bar{c})(\overline{ab} + \overline{cd})} + (\overline{bcd})$

$\qquad\qquad = [(a + b + \bar{c}) + (\overline{ab} + \overline{cd})](bcd)$

$\qquad\qquad = [(a + b + \bar{c}) + (\bar{a} + \bar{b} + \bar{c} + \bar{d})](bcd)$

$\qquad\qquad = (a + \bar{a} + b + \bar{b} + \bar{c} + \bar{d})(bcd)$

Thus,$\qquad\qquad T = bcd$

(c) $\qquad T = \overline{\overline{(abc + b\bar{c}d)} + \overline{(\overline{acd} + \bar{b}\bar{c}\bar{d} + bcd)}}$

$\qquad\qquad = (abc + b\bar{c}d)(\overline{\overline{acd} + \bar{b}\bar{c}\bar{d} + bcd})$

$\qquad\qquad = (abc + b\bar{c}d)(\bar{a} + \bar{c} + \bar{d} + \bar{b}\bar{c}\bar{d} + bcd)$

$\qquad\qquad = (abc + b\bar{c}d)(\bar{a} + \bar{c} + \bar{d})$

$\qquad\qquad = abc\bar{a} + abc\bar{c} + abc\bar{d} + \bar{a}b\bar{c}d + b\bar{c}\bar{c}d + b\bar{c}d\bar{d}$

$\qquad\qquad = abc\bar{d} + \bar{a}b\bar{c}d + b\bar{c}d$

$\qquad T = abc\bar{d} + b\bar{c}d$

2-3 (a) The equation for the circuit, including all nets, is

$$T = \bar{A}BD + \bar{A}\bar{B}CD + ABCD + A\bar{B}D + ABD$$

Expanding into canonical sum-of-products we have

$$T = \bar{A}BD(C + \bar{C}) + A\bar{B}D(C + \bar{C}) + ABD(C + \bar{C}) + \bar{A}\bar{B}CD + ABCD$$

Thus $\quad T = \bar{A}BCD + \bar{A}B\bar{C}D + A\bar{B}CD + A\bar{B}\bar{C}D + ABCD + AB\bar{C}D + \bar{A}\bar{B}CD$

(a)

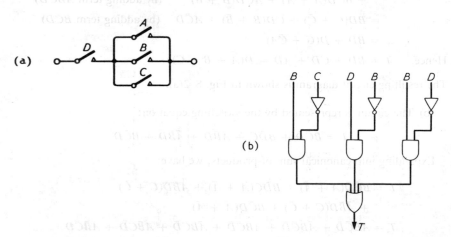

(b)

Fig. S–2 Problem 2–3

Alternatively, the formula may be used:

$$T = (\bar{A}\bar{B}\bar{C}\bar{D} \cdot 0) + (\bar{A}\bar{B}\bar{C}D \cdot 0) + (\bar{A}\bar{B}C\bar{D} \cdot 0) + (\bar{A}\bar{B}CD \cdot 1) + (\bar{A}B\bar{C}\bar{D} \cdot 0)$$
$$+ (\bar{A}B\bar{C}D \cdot 1) + (\bar{A}BC\bar{D} \cdot 0) + (\bar{A}BCD \cdot 1) + (A\bar{B}\bar{C}\bar{D} \cdot 0)$$
$$+ (A\bar{B}\bar{C}D \cdot 1) + (A\bar{B}C\bar{D} \cdot 0) + (A B\bar{C}D \cdot 1) + (A B C\bar{D} \cdot 0)$$
$$+ (A B\bar{C}D \cdot 1) + (A B C\bar{D} \cdot 0) + (A B C D \cdot 1)$$

Hence,

$$T = \bar{A}\bar{B}CD + \bar{A}B\bar{C}D + \bar{A}BCD + A\bar{B}\bar{C}D + A\bar{B}CD + A B\bar{C}D + A B C D$$

To obtain the canonical product-of-sums we again apply the formula:

$$T = (\bar{A} + \bar{B} + \bar{C} + \bar{D} + 1)(\bar{A} + \bar{B} + \bar{C} + D + 0)(\bar{A} + \bar{B} + C + \bar{D} + 1)$$
$$(\bar{A} + \bar{B} + C + D + 0)(\bar{A} + B + \bar{C} + \bar{D} + 1)(\bar{A} + B + \bar{C} + D + 0)$$
$$(\bar{A} + B + C + \bar{D} + 1)(\bar{A} + B + C + D + 0)(A + \bar{B} + \bar{C} + \bar{D} + 1)$$
$$(A + \bar{B} + \bar{C} + D + 0)(A + \bar{B} + C + \bar{D} + 1)(A + \bar{B} + C + D + 0)$$
$$(A + B + \bar{C} + \bar{D} + 1)(A + B + \bar{C} + D + 0)(A + B + C + \bar{D} + 0)$$
$$(A + B + C + D + 0)$$

And,

$$T = (\bar{A} + \bar{B} + \bar{C} + D)(\bar{A} + \bar{B} + C + D)(\bar{A} + B + \bar{C} + D)$$
$$(\bar{A} + B + C + D)(A + \bar{B} + \bar{C} + D)(A + \bar{B} + C + D)$$
$$(A + B + \bar{C} + D)(A + B + C + \bar{D})(A + B + C + D)$$

The equation may be simplified

$$T = BCD(A + \bar{A}) + B\bar{C}D(A + \bar{A})$$
$$+ \bar{B}CD(A + \bar{A}) + A\bar{C}D(B + \bar{B}) \qquad \text{(by adding term } AB\bar{C}D)$$
$$= BD(C + \bar{C}) + CD(B + \bar{B}) + A\bar{C}D \qquad \text{(by adding term } BCD)$$
$$= BD + D(C + \bar{C}A)$$

Hence, $T = BD + CD + AD = D(A + B + C)$

The resulting circuit diagram is shown in Fig. S–2(a).

(b) The circuit is represented by the switching equation:

$$T = B\bar{C}\bar{D} + B\bar{D}C + A\bar{B}D + \bar{A}\bar{B}D + B\bar{C}D$$

Expanding into canonical sum-of-products, we have:

$$T = B\bar{C}\bar{D}(A + \bar{A}) + B\bar{D}C(A + \bar{A}) + A\bar{B}D(C + \bar{C})$$
$$+ \bar{A}\bar{B}D(C + \bar{C}) + B\bar{C}D(A + \bar{A})$$
$$T = AB\bar{C}\bar{D} + \bar{A}B\bar{C}\bar{D} + ABC\bar{D} + \bar{A}BC\bar{D} + A\bar{B}CD + A\bar{B}\bar{C}D$$
$$+ \bar{A}\bar{B}\bar{C}D + \bar{A}\bar{B}CD + AB\bar{C}D + \bar{A}B\bar{C}D$$

Having found this canonical form, it is easier perhaps to obtain the product-of-sums using De Morgan's theorem; writing down the excluded terms and finding the inverse we have:

$$T = \overline{\bar{A}\bar{B}\bar{C}\bar{D} + \bar{A}B\bar{C}\bar{D} + \bar{A}BCD + A\bar{B}\bar{C}\bar{D} + AB\bar{C}\bar{D} + ABCD}$$

Thus, $T = (A + B + C + D)(A + B + \bar{C} + D)(A + \bar{B} + \bar{C} + \bar{D})$

$(\bar{A} + B + C + D)(\bar{A} + B + \bar{C} + D)(\bar{A} + \bar{B} + \bar{C} + \bar{D})$

The expression may be simplified thus:

$$T = B\bar{C}\bar{D} + B\bar{D}C + A\bar{B}D + \bar{A}\bar{B}D + BCD$$

$$= B\bar{C}(\bar{D} + D) + \bar{B}D(\bar{A} + A) + B\bar{D}C$$

$$= \bar{B}D + B(\bar{C} + C\bar{D})$$

and $T = \bar{B}D + B\bar{C} + B\bar{D}$

or $T = B\bar{D}(C + \bar{C}) + \bar{B}D(A + \bar{A}) + B\bar{C}D$

$$= B\bar{D} + D(\bar{B} + B\bar{C})$$

Hence $T = B\bar{D} + \bar{B}D + \bar{C}D$

Both are equally valid minimal solutions, the circuit is shown in Fig. S–2(b).

2-4 The subsets of the set $A = \{x_1, x_2, x_3, x_4\}$ are:

$(\bar{x}_1\bar{x}_2\bar{x}_3\bar{x}_4)$, $(\bar{x}_1\bar{x}_2\bar{x}_3x_4)$, $(\bar{x}_1\bar{x}_2x_3\bar{x}_4)$, $(\bar{x}_1\bar{x}_2x_3\bar{x}_4)$, $(\bar{x}_1x_2\bar{x}_3\bar{x}_4)$, $(\bar{x}_1x_2\bar{x}_3x_4)$,

$(\bar{x}_1x_2x_3\bar{x}_4)$, $(\bar{x}_1x_2x_3x_4)$, $(x_1\bar{x}_2\bar{x}_3\bar{x}_4)$, $(x_1\bar{x}_2\bar{x}_3x_4)$, $(x_1\bar{x}_2x_3\bar{x}_4)$, $(x_1\bar{x}_2x_3x_4)$,

$(x_1x_2\bar{x}_3\bar{x}_4)$, $(x_1x_2\bar{x}_3x_4)$, $(x_1x_2x_3\bar{x}_4)$, $(x_1x_2x_3x_4)$

The Venn diagram is shown in Fig. S–3. The diagram may be used to simplify switching equations as adjacent terms differ in one variable, hence it can be clearly recognized that $x_2x_1 + x_2\bar{x}_1 = x_2$ applies. See Chapter 3 for further description.

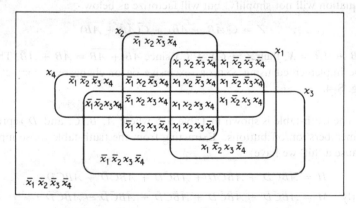

Fig. S–3 Problem 2–4

Table S–4 **Fig. S–4 Problem 2–5**
Problem 2–5

A	B	C		Z
0	0	0		0
0	0	1		1
0	1	0		1
0	1	1		0
1	0	0		1
1	0	1		0
1	1	0		0
1	1	1		1

2-5 The problem is first stated in truth-table form; let the three on/off switches be A, B, and C and the 'light-on' condition be represented by $Z = 1$. The truth table is shown in Table S–4.

In this way we have considered all possible input conditions for the three on/off switches A, B, and C. The next step is to read down the switching function from the table, this is for the terms $Z = 1$:

$$Z = \bar{A}\bar{B}C + \bar{A}B\bar{C} + A\bar{B}\bar{C} + ABC$$

The equation will not simplify, but will factorize as below

$$Z = \bar{C}(\bar{A}B + A\bar{B}) + C(\bar{A}\bar{B} + AB)$$

Let $\bar{A}B + A\bar{B} = X$, then $Z = \bar{C}X + C\bar{X}$ since $\overline{\bar{A}\bar{B} + AB} = \bar{A}B + A\bar{B}$. The circuit may be implemented using AND/OR, exclusive OR or changeover contact circuits, see Fig. S–4.

2-6 The truth-table is shown in Table S–5 where A, B, C, and D represent the panel members' on/off buttons. Extracting from the truth-table those input terms that cause a 'hit' we have:

$$H = \bar{A}BCD + A\bar{B}CD + ABC\bar{D} + ABC\bar{D} + ABCD$$

Similarly $M = \bar{A}\bar{B}\bar{C}\bar{D} + \bar{A}\bar{B}C\bar{D} + \bar{A}B\bar{C}\bar{D} + \bar{A}B\bar{C}\bar{D} + A\bar{B}\bar{C}\bar{D}$

$$T = \bar{A}\bar{B}CD + \bar{A}B\bar{C}D + \bar{A}BC\bar{D} + A\bar{B}\bar{C}D + A\bar{B}C\bar{D} + AB\bar{C}\bar{D}$$

Table S–5 Problem 2–6

A	B	C	D	Hit	Miss	Tie
0	0	0	0	0	1	0
0	0	0	1	1	0	0
0	0	1	0	0	1	0
0	0	1	1	0	0	1
0	1	0	0	0	1	0
0	1	0	1	1	0	0
0	1	1	0	0	0	1
0	1	1	1	1	0	0
1	0	0	0	0	1	0
1	0	0	1	0	0	1
1	0	1	0	0	0	1
1	0	1	1	1	0	0
1	1	0	0	0	0	1
1	1	0	1	1	0	0
1	1	1	0	1	0	0
1	1	1	1	1	0	0

Simplifying the function, we have:

$$H = ABD(C + \bar{C}) + ABC(D + \bar{D}) + ACD(B + \bar{B})$$
$$+ BCD(\bar{A} + A) \qquad \text{(adding redundant terms } ABCD)$$

Hence $\qquad H = ABD + ABC + ACD + BCD$

Also $\qquad M = \bar{A}\bar{B}\bar{C}(D + \bar{D}) + \bar{A}\bar{B}\bar{D}(C + \bar{C}) + \bar{A}\bar{C}\bar{D}(B + \bar{B})$
$$+ \bar{B}\bar{C}\bar{D}(A + \bar{A}) \qquad \text{(adding redundant terms } \bar{A}\bar{B}\bar{C}\bar{D})$$

Thus $\qquad M = \bar{A}\bar{C}\bar{D} + \bar{A}\bar{B}\bar{C} + \bar{B}\bar{C}\bar{D} + \bar{A}\bar{B}\bar{D}$

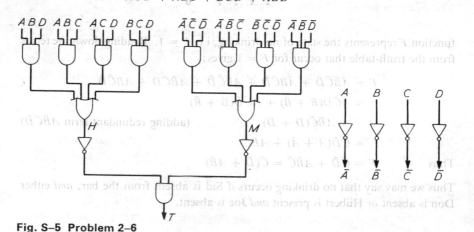

Fig. S–5 Problem 2–6

The equation for the 'tie' condition cannot be simplified; however, the 'tie' condition occurs when there is not a 'hit' ($\bar{H}$) and not a 'miss' ($\bar{M}$), i.e.

$$T = \bar{H}\bar{M}$$

The logic diagram is shown in Fig. S–5. If only two-input gates were available, it would be better to factorize the equations as

$$M = \bar{A}\bar{C}(\bar{B} + \bar{D}) + \bar{B}\bar{D}(\bar{A} + \bar{C})$$

and

$$H = AB(C + D) + CD(A + B)$$

2-7 The truth-table for this problem is shown in Table S–6, where A, B, C, and D represent the absence or presence of Hubert, Joe, Sid, and Don in the bar. The

Table S–6	A	B	C	D	F
Problem 2–7	0	0	0	0	1
	0	0	0	1	0
	0	0	1	0	0
	0	0	1	1	0
	0	1	0	0	1
	0	1	0	1	0
	0	1	1	0	0
	0	1	1	1	0
	1	0	0	0	1
	1	0	0	1	1
	1	0	1	0	0
	1	0	1	1	0
	1	1	0	0	1
	1	1	0	1	0
	1	1	1	0	0
	1	1	1	1	0

function F represents the state of no drinking, i.e. $F = 1$. Reading down the terms from the truth-table that occur for $F = 1$ gives:

$$F = \bar{A}\bar{B}\bar{C}\bar{D} + \bar{A}B\bar{C}\bar{D} + A\bar{B}\bar{C}\bar{D} + A\bar{B}\bar{C}D + AB\bar{C}\bar{D}$$
$$= \bar{A}\bar{C}\bar{D}(B + \bar{B}) + A\bar{C}\bar{D}(B + \bar{B})$$
$$+ A\bar{B}\bar{C}(D + \bar{D}) \qquad \text{(adding redundant term } A\bar{B}\bar{C}\bar{D})$$
$$= \bar{C}\bar{D}(A + \bar{A}) + A\bar{B}\bar{C}$$

Thus $$F = \bar{C}\bar{D} + A\bar{B}\bar{C} = \bar{C}(\bar{D} + A\bar{B})$$

Thus we may say that no drinking occurs if Sid is absent from the bar, *and* either Don is absent *or* Hubert is present *and* Joe is absent.

Chapter 3

3-1 The truth-table for this problem is shown in Table S-7, where M represents the add/subtract control signal, x and y the digits to be added (or subtracted), b/c the borrow (or carry), and S/D the sum (or difference). Note that the sum and difference outputs are identical, i.e. independent of M. Thus

$$S/D = \bar{M}\bar{x}\bar{y}\,b/c + \bar{M}\bar{x}y\,\overline{b/c} + \bar{M}x\bar{y}\,\overline{b/c} + \bar{M}xy\,b/c + M\bar{x}\bar{y}\,b/c$$
$$+ M\bar{x}y\,\overline{b/c} + Mx\bar{y}\,\overline{b/c} + Mxy\,b/c$$
$$= (\bar{x}\bar{y}\,b/c + \bar{x}y\,\overline{b/c} + x\bar{y}\,\overline{b/c} + xy\,b/c)(M + \bar{M})$$

Thus $S/D = \bar{x}\bar{y}\,b/c + \bar{x}y\,b/c + x\bar{y}\,b/c + xy\,b/c$

The borrow/carry output is given by

$$b_+/c_+ = \bar{M}\bar{x}\bar{y}\,b/c + \bar{M}\bar{x}y\,\overline{b/c} + \bar{M}\bar{x}y\,b/c + \bar{M}xy\,b/c$$
$$+ M\bar{x}y\,b/c + Mx\bar{y}\,b/c + Mxy\,\overline{b/c} + Mxy\,b/c$$

M	x	y	b/c	S/D	b+/c+
0	0	0	0	0	0
0	0	0	1	1	1
0	0	1	0	1	1
0	0	1	1	0	1
0	1	0	0	1	0
0	1	0	1	0	0
0	1	1	0	0	0
0	1	1	1	1	1
1	0	0	0	0	0
1	0	0	1	1	0
1	0	1	0	1	0
1	0	1	1	0	1
1	1	0	0	1	0
1	1	0	1	0	1
1	1	1	0	0	1
1	1	1	1	1	1

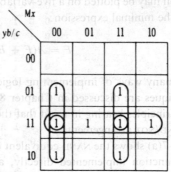

Table S–7 (left) Problem 3–1

Table S–8 (above) Problem 3–1

Fig. S–6 (below) Problem 3–1

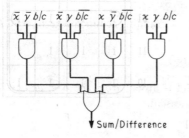

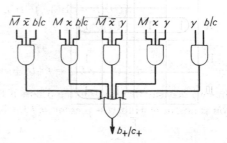

Table S–8 shows the Karnaugh map for the problem, thus the minimal expression for the borrow/carry is

$$b_+/c_+ = \bar{M}\bar{x}\ b/c + Mx\ b/c + \bar{M}\bar{x}y + Mxy + y\ b/c$$

The complete logic diagram for the adder/subtractor is shown in Fig. S–6.

3-2 From the circuit diagram (Fig. 3–8) we have six variables, A, B, C, D, E, and F. However, A is common to all terms and may be ignored in the minimization. Ideal contacts are assumed throughout, and all possible paths are included in the transmission function F. Thus

$$F = AB\bar{C} + AB\bar{E} + ABD + AE\bar{D} + AF$$
$$= A(B\bar{C} + B\bar{E} + BD + E\bar{D} + F)$$

The function may be plotted on a five-variable Karnaugh map, shown in Table S–9. This gives the minimal expression:

$$F = A(F + B + \bar{D}E)$$

There are many ways of implementing logic in terms of NAND/NOR elements, and these techniques are discussed in Chapter 8. We may, however, deduce a circuit from first principles bearing in mind that the NAND unit is logically equivalent to a cascaded AND/NOT arrangement.

Figure S–7(a) shows the NAND equivalent of AND/OR gates, Fig. S–7(b) shows the switching function implemented directly, and Fig. S–7(c) the final circuit after eliminating redundant elements. This configuration is a sequential switching circuit; note the feedback of F, and the bistable element formed by NANDs II and III.

Table S–9 Problem 3–2

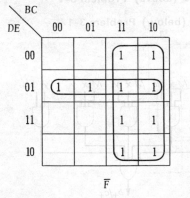

$\bar{F}$

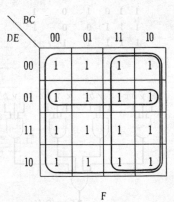

F

$A = 1$

Fig. S–7 Problem 3–2

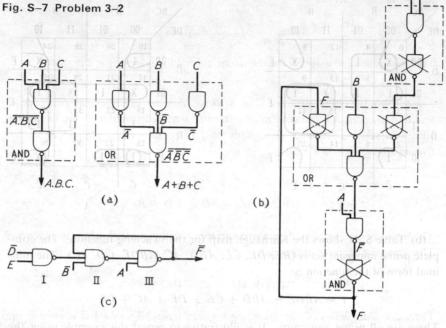

(a)   (b)

(c)

3-3 (a) The Karnaugh map is shown in Table S–10. From this the minimal expression is given by:

$$T = D + AB + \bar{B}\bar{C}$$

All these terms are essential prime implicants.

Table S–10 Problem 3–3(a)

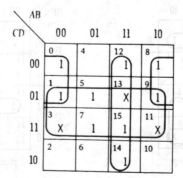

Table S-11 Problem 3-3(b)

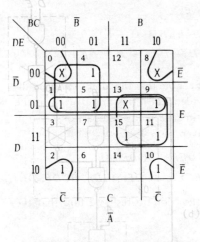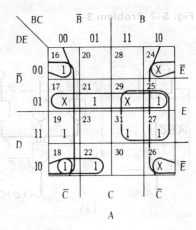

(b) Table S-11 shows the Karnaugh map for the switching function. The complete prime implicant set is $(BE, \bar{D}E, \bar{C}\bar{E}, \bar{A}\bar{B}\bar{D}, A\bar{C}, A\bar{B}D\bar{E}, \bar{C}\bar{D}, B\bar{C})$. The minimal form of the function is:

$$T = A\bar{B}D\bar{E} + \bar{A}\bar{B}\bar{D} + \bar{C}\bar{E} + \bar{D}E + A\bar{C} + BE$$

These are all prime implicants. It is illustrative to repeat this example using the McCluskey tabular method, it is more time-consuming but ensures the best use of the unspecified conditions. Furthermore the minimal prime implicant set may be more easily arrived at by using the chart technique.

(c) Product-of-sums equations may be plotted directly on a Karnaugh map in exactly the same way as sums-of-products. Table S-12 shows the function plotted

Table S-12 Problem 3-3(c)

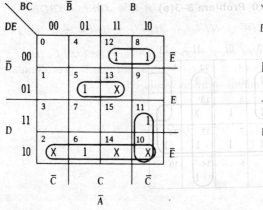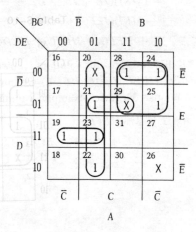

on a map. The terms are read from the map in the normal way, but expressed as a product-of-sums. Thus from Table S–12 we have:

$$T = (\bar{A} + D + \bar{E})(\bar{A} + B + \bar{C} + D)(C + \bar{D} + E)(B + \bar{D} + \bar{E})$$

$$(A + \bar{B} + D + E)(A + B + \bar{D})(A + \bar{B} + C)$$

3-4 Table S–13 shows the tabular arrangement, note that the 'don't care' conditions have been included in the table. Many identical terms are evolved in the computation process, these are simply ignored in succeeding comparisons. From the table, the complete prime implicant set is given by:

$$PI = (\bar{B}\bar{C}\bar{D}EF, AB\bar{C}\bar{D}F, AB\bar{C}\bar{E}F, ABC\bar{D}F, AB\bar{D}EF, ABC\bar{D}E, ABCEF,$$

$$\bar{A}\bar{B}CD, BC\bar{E}\bar{F}, \bar{A}CDF, \bar{A}BDF, BCDF, D\bar{E})$$

Drawing the prime implicant table, ignoring the 'don't cares', we find that the essential prime implicants are:

$$PIE = (BC\bar{E}\bar{F}, \bar{A}BDF, D\bar{E})$$

This leaves terms 15, 51, 58, 59 and 63 still to be covered, with the resulting PI chart having a cyclic form. The algebraic approach will give all possible solutions, thus:

$$PI = (M)(M + H)(M + J + H)(J + H)(M + K)(K)(I)(M + L + K + J)$$

$$(L + K + J)(M)(M)(M)(M)(E + B)(M)(M + C)$$

$$(I + D)(F + D)(G + F + E)(M + I)(G + L)$$

Simplifying we have

$$PI = (M)(J + H)(K)(I)(E + B)(F + D)(G + F + E)(G + L)$$

$$= (MKI)(JE + JB + HE + HB)(F + D)(G + EL + FL)$$

$$= (MKI)(JE + JB + HE + HB)(FG + FL + DG + DEL)$$

$$= (MKI)(JEFG + JEFL + JEDG + JEDL + JBFG + JBFL + JBDG$$

$$+ HEFG + HEFL + HEDG + HEDL + HBFG + HBFL + HBDG)$$

All these are possible solutions; however, the prime implicant sets (*JEFL, HEFL, JBFL, HBFL, JEDL, HEDL*) contain the fewest literals and hence give minimal solutions. Thus, for example, a minimal solution would be

$$T = MKIJEFL$$

$$= D\bar{E} + \bar{A}BDF + BC\bar{E}\bar{F} + \bar{A}CDF + AB\bar{D}EF + ABC\bar{D}E + BCDF$$

Table S–13 Problem 3–4

	A	B	C	D	E	F	
2	0	0	0	0	1	0	√
4	0	0	0	1	0	0	√
5	0	0	0	1	0	1	√
12	0	0	1	1	0	0	√
20	0	1	0	1	0	0	√
24	0	1	1	0	0	0	√
34	1	0	0	0	1	0	√
36	1	0	0	1	0	0	√
13	0	0	1	1	0	1	√
14	0	0	1	1	1	0	√
21	0	1	0	1	0	1	√
28	0	1	1	1	0	0	√
37	1	0	0	1	0	1	√
44	1	0	1	1	0	0	√
49	1	1	0	0	0	1	√
52	1	1	0	1	0	0	√
56	1	1	1	0	0	0	√
15	0	0	1	1	1	1	√
23	0	1	0	1	1	1	√
29	0	1	1	1	0	1	√
45	1	0	1	1	0	1	√
51	1	1	0	0	1	1	√
53	1	1	0	1	0	1	√
58	1	1	1	0	1	0	√
60	1	1	1	1	0	0	√
31	0	1	1	1	1	1	√
59	1	1	1	0	1	1	√
61	1	1	1	1	0	1	√
63	1	1	1	1	1	1	√

List 1

	A	B	C	D	E	F	
2,34	–	0	0	0	1	0	A
4,5	0	0	0	1	0	–	√
4,12	0	0	–	1	0	0	√
4,20	0	–	0	1	0	0	√
4,36	–	0	0	1	0	0	√
5,13	0	0	–	1	0	1	√
5,21	0	–	0	1	0	1	√
5,37	–	0	0	1	0	1	√
12,13	0	0	1	1	0	–	√
12,14	0	0	1	1	–	0	√
12,28	0	–	1	1	0	0	√

	A	B	C	D	E	F	
12,44	–	0	1	1	0	0	√
20,21	0	1	0	1	0	–	√
20,28	0	1	–	1	0	0	√
20,52	–	1	0	1	0	0	√
24,28	0	1	1	–	0	0	√
24,56	–	1	1	0	0	0	√
36,37	1	0	0	1	0	–	√
36,44	1	0	–	1	0	0	√
36,52	1	–	0	1	0	0	√
13,15	0	0	1	1	–	1	√
13,29	0	–	1	1	0	1	√
13,45	–	0	1	1	0	1	√
14,15	0	0	1	1	1	–	√
21,23	0	1	0	1	–	1	√
21,29	0	1	–	1	0	1	√
21,53	–	1	0	1	0	1	√
28,29	0	1	1	1	0	–	√
28,60	–	1	1	1	0	0	√
37,45	1	0	–	1	0	1	√
37,53	1	–	0	1	0	1	√
44,45	1	0	1	1	0	–	√
44,60	1	–	1	1	0	0	√
49,51	1	1	0	0	–	1	B
49,53	1	1	0	–	0	1	C
52,53	1	1	0	1	0	–	√
52,60	1	1	–	1	0	0	√
56,58	1	1	1	0	–	0	D
56,60	1	1	1	–	0	0	√
15,31	0	–	1	1	1	1	√
23,31	0	1	–	1	1	1	√
29,31	0	1	1	1	–	1	√
29,61	–	1	1	1	0	1	√
45,61	1	–	1	1	0	1	√
51,59	1	1	–	0	1	1	E
53,61	1	1	–	1	0	1	√
58,59	1	1	1	0	1	–	√
60,61	1	1	1	1	0	–	√
31,63	–	1	1	1	1	1	√
59,63	1	1	1	–	1	1	G
61,63	1	1	1	1	–	1	√

List 2

Table S–13 continued

	A	B	C	D	E	F
4,5/12,13	0	0	-	1	0	- √
4,5/20,21	0	-	0	1	0	- √
4,5/36,37	-	0	0	1	0	- √
4,12/5,13	0	0	-	1	0	-
4,12/20,28	0	-	-	1	0	0 √
4,12/36,44	-	0	-	1	0	0 √
4,20/5,21	0	-	0	1	0	-
4,20/12,28	0	-	-	1	0	0
4,20/36,52	-	-	0	1	0	0 √
4,36/5,37	-	0	0	1	0	-
4,36/12,44	-	0	-	1	0	0
4,36/20,52	-	-	0	1	0	0
5,13/21,29	0	-	-	1	0	1 √
5,13/37,45	-	0	-	1	0	1 √
5,21/13,29	0	-	-	1	0	1
5,21/37,53	-	-	0	1	0	1 √
5,37/13,45	-	0	-	1	0	1
5,37/21,53	-	-	0	1	0	1
12,13/14,15	0	0	1	1	-	- H
12,13/28,29	0	-	1	1	0	- √
12,13/44,45	-	0	1	1	0	- √
12,14/13,15	0	0	1	1	-	-
12,28/13,29	0	-	1	1	0	-
12,28/44,60	-	-	1	1	0	0 √
12,44/13,45	-	0	1	1	0	-
12,44/28,60	-	-	1	1	0	0
20,21/28,29	0	1	-	1	0	- √
20,21/52,53	-	1	0	1	0	- √
20,28/21,29	0	1	-	1	0	-
20,28/52,60	-	1	-	1	0	0 √
20,52/21,53	-	1	0	1	0	-
20,52/28,60	-	1	-	1	0	0
24,28/56,60	-	1	1	-	0	0 I
24,56/28,60	-	1	1	-	0	0
36,37/44,45	1	0	-	1	0	- √
36,37/52,53	1	-	0	1	0	- √
36,44/37,45	1	0	-	1	0	-
36,44/52,60	1	-	-	1	0	0 √
36,52/37,53	1	-	0	1	0	-
36,52/44,60	1	-	-	1	0	0
13,15/29,31	0	-	1	1	-	1 J
13,29/15,31	0	-	1	1	-	1

	A	B	C	D	E	F
13,29/45,61	-	-	1	1	0	1 √
13,45/29,61	-	-	1	1	0	1
21,23/29,31	0	1	-	1	-	1 K
21,29/23,31	0	1	-	1	-	1
21,29/53,61	-	1	-	1	0	1 √
21,53/29,61	-	1	-	1	0	1
28,29/60,61	-	1	1	1	0	- √
28,60/29,61	-	1	1	1	0	-
37,45/53,61	1	-	-	1	0	1 √
37,53/45,61	1	-	-	1	0	1
44,45/60,61	1	-	1	1	0	- √
44,60/45,61	1	-	1	1	0	-
52,53/60,61	1	1	-	1	0	- √
52,60/53,61	1	1	-	1	0	-
29,61/31,63	-	1	1	1	-	1 L
29,31/61,63	-	1	1	1	-	1
29,61/31,63	-	1	1	1	-	1

List 3.

	A	B	C	D	E	F
4,5/12,13/20,21/28,29	0	-	-	1	0	- √
4,5/12,13/36,37/44,45	-	0	-	1	0	- √
4,5/20,21/12,13/28,29	0	-	-	1	0	-
4,5/20,21/36,37/52,53	-	-	0	1	0	- √
4,5/36,37/12,13/44,45	-	0	-	1	0	-
4,5/36,37/20,21/52,53	-	-	0	1	0	-
4,12/20,28/5,13/21,29	0	-	-	1	0	-
4,12/20,28/36,44/52,60	-	-	-	1	0	0 √
4,12/36,44/5,13/37,45	-	0	-	1	0	-
4,12/36,44/20,28/52,60	-	-	-	1	0	0
4,20/36,52/5,21/37,53	-	-	0	1	0	-
4,20/36,52/12,28/44,60	-	-	-	1	0	0
5,13/21,29/37,45/53,61	-	-	-	1	0	1 √
5,13/37,45/21,29/53,61	-	-	-	1	0	1
5,21/37,53/13,29/45,61	-	-	-	1	0	1
12,13/28,29/44,45/60,61	-	-	1	1	0	- √
12,13/44,45/28,29/60,61	-	-	1	1	0	-
12,28/44,60/13,29/45,61	-	-	1	1	0	-
20,21/28,29/52,53/60,61	-	1	-	1	0	- √
20,21/52,53/28,29/60,61	-	1	-	1	0	-
20,28/52,60/21,29/53,61	-	1	-	1	0	-

Table S–13 continued

```
                            A B C D E F
36,37/44,45/52,53/60,61     1 – – 1 0 – √
36,37/52,53/44,45/60,61     1 – – 1 0 –
36,44/52,60/37,45/53,61     1 – – 1 0 –
```

List 4

```
4,5/12,13/20,21/28,29/
36,37/44,45/52,53/60,61     – – – 1 0 – M
4,5/12,13/36,37/44,45/
20,21/28,29/52,53/60,61.    – – – 1 0 –
4,5/20,21/36,37/52,53/
12,13/38,29/44,45/60,61.    – – – 1 0 –
4,12/20,28/36,44/52,60/
5,13/21,29/37,45/53,61-     – – – 1 0 –
```

List 5

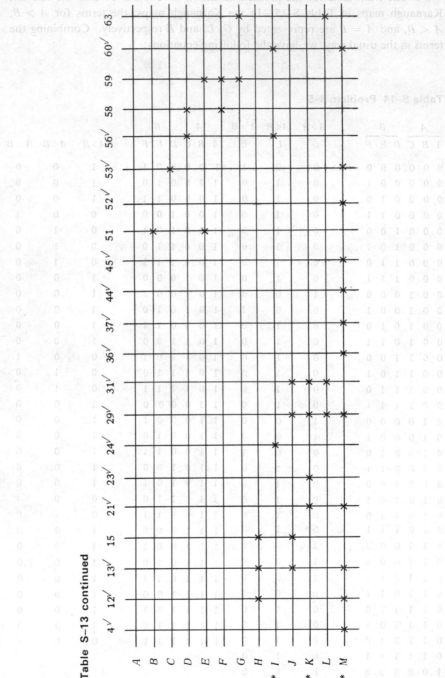

Table S-13 continued

3-5 The truth-table for the problem is shown in Table S–14 and the relevant Karnaugh maps in Table S–15. In the Karnaugh maps, the terms for $A > B$, $A < B$, and $A = B$ are represented by G, L, and E respectively. Combining the terms in the usual way, we have the following equations:

Table S–14 Problem 3–5

A	B	C	D	E	F	A>B (G)	A<B (L)	A=B (E)	A	B	C	D	E	F	A>B	A<B	A=B
0	0	0	0	0	0	0	0	1	1	0	0	0	0	1	1	0	0
0	0	0	0	0	1	0	1	0	1	0	0	0	1	0	1	0	0
0	0	0	0	1	0	0	1	0	1	0	0	0	1	1	1	0	0
0	0	0	0	1	1	0	1	0	1	0	0	1	0	0	0	0	1
0	0	0	1	0	0	0	1	0	1	0	0	1	0	1	0	1	0
0	0	0	1	0	1	0	1	0	1	0	0	1	1	0	0	1	0
0	0	0	1	1	0	0	1	0	1	0	0	1	1	1	0	1	0
0	0	0	1	1	1	0	1	0	1	0	1	0	0	0	1	0	0
0	0	1	0	0	0	1	0	0	1	0	1	0	0	1	1	0	0
0	0	1	0	0	1	0	0	1	1	0	1	0	1	0	1	0	0
0	0	1	0	1	0	0	1	0	1	0	1	0	1	1	1	0	0
0	0	1	0	1	1	0	1	0	1	0	1	1	0	0	1	0	0
0	0	1	1	0	0	0	1	0	1	0	1	1	0	1	0	0	1
0	0	1	1	0	1	0	1	0	1	0	1	1	1	0	0	1	0
0	0	1	1	1	0	0	1	0	1	0	1	1	1	1	0	1	0
0	0	1	1	1	1	0	1	0	1	1	0	0	0	0	1	0	0
0	1	0	0	0	0	1	0	0	1	1	0	0	0	1	1	0	0
0	1	0	0	0	1	1	0	0	1	1	0	0	1	0	1	0	0
0	1	0	0	1	0	0	0	1	1	1	0	0	1	1	1	0	0
0	1	0	0	1	1	0	1	0	1	1	0	1	0	0	1	0	0
0	1	0	1	0	0	0	1	0	1	1	0	1	0	1	1	0	0
0	1	0	1	0	1	0	1	0	1	1	0	1	1	0	0	0	1
0	1	0	1	1	0	0	1	0	1	1	0	1	1	1	0	1	0
0	1	0	1	1	1	0	1	0	1	1	1	0	0	0	1	0	0
0	1	1	0	0	0	1	0	0	1	1	1	0	0	1	1	0	0
0	1	1	0	0	1	1	0	0	1	1	1	0	1	0	1	0	0
0	1	1	0	1	0	1	0	0	1	1	1	0	1	1	1	0	0
0	1	1	0	1	1	0	0	1	1	1	1	1	0	0	1	0	0
0	1	1	1	0	0	0	1	0	1	1	1	1	0	1	1	0	0
0	1	1	1	0	1	0	1	0	1	1	1	1	1	0	1	0	0
0	1	1	1	1	0	0	1	0	1	1	1	1	1	1	0	0	1
0	1	1	1	1	1	0	1										
1	0	0	0	0	0	1	0	0									

Table S–15 Problem 3–5

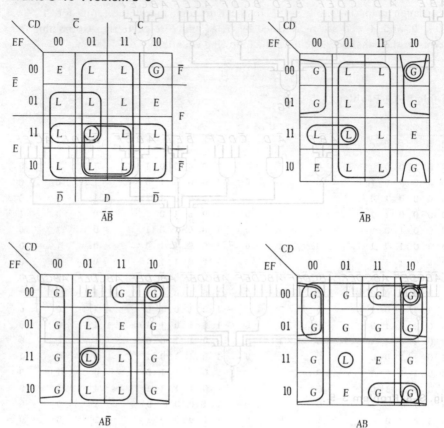

$$G = AB\bar{E} + A\bar{D} + C\bar{D}\bar{E}\bar{F} + B\bar{E}\bar{D} + BC\bar{D}\bar{F} + AC\bar{E}\bar{F} + ABCEF$$
$$L = \bar{A}\bar{B}E + \bar{A}D + \bar{C}DEF + \bar{B}ED + \bar{A}\bar{B}\bar{C}F + \bar{B}\bar{C}DF + \bar{A}\bar{C}EF$$
$$E = \bar{A}\bar{B}\bar{C}\bar{D}\bar{E}\bar{F} + \bar{A}\bar{B}C\bar{D}\bar{E}\bar{F} + \bar{A}\bar{B}C\bar{D}EF + \bar{A}B\bar{C}\bar{D}\bar{E}\bar{F} + A\bar{B}\bar{C}D\bar{E}\bar{F}$$
$$+ A\bar{B}CDE\bar{F} + ABCDEF + AB\bar{C}DEF$$

These equations are shown implemented in terms of NAND logic in Fig. S–8. Consider how this would be implemented if only three-input NAND elements were available. Note the equations could be factored as

$$G = AB\bar{E} + A\bar{D} + \bar{E}\bar{D}(C\bar{F} + B) + C\bar{F}(ABE + B\bar{D} + A\bar{E})$$
$$L = \bar{A}\bar{B}E + \bar{A}D + ED(\bar{C}\bar{F} + \bar{B}) + \bar{C}F(\bar{A}\bar{B} + \bar{B}D + \bar{A}E)$$
$$E = \bar{A}\bar{C}\bar{D}(\bar{B}\bar{E}\bar{F} + BEF) + \bar{A}DC(\bar{B}\bar{E}\bar{F} + BEF)$$
$$+ A\bar{B}\bar{E}(\bar{C}D\bar{F} + CDF) + ABD(CEF + \bar{C}E\bar{F})$$

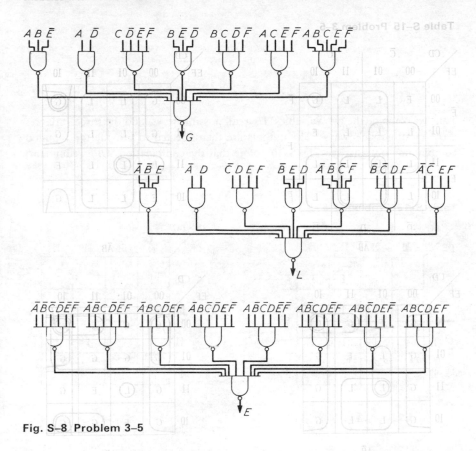

Fig. S–8 Problem 3–5

3-6 The relay tree will be designed by first assuming that there are no 'don't care' conditions; Table S–16 shows the relevant stages using the Karnaugh map technique. The combinations are first plotted on the maps, and the maps subdivided, indicating the order of subdivision by inserting the appropriate variable in the squares.

The corresponding relay circuit is shown in Fig. S–9(a). If, however, we assume that only the required combinations can occur, the circuit can be simplified, see Table S–17 and Fig. S–9(b). Note that many alternative solutions are possible for this problem.

Note also the simplified circuit uses 11 change-over contacts, compared with the original circuit which uses 11 change-over and 5 normally open contacts. To design an electronic tree circuit, we split the number of variables thus:

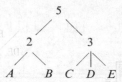

Thus we combine the two variables AB in all possible ways, and the three variables CDE in all possible ways. The outputs are then selected to provide the required combination outputs, see Fig. S–10. Note that the combination $A\bar{B}$ is redundant.

Table S–16 Problem 3–6

DE \ BC	00 ($\bar{B}$)	01	11 (B)	10	
00 ($\bar{D}$)	0	4	12 · 1	8 · 1	$\bar{E}$
01	1	5 · 1	13 · 1	9 · 1	E
11 (D)	3 · 1	7 · 1	15 · 1	11 · 1	
10	2	6	14	10	$\bar{E}$
	$\bar{C}$	C ($\bar{A}$)		$\bar{C}$	

DE \ BC	00	01	11	10
00	16	20	28	24
01	17	21	29 · 1	25 · 1
11	19	23	31 · 1	27 · 1
10	18	22	30	26
		A		

DE \ BC	$\bar{B}$		B		
$\bar{D}$			$\bar{A}BD\bar{E}\bar{C}$ · 1	$\bar{A}BD\bar{E}C$ · 1	$\bar{E}$
		$\bar{A}BCE\bar{D}$ · 1	$\bar{A}BD\bar{E}C$ · 1	$\bar{A}BD\bar{E}\bar{C}$ · 1	E
D		$\bar{A}BCE\bar{D}$ · 1	$\bar{A}BDEC$ · 1	$\bar{A}BD\bar{E}\bar{C}$ · 1	
					$\bar{E}$
	$\bar{C}$	C ($\bar{A}$)		$\bar{C}$	

DE \ BC	$\bar{B}$		B		
$\bar{D}$					$\bar{E}$
			$ABEC\bar{D}$ · 1	$ABE\bar{C}\bar{D}$ · 1	E
D			$ABECD$ · 1	$ABE\bar{C}D$ · 1	
					$\bar{E}$
	$\bar{C}$	C (A)		$\bar{C}$	

Table S–17 Problem 3–6

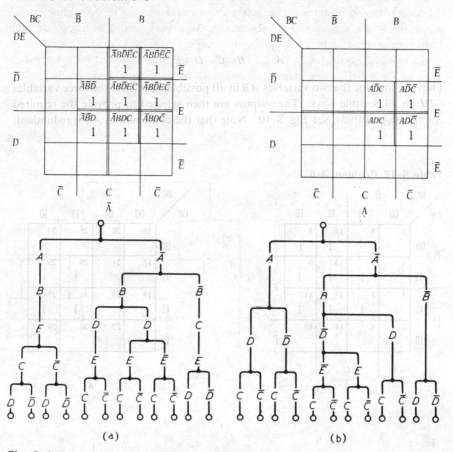

BC / DE		$\bar{B}$	B	
			$\bar{A}B\bar{D}\bar{E}C$ 1	$\bar{A}B\bar{D}\bar{E}\bar{C}$ 1	$\bar{E}$
$\bar{D}$	$\bar{A}\bar{B}\bar{D}$ 1	$\bar{A}B\bar{D}EC$ 1	$\bar{A}B\bar{D}E\bar{C}$ 1	E
D	$\bar{A}\bar{B}D$ 1	$\bar{A}BDC$ 1	$\bar{A}BD\bar{C}$ 1	
				$\bar{E}$
	$\bar{C}$	C	$\bar{C}$	

$\bar{A}$

		$\bar{B}$	B	
BC / DE				$\bar{E}$
$\bar{D}$			$A\bar{D}C$ 1	$A\bar{D}\bar{C}$ 1	E
D			ADC 1	$AD\bar{C}$ 1	
				$\bar{E}$
	$\bar{C}$	C	$\bar{C}$	

A

Fig. S–9 Problem 3–6

(a) (b)

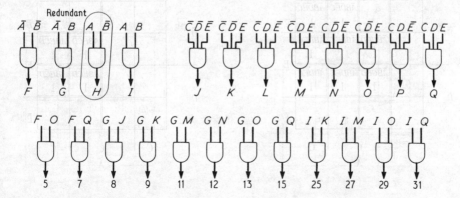

Fig. S–10 Problem 3–6

3-7 The truth-table for the problem is shown in Table S–18, note that there are 22 'don't care' conditions. The best way of implementing this decoding circuit would be to use a relay tree. An alternative approach would be to decode each combination separately using AND gates, utilizing the 'don't care' condition to effect minimal expressions. The combinations are shown plotted on a Karnaugh map in Table S–19. The maps are subdivided in the normal way, producing the relay tree shown in Fig. S–11.

Table S–18 Problem 3–7

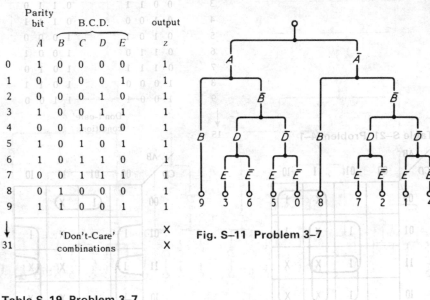

	Parity bit	B.C.D.				output
	A	B	C	D	E	z
0	1	0	0	0	0	1
1	0	0	0	0	1	1
2	0	0	0	1	0	1
3	1	0	0	1	1	1
4	0	0	1	0	0	1
5	1	0	1	0	1	1
6	1	0	1	1	0	1
7	0	0	1	1	1	1
8	0	1	0	0	0	1
9	1	1	0	0	1	1
↓						X
31		'Don't-Care' combinations				X

Fig. S–11 Problem 3–7

Table S–19 Problem 3–7

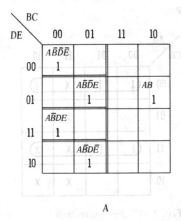

Chapter 4

4-1 The truth-table is shown in Table S–20, note that there are six 'don't care'

Table S–20	Problem 4–1	B.C.D. Decimal				Excess-three code			
		A	*B*	*C*	*D*	*W*	*X*	*Y*	*Z*
0		0	0	0	0	0	0	1	1
1		0	0	0	1	0	1	0	0
2		0	0	1	0	0	1	0	1
3		0	0	1	1	0	1	1	0
4		0	1	0	0	0	1	1	1
5		0	1	0	1	1	0	0	0
6		0	1	1	0	1	0	0	1
7		0	1	1	1	1	0	1	0
3		1	0	0	0	1	0	1	1
9		1	0	0	1	1	1	0	0
↓ 15						'Don't-care' conditions			

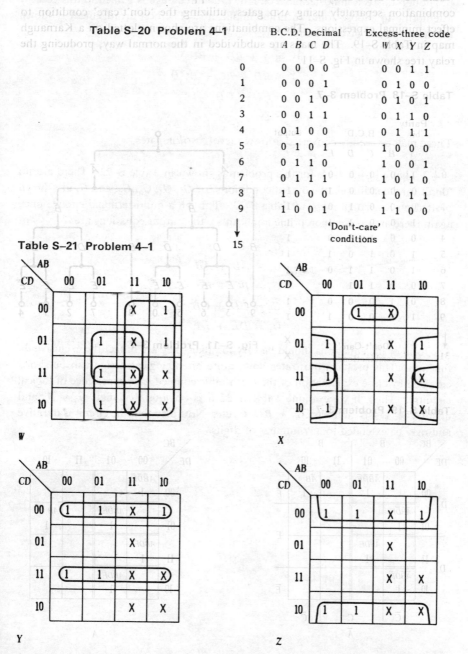

Table S–21 Problem 4–1

W

X

Y

Z

conditions. The output conditions for W, X, Y, and Z are plotted on Karnaugh maps together with the 'don't cares' in Table S–21.

Though this is a multi-terminal circuit, little advantage is gained in this case by attempting to choose common prime implicants. The best arrangement is shown on the maps and gives the equations

$$W = A + BD + BC$$
$$X = \bar{B}D + \bar{B}C + BC\bar{D}$$
$$Y = \bar{C}\bar{D} + CD$$
$$Z = \bar{D}$$

These may be readily converted into two level AND/OR gates.

4-2 The full truth-table for this problem is shown in Table S–22. There are no 'don't care' conditions, the output conditions for G_5, G_4, G_3, G_2, and G_1 are shown plotted on Karnaugh maps in Table S–23. Though a multi-terminal circuit, once again there are no common prime implicants; the output equations are

$$G_5 = A$$
$$G_4 = \bar{A}B + A\bar{B}$$
$$G_3 = B\bar{C} + \bar{B}C$$
$$G_2 = \bar{C}D + C\bar{D}$$
$$G_1 = D\bar{E} + \bar{D}E$$

The form of the equations should be very familiar, they are in fact the exclusive OR function. This problem illustrates how, quite often, logical design can be short-circuited by close examination of the truth-table coupled with experience of logical circuitry. Thus, if we examine Table S–22 it is obvious that digit $G_5 = A$, and digit $G_4 = A \oplus B$, and digit $G_3 = B \oplus C$, etc. Note also that the circuit is iterative and may be extended to any number of digits.

Table S–22 Problem 4–2

Pure binary					Gray code				
A	B	C	D	E	G_5	G_4	G_3	G_2	G_1
0	0	0	0	0	0	0	0	0	0
0	0	0	0	1	0	0	0	0	1
0	0	0	1	0	0	0	0	1	1
0	0	0	1	1	0	0	0	1	0
0	0	1	0	0	0	0	1	1	0
0	0	1	0	1	0	0	1	1	1
0	0	1	1	0	0	0	1	0	1
0	0	1	1	1	0	0	1	0	0
0	1	0	0	0	0	1	1	0	0
0	1	0	0	1	0	1	1	0	1
0	1	0	1	0	0	1	1	1	1
0	1	0	1	1	0	1	1	1	0
0	1	1	0	0	0	1	0	1	0
0	1	1	0	1	0	1	0	1	1
0	1	1	1	0	0	1	0	0	1
0	1	1	1	1	0	1	0	0	0
1	0	0	0	0	1	1	0	0	0
1	0	0	0	1	1	1	0	0	1
1	0	0	1	0	1	1	0	1	1
1	0	0	1	1	1	1	0	1	0
1	0	1	0	0	1	1	1	1	0
1	0	1	0	1	1	1	1	1	1
1	0	1	1	0	1	1	1	0	1
1	0	1	1	1	1	1	1	0	0
1	1	0	0	0	1	0	1	0	0
1	1	0	0	1	1	0	1	0	1
1	1	0	1	0	1	0	1	1	1
1	1	0	1	1	1	0	1	1	0
1	1	1	0	0	1	0	0	1	0
1	1	1	0	1	1	0	0	1	1
1	1	1	1	0	1	0	0	0	1
1	1	1	1	1	1	0	0	0	0

Table S–23 Problem 4–2

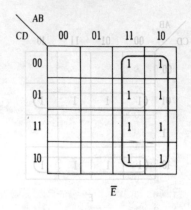

G_5

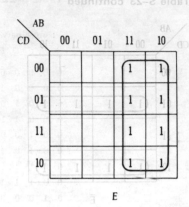

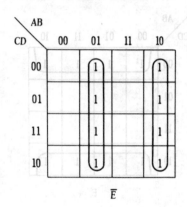

G_4

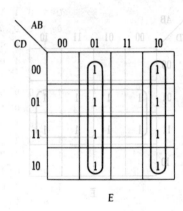

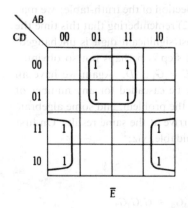

G_3

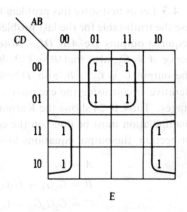

Table S–23 continued

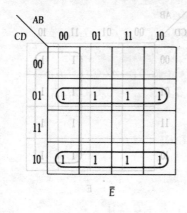

G_2

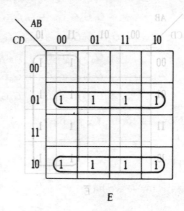

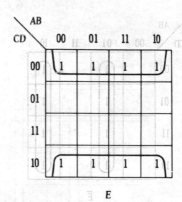

G_1

4-3 Let us first solve this problem by simple inspection of the truth-table; we may use the truth-table for the last problem (Table S–22) remembering that this time the required outputs are $ABCDE$. Note that the most significant digit is unchanged, hence $A = G_5$, also that $B = G_5 \oplus G_4$. The next step is perhaps not so obvious, the output $C = G_3 \oplus B$, also $D = G_2 \oplus C$ and $E = G_1 \oplus D$. Again we have an iterative circuit using the exclusive OR which may be cascaded for any number of stages. Table S–24 shows the Karnaugh maps for the problem, and some algebraic manipulation must be done on the equations to arrive at the same result. On first inspection, the output equations look rather formidable, viz:

$$A = G_5$$
$$B = \bar{G}_5 G_4 + G_5 \bar{G}_4$$
$$C = \bar{G}_5 G_4 \bar{G}_3 + G_5 \bar{G}_4 \bar{G}_3 + \bar{G}_5 \bar{G}_4 G_3 + G_5 G_4 G_3$$

$$D = \bar{G}_5\bar{G}_4\bar{G}_3G_2 + \bar{G}_5\bar{G}_4G_3\bar{G}_2 + \bar{G}_5G_4\bar{G}_3\bar{G}_2 + \bar{G}_5G_4G_3G_2 + G_5\bar{G}_4\bar{G}_3G_2$$
$$+ G_5\bar{G}_4G_3\bar{G}_2 + G_5\bar{G}_4\bar{G}_3\bar{G}_2 + G_5\bar{G}_4G_3G_2$$

$$E = \bar{G}_5\bar{G}_4\bar{G}_3G_2\bar{G}_1 + \bar{G}_5\bar{G}_4G_3\bar{G}_2\bar{G}_1 + \bar{G}_5G_4\bar{G}_3G_2\bar{G}_1 + \bar{G}_5G_4G_3G_2\bar{G}_1$$
$$+ G_5\bar{G}_4\bar{G}_3G_2\bar{G}_1 + G_5\bar{G}_4G_3\bar{G}_2\bar{G}_1 + G_5\bar{G}_4\bar{G}_3\bar{G}_2\bar{G}_1 + G_5\bar{G}_4G_3G_2\bar{G}_1$$
$$+ \bar{G}_5\bar{G}_4\bar{G}_3G_2G_1 + \bar{G}_5\bar{G}_4G_3\bar{G}_2G_1 + \bar{G}_5G_4\bar{G}_3G_2G_1 + \bar{G}_5G_4G_3G_2G_1$$
$$+ G_5\bar{G}_4\bar{G}_3G_2G_1 + G_5\bar{G}_4G_3\bar{G}_2G_1 + G_5\bar{G}_4\bar{G}_3\bar{G}_2G_1 + G_5\bar{G}_4G_3G_2G_1$$

Now, factoring C, we have:

$$C = \bar{G}_3(\bar{G}_5G_4 + G_5\bar{G}_4) + G_3(\bar{G}_5\bar{G}_4 + G_5G_4)$$

Thus $\qquad\qquad C = \bar{G}_3B + G_3\bar{B}$

Also for D we have:

$$D = G_2[\bar{G}_3(\bar{G}_5G_4 + G_5\bar{G}_4) + G_3(\bar{G}_5\bar{G}_4 + G_5G_4)]$$
$$+ \bar{G}_2[\bar{G}_3(\bar{G}_5\bar{G}_4 + G_5G_4) + G_3(\bar{G}_5G_4 + G_5\bar{G}_4)]$$

Table S–24 Problem 4–3

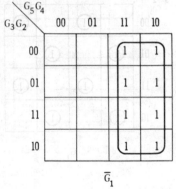

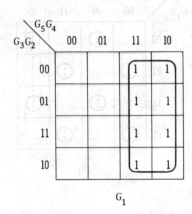

A

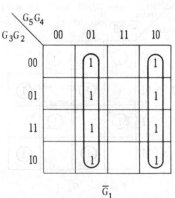

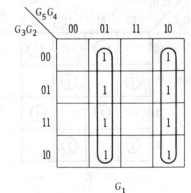

B

Table S-24 continued

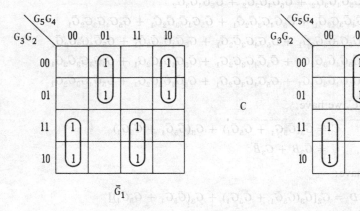

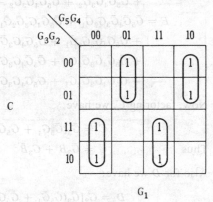

C

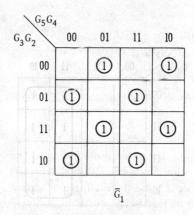

$\bar{G}_1$

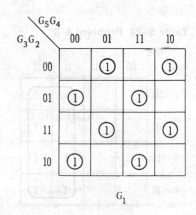

G_1

D

$\bar{G}_1$

G_1

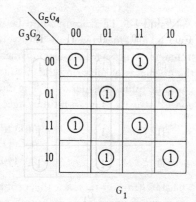

E

$\bar{G}_1$

G_1

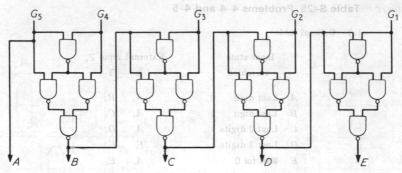

Fig. S–12 Problem 4–3

Thus $$D = G_2\bar{C} + \bar{G}_2 C$$

Similarly we may factorize for E:

$$E = \bar{G}_1\{\bar{G}_2[\bar{G}_3(\bar{G}_5 G_4 + G_5\bar{G}_4) + G_3(\bar{G}_5\bar{G}_4 + G_5 G_4)]$$
$$+ G_2[\bar{G}_3(\bar{G}_5\bar{G}_4 + G_5 G_4) + G_3(\bar{G}_5 G_4 + G_5\bar{G}_4)]\}$$
$$+ G_1\{\bar{G}_2[\bar{G}_3(\bar{G}_5\bar{G}_4 + G_5 G_4) + G_3(\bar{G}_5 G_4 + G_5\bar{G}_4)]$$
$$+ G_2[\bar{G}_3(\bar{G}_5 G_4 + G_5\bar{G}_4) + G_3(\bar{G}_5\bar{G}_4 + G_5 G_4)]\}$$

Hence $$E = \bar{G}_1 D + G_1 \bar{D}$$

This example illustrates that switching theory must be applied intelligently, and cannot be expected always to yield the final result. Direct implementation of the unfactorized equations would result in a very uneconomical (though correct) circuit. To implement the circuit in NAND logic we can use the exclusive OR circuit shown in Fig. S–1, for each stage, this is shown in Fig. S–12. Note that only 16 NAND elements are required compared with 20 using the AND/OR invertor system.

4-4 and **4-5** This circuit could be designed using normal truth-table techniques, and for small message words this would yield the most economical result. However, a change of message length would mean redesigning the circuit, and for long messages the problems of factoring the circuits to suit the fan-in factor of the logic modules could be quite considerable. The circuit is required to detect the presence of three consecutive 1's in a ten-bit message, for example:

0011101101	valid
0011110000	invalid
0011101110	valid

The state transfer table for this problem is shown in Table S-25, note that six input states are required necessitating three bits for the state coding. Note also that only

Table S–25 Problems 4–4 and 4–5

(a) General table

	Input state variables		External input Z_n	
			0	1
A	Last digit	0	A_+	B_+
B	Last digit	1	A_+	C_+
C	Last 2 digits	1	A_+	D_+
D	Last 3 digits	1	F_+	E_+
E	Wait for 0		A_+	E_+
F	Output		F_+	F_+

(b) Assigned table for NAND implementation

	Input state variables			External input Z_n	
	w	x	y	0	1
A	0	0	0	000	001
B	0	0	1	000	011
C	0	1	1	000	010
D	0	1	0	100	110
E	1	1	0	000	110
F	1	0	0	100	100

(c) Alternative assignment

	Input state variables			External input Z_n	
	w	x	y	0	1
A	0	0	0	000	001
B	0	0	1	000	011
C	0	1	1	000	010
D	0	1	0	111	110
E	1	1	0	000	110
F	1	1	1	111	111

six of the combinations are used, the remaining two being 'don't care' conditions. Table S–26 shows the Karnaugh maps for the logic gate implementation; two possible state assignments are given, both giving rather similar results; note the grouping of common prime implicants for the assignment shown in Table S–26(b). The next input state equations for W, X, and Y are, for the initial assignment, Table S–26(a)

$$W = wz_n + w\bar{x} + \bar{w}x\bar{y}$$
$$X = xz_n + yz_n$$
$$Y = \bar{w}\bar{x}z_n$$

The logic diagram for the cells is shown in Fig. S–13; note that the first cell can be simplified since the input states wxy must indicate that the last digit is 0, i.e. $\bar{w}x\bar{y}$, therefore the output from the first cell depends on the external input z_1. The last cell must be modified because, though the actual output state is given by $w\bar{x}\bar{y}$, we must account for the case when the sequence 0000000111 occurs, thus we also need to know the input state 'last three digits 1', i.e. $\bar{w}x\bar{y}$; this is accomplished by the additional gating circuitry. Note that the actual cell circuit requires 11 NAND elements, and the complete ten-bit circuit 105 elements.

To design the contact circuit we use Table S–25(a) direct to give the equations:

$$A_+ = A\bar{z}_n + B\bar{z}_n + C\bar{z}_n + E\bar{z}_n \qquad\qquad D_+ = Cz_n$$
$$B_+ = Az_n \qquad\qquad\qquad\qquad\qquad\quad E_+ = Dz_n + Ez_n$$
$$C_+ = Bz_n \qquad\qquad\qquad\qquad\qquad\quad F_+ = Fz_n + F\bar{z}_n + D\bar{z}_n = 1 + D\bar{z}_n$$

Table S–26 Problems 4–4 and 4–5

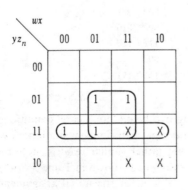

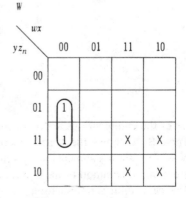

Table S–26 continued

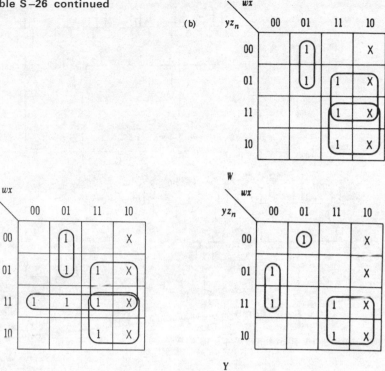

(b)

The circuit may be simplified in the initial and final cells (Fig. S–14). Note that two outputs are required: D and F. The F line may be a straight-through connection.

It is interesting to consider how the circuit may be redesigned to detect the occurrence of *one group only* of three consecutive 1's. Symmetric functions cannot be used to design this circuit. It is normal practice to use one external input per cell, but there is no reason in theory why more should not be used. Table S–27 shows the same circuit allocated with two external inputs $z_1 z_2$. The cell relay equations are:

$$A_+ = A\bar{z}_1\bar{z}_2 + Az_1\bar{z}_2 + B\bar{z}_1\bar{z}_2 + Bz_1\bar{z}_2 + C\bar{z}_1\bar{z}_2 + Dz_1\bar{z}_2 + E\bar{z}_1\bar{z}_2 + Ez_1\bar{z}_2$$

Thus $\quad A_+ = A\bar{z}_2 + B\bar{z}_2 + C\bar{z}_1\bar{z}_2 + Dz_1\bar{z}_2 + E\bar{z}_2$

$$B_+ = A\bar{z}_1 z_2 + B\bar{z}_1 z_2 + C\bar{z}_1 z_2 + E\bar{z}_1 z_2$$

$$C_+ = Az_1 z_2$$

$$D_+ = Bz_1 z_2$$

$$E_+ = Cz_1 z_2 + Dz_1 z_2 + Ez_1 z_2$$

$$F_+ = F\bar{z}_1\bar{z}_2 + F\bar{z}_1 z_2 + Fz_1\bar{z}_2 + Fz_1 z_2 + Cz_1\bar{z}_2 + D\bar{z}_1\bar{z}_2 + D\bar{z}_1 z_2$$

Hence $\quad F_+ = 1 + Cz_1\bar{z}_2 + D\bar{z}_1$

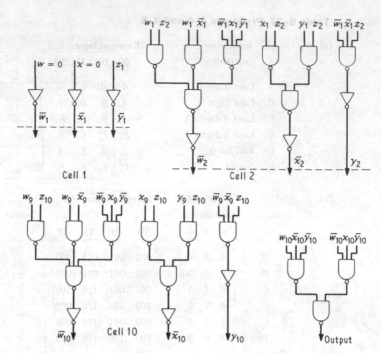

Fig. S–13 Problems 4–4 and 4–5

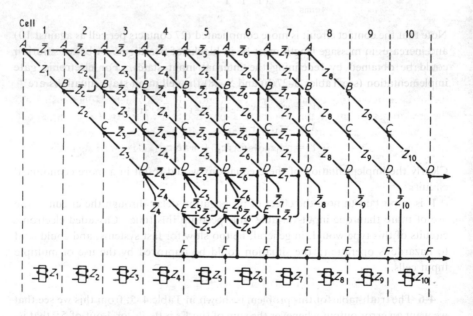

Fig. S–14 Problems 4–4 and 4–5

Table S-27 Problems 4-4 and 4-5

(a)

Input state variables		External inputs Z_1Z_2			
		00	01	11	10
A	Last digit 0	A_+	B_+	C_+	A_+
B	Last digit 1	A_+	B_+	D_+	A_+
C	Last 2 digits 1	A_+	B_+	E_+	F_+
D	Last 3 digits 1	F_+	F_+	E_+	A_+
E	Wait for 0	A_+	B_+	E_+	A_+
F	Output	F_+	F_+	F_+	F_+

(b)

Input state variables				External inputs Z_1Z_2			
	w	x	y	00	01	11	10
A	0	0	0	000	001	011	000
B	0	0	1	000	001	010	000
C	0	1	1	000	001	110	100
D	0	1	0	100	100	110	000
E	1	1	0	000	001	110	000
F	1	0	0	100	100	100	100
'Don't care' terms	1	0	1				
	1	1	1				

Note that the contact circuit is more complicated (27 contacts per cell as against 10) and increases in message length must be in blocks of two digits. A better solution could be obtained by redefining the internal input states. For electronic gate implementation (see Tables S-27(b) and S-28) the cell input state equations are

$$W = w\bar{x} + xz_1z_2 + xyz_1 + \bar{w}x\bar{y}\bar{z}_1$$

$$X = xz_1z_2 + \bar{w}z_1z_2$$

$$Y = y\bar{z}_1z_2 + \bar{w}\bar{x}\bar{y}z_2 + wx\bar{z}_1z_2$$

Clearly the implementation of these equations would result in a more economical circuit.

It is important to note the effect of propagation delay through the circuits; the use of more than one input-variable will speed up this time. Cascaded electronic circuits of this type would, in general, be too slow for fast systems, and could lead to hazardous operation; the situation could be improved by the use of multiple input cells.

4-6 The truth-table for this problem is shown in Table 4-5, from this we see that we want an error output whenever the sum of the 1's is 0-, 2-, or 4-out-of-5; that is,

Table S–28 Problems 4–4 and 4–5

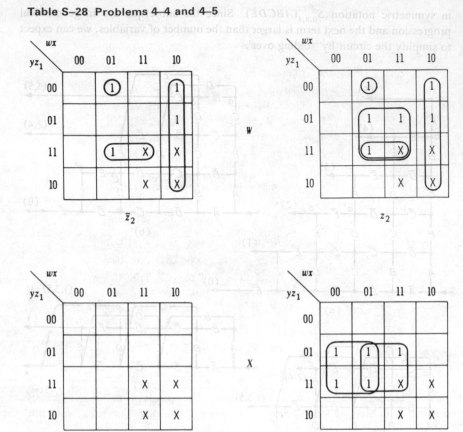

W

X

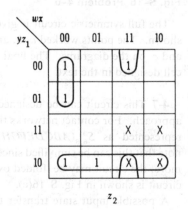

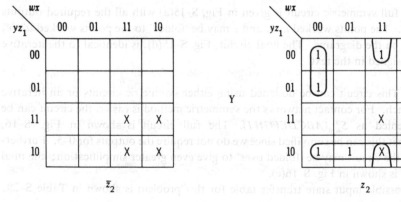

Y

in symmetric notation $S^5_{0,2,4}(ABCDE)$. Since the subscripts are in geometrical progression and the next term is larger than the number of variables, we can expect to simplify the circuit by 'folding over'.

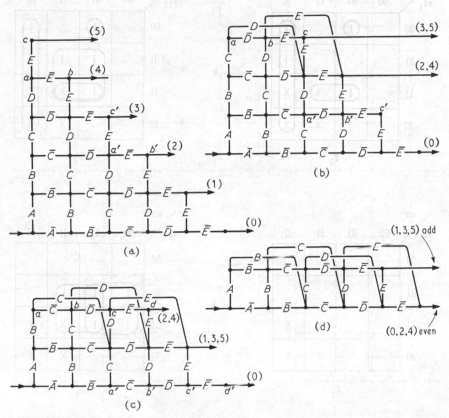

Fig. S–15 Problem 4–6

The full symmetric circuit is given in Fig. S–15(a) with all the required outputs shown. The points worked a, b, and c may be 'folded' to the points worked a', b', and c' on the diagrams. The final circuit, Fig. S–15(d), is identical to the iterative cell designed in the text.

4-7 This circuit can be designed using either symmetric circuits or an iterative approach. For contact networks the symmetric method is easier, the circuit can be represented as $S^9_{6,8}(ABCDEFGHI)$. The full circuit is shown in Fig. S–16, note that this can be simplified since we do not require the outputs for 0–5. Furthermore, the circuit may be 'folded over' to give even greater simplification; the final circuit is shown in Fig. S–16(c).

A possible input state transfer table for this problem is shown in Table S–29,

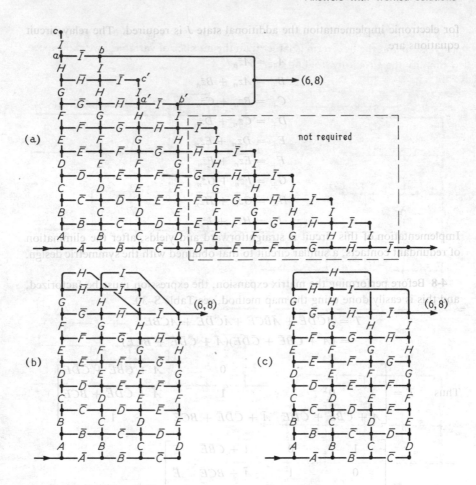

Fig. S–16 Problem 4–7

Table S–29 Problem 4–7

Input state variables		External inputs Z	
		0	1
A	Sum zero	A_+	B_+
B	Sum one	B_+	C_+
C	Sum two	C_+	D_+
D	Sum three	D_+	E_+
E	Sum four	E_+	F_+
F	Sum five	F_+	G_+
G	Sum six	G_+	H_+
H	Sum seven	H_+	I_+
I	Sum eight	I_+	J_+
J	Abortive	J_+	J_+

for electronic implementation the additional state J is required. The relay circuit equations are

$$A_+ = A\bar{z}_n$$
$$B_+ = Az_n + B\bar{z}_n$$
$$C_+ = Bz_n + C\bar{z}_n$$
$$D_+ = Cz_n + D\bar{z}_n$$
$$E_+ = Dz_n + E\bar{z}_n$$
$$F_+ = Ez_n + F\bar{z}_n$$
$$G_+ = Fz_n + G\bar{z}_n$$
$$H_+ = Gz_n + H\bar{z}_n$$
$$I_+ = Hz_n + I\bar{z}_n$$

Implementation of this circuit is straightforward and yields, after the elimination of redundant contacts, a similar circuit to that obtained with the symmetric design.

4-8 Before performing the matrix expansion, the expression must be factorized, and this is easily done using the map method, see Table S–30.

$$T = A\bar{C}\bar{D}\bar{E} + \bar{A}BC\bar{E} + \bar{A}\bar{C}\bar{D}E + ACBE$$
$$= (A + C\bar{B}\bar{F} + \bar{C}\bar{D}E)(\bar{A} + \bar{C}\bar{D}\bar{E} + BCE)$$

Thus
$$T = \begin{bmatrix} 1 & 0 & A + C\bar{B}\bar{E} + \bar{C}\bar{D}E \\ 0 & 1 & \bar{A} + \bar{C}\bar{D}\bar{E} + BCE \\ A + C\bar{B}\bar{E} + \bar{C}\bar{D}E & \bar{A} + \bar{C}\bar{D}\bar{E} + BCE & 1 \end{bmatrix}$$

$$= \begin{bmatrix} 1 & 0 & A + C\bar{B}\bar{E} & E \\ 0 & 1 & \bar{A} + BCE & \bar{E} \\ A + C\bar{B}\bar{E} & \bar{A} + BCE & 1 & \bar{C}\bar{D} \\ E & \bar{E} & \bar{C}\bar{D} & 1 \end{bmatrix}$$

Hence
$$T = \begin{array}{c} \\ 1 \\ 2 \\ 3 \\ 4 \\ 5 \end{array} \begin{array}{ccccc} 1 & 2 & 3 & 4 & 5 \\ \begin{bmatrix} 1 & 0 & A & E & \bar{B}\bar{E} \\ 0 & 1 & \bar{A} & \bar{E} & BE \\ A & \bar{A} & 1 & \bar{C}\bar{D} & C \\ E & \bar{E} & \bar{C}\bar{D} & 1 & 0 \\ \bar{B}\bar{E} & BE & C & 0 & 1 \end{bmatrix} \end{array}$$

The circuit is shown implemented in Fig. S–17.

Table S–30 Problem 4–8

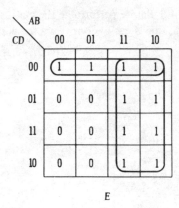
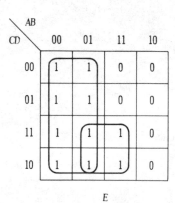

Top left (Ē):

CD\AB	00	01	11	10
00			1	1
01				
11	1			
10	1			

$\bar{E}$

Top right (E):

CD\AB	00	01	11	10
00	1	1		
01				
11			1	
10			1	

E

Middle left (Ē):

CD\AB	00	01	11	10
00	0	0	1	1
01	0	0	1	1
11	1	0	1	1
10	1	0	1	1

$\bar{E}$

Middle right (E):

CD\AB	00	01	11	10
00	1	1	1	1
01	0	0	1	1
11	0	0	1	1
10	0	0	1	1

E

Bottom left (Ē):

CD\AB	00	01	11	10
00	1	1	1	1
01	1	1	0	0
11	1	1	0	0
10	1	1	0	0

$\bar{E}$

Bottom right (E):

CD\AB	00	01	11	10
00	1	1	0	0
01	1	1	0	0
11	1	1	1	0
10	1	1	1	0

E

$$T = (A + C\bar{B}\bar{E} + \bar{C}\bar{D}E)(\bar{A} + \bar{C}\bar{D}\bar{E} + BCE)$$

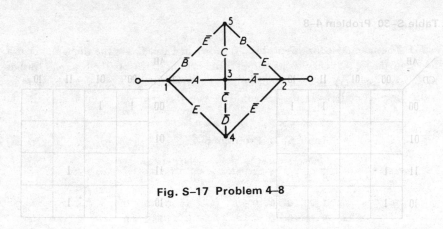

Fig. S–17 Problem 4–8

Chapter 5

5-1 The state-table for this problem is shown in Table S–31; the ring-counter is a five-state device that changes its output, obtained directly from the bistables (rather like a shift-register) on each input pulse. The remaining 27 states can be used as 'don't care' conditions in the design. This is a rather trivial example and the set

Table S–31 Problem 5–1

Present states					Next states				
A	B	C	D	E	A_+	B_+	C_+	D_+	E_+
1	0	0	0	0	0	1	0	0	0
0	1	0	0	0	0	0	1	0	0
0	0	1	0	0	0	0	0	1	0
0	0	0	1	0	0	0	0	0	1
0	0	0	0	1	1	0	0	0	0

and reset conditions can be ascertained by direct inspection of the state-table. For example, the condition for setting bistable A is 00001; however, since this is the only state with $E = 1$ (all the others are 'don't cares'), we can simply use E to set the bistable. All the other conditions follow in the same way to give, for the SR-FF bistable:

$$\text{Set} \quad S_A = E \qquad \text{Reset} \quad R_A = A$$
$$S_B = A \qquad\qquad R_B = B$$
$$S_C = B \qquad\qquad R_C = C$$
$$S_D = C \qquad\qquad R_D = D$$
$$S_E = D \qquad\qquad R_E = E$$

The trigger bistable may be treated similarly to give:

$$T_A = A + E$$
$$T_B = A + B$$
$$T_C = B + C$$
$$T_D = C + D$$
$$T_E = D + E$$

Figure S–18 shows the logic diagrams for the two cases. It is worth noting that the circuit is on the conservative side. In practice more economical circuits can be designed by utilizing the circuit characteristics of the bistable device. Suppose for example we have an a.c. pulse bistable which operates on a negative-going edge, and that the system employs a positive logic convention. In this case the set conditions may be taken directly to the set input terminals without gating with the input

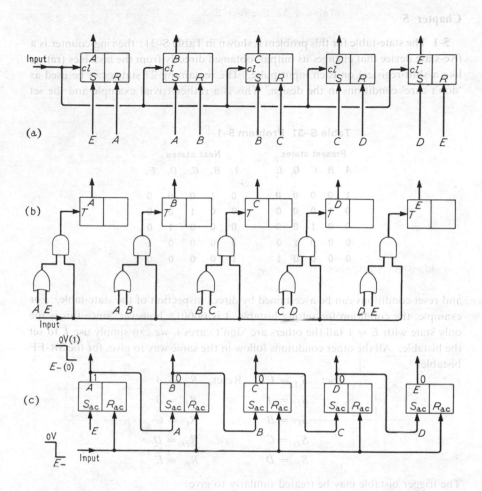

Fig. S–18 Problem 5–1

(clock), the input being used as a common reset line to all the bistables [see Fig. S–18(c)]. The action is that the input comes along and resets the bistables, the change of output state at one bistable only (going from 1 → 0) produces a negative-going pulse which sets the next bistable. In all cases provision must be made to set an initial 1 into the ring-counter circuit before operation.

5–2 Table S–32 shows the state-table for this problem, with the Karnaugh maps for the SR-FF bistable input conditions in Table S–33. Note that there are six

Table S–32 Problem 5–2

Present states				Next states			
5	4	2	1				
A	B	C	D	A_+	B_+	C_+	D_+
0	0	0	0	0	0	0	1
0	0	0	1	0	0	1	0
0	0	1	0	0	0	1	1
0	0	1	1	0	1	0	0
0	1	0	0	1	0	0	0
1	0	0	0	1	0	0	1
1	0	0	1	1	0	1	0
1	0	1	0	1	0	1	1
1	0	1	1	1	1	0	0
1	1	0	0	0	0	0	0

Table S–33 Problem 5–2

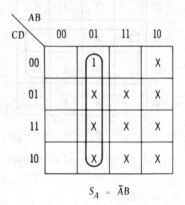

$S_A = \bar{A}B$

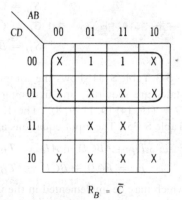

$R_A = AB$

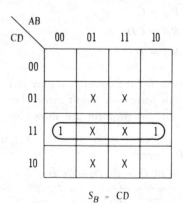

$S_B = CD$

$R_B = \bar{C}$

Table S–33 continued

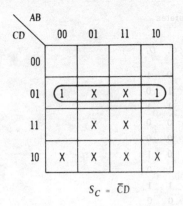

AB CD	00	01	11	10
00				
01	1	X	X	1
11		X	X	
10	X	X	X	X

$$S_C = \bar{C}D$$

AB CD	00	01	11	10
00	X	X	X	X
01		X	X	
11	1	X	X	1
10		X	X	

$$R_C = CD$$

AB CD	00	01	11	10
00	1			1
01		X	X	
11		X	X	
10	1	X	X	1

$$S_D = \bar{B}\bar{D}$$

AB CD	00	01	11	10
00		X	X	
01	1	X	X	1
11	1	X	X	1
10		X	X	

$$R_D = D$$

'don't care' conditions, i.e. $D = (5, 6, 7, 13, 14, 15)$, due to the unused combinations. The input equations are:

$$\text{Set} \quad S_A = \bar{A}B \qquad \text{Reset} \quad R_A = AB$$
$$S_B = CD \qquad\qquad\qquad R_B = \bar{C}$$
$$S_C = \bar{C}D \qquad\qquad\qquad R_C = CD$$
$$S_D = \bar{B}\bar{D} \qquad\qquad\qquad R_D = D$$

5-3 Table S–34 shows the complete transition table for the counter, if only ten states are required, and assuming the first ten, this leaves six 'don't cares', i.e. $D = (15, 14, 10, 11, 9, 8)$. The Karnaugh maps for this problem are shown in Table S–35. The input equations are:

$$T_A = \bar{A}B\bar{C}\bar{D} + AD \qquad T_B = \bar{B}C\bar{D} + AD$$
$$T_C = BCD + \bar{B}\bar{C}D \qquad T_D = A + B\bar{C}D + BC\bar{D} + \bar{B}CD + \bar{B}\bar{C}\bar{D}$$

which may be implemented in the usual way.

Table S–34 Problem 5–3

Present states				Next states			
A	B	C	D	A_+	B_+	C_+	D_+
0	0	0	0	0	0	0	1
0	0	0	1	0	0	1	1
0	0	1	1	0	0	1	0
0	0	1	0	0	1	1	0
0	1	1	0	0	1	1	1
0	1	1	1	0	1	0	1
0	1	0	1	0	1	0	0
0	1	0	0	1	1	0	0
1	1	0	0	1	1	0	1
1	1	0	1	0	0	0	0

Table S–35 Problem 5–3

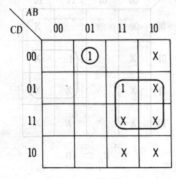

$$T_A = \bar{A}B\bar{C}\bar{D} + AD$$

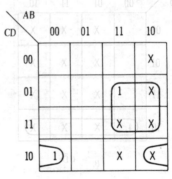

$$T_B = \bar{B}C\bar{D} + AD$$

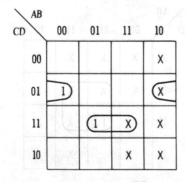

$$T_C = BCD + \bar{B}\bar{C}D$$

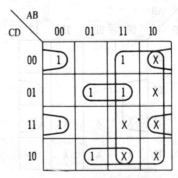

$$T_D = A + \bar{B}\bar{C}\bar{D} + B\bar{C}D + \bar{B}CD + BC\bar{D}$$

Table S–36 Problem 5–3

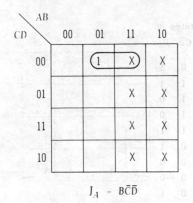

$J_A = B\bar{C}\bar{D}$

AB
CD	00	01	11	10
00	X	X		X
01	X	X	1	X
11	X	X	X	X
10	X	X	X	X

$K_A = D$

AB
CD	00	01	11	10
00		X	X	X
01		X	X	X
11		X	X	X
10	1	X	X	X

$J_B = C\bar{D}$

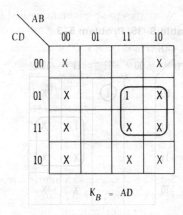

$K_B = AD$

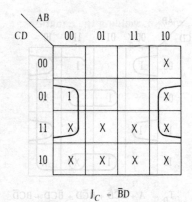

$J_C = \bar{B}D$

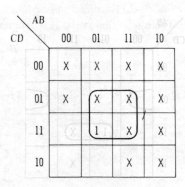

$K_C = BD$

Table S–36 continued

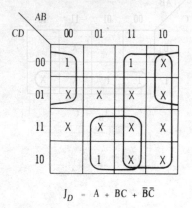

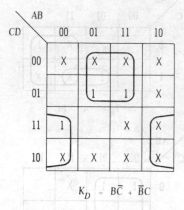

$$J_D = A + BC + \bar{B}\bar{C}$$

$$K_D = B\bar{C} + \bar{B}C$$

When designing counter circuits, it is worthwhile trying several different types of bistable (if available) to find the most economical circuit; in general the JK bistables give the best results. For example the same Gray-code counter using JK bistables yields the following input equations (see Table S–36)

$$J_A = B\bar{C}\bar{D} \qquad\qquad K_A = D$$
$$J_B = C\bar{D} \qquad\qquad K_B = AD$$
$$J_C = \bar{B}D \qquad\qquad K_C = BD$$
$$J_D = A + BC + \bar{B}\bar{C} \qquad K_D = B\bar{C} + \bar{B}C$$

5-4 The divide-by-5 counter circuit has five states, requiring three bistables, thus leaving three 'don't care' conditions, i.e. $D = (5, 6, 7)$. Table S–37 shows the transition table; note that bistable A is set for every fifth input pulse. If this is used in conjunction with a divide-by-2 circuit, preferably preceding the divide-by-5, a divide-by-10 counter will result.

Table S–38 shows the Karnaugh maps for the problem, yielding the equations:

$$T_A = A + BC \qquad T_B = C \qquad T_C = \bar{A}$$

Table S–37 Problem 5–4

Present state				Next state		
A	B	C		A_+	B_+	C_+
0	0	0		0	0	1
0	0	1		0	1	0
0	1	0		0	1	1
0	1	1		1	0	0
1	0	0		0	0	0

Table S–38 Problem 5–4

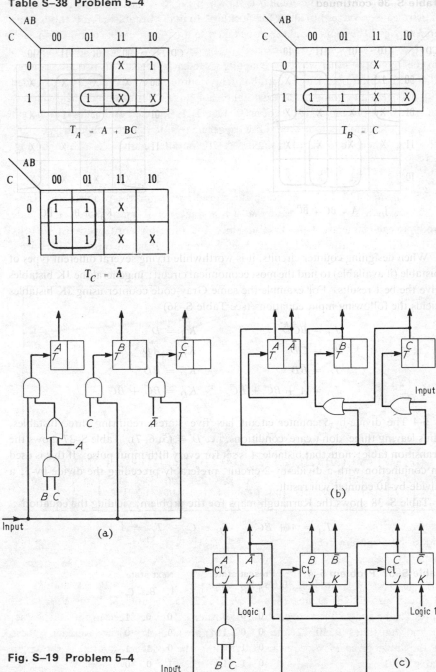

$$T_A = A + BC$$

$$T_B = C$$

$$T_C = \bar{A}$$

Fig. S–19 Problem 5–4

(a)

(b)

(c)

The circuit diagram for the counter is shown in Fig. S–19(a), note the inclusion of an extra gate on stage A to allow for clocking. In many bistable circuits this is done internally and the input would then be taken to a gate, or clock, terminal on each bistable. It is important to realize that all the counters we have designed have had parallel inputs, in other words, the input goes to each stage. This produces a more reliable and faster operating circuit, but many counters used in practice are cascaded with a single input going to the least significant stage. For example, the divide-by-5 circuit shown in Fig. S–19(b) counts 0, 1, 2, 3, 7, 0, 1 etc., and relies on inherent delays in the elements to prevent false triggering. Note that the stages trigger, one after the other, in a serial fashion. A JK parallel counter is shown in Fig. S–19(c).

5-5 Figure S–20 shows the complete state-diagram for the problem and Table S–39 shows the state-table. Note that it is a single serial input, therefore the only inputs to each state are 0 and 1; also, since it is a five-bit word, we must go back to the initial state after five bits have been examined. It is obvious that there are a

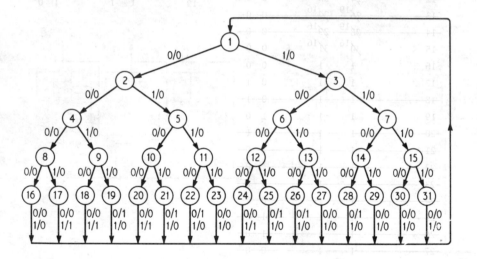

Fig. S–20 Problem 5–5

large number of redundant states, for example, 16, 23, 27, 29, 30, and 31 are identical, also 17, 18, 20, and 24, and 19, 21, 22, 25, 26, and 28. If these are called states 16, 17 and 19 respectively, and the other entries replaced in the state-table, we find that states (9, 10, 12) and (11, 13, 14) are also equivalent. Replacing these in the table gives (5, 6) equivalent, yielding the reduced state-table shown in Table S–40.

Table S–39 Problem 5–5

Present states	Input x Next states		Outputs	
	0	1	0	1
1	2	3	0	0
2	4	5	0	0
3	6^5	7	0	0
4	8	9	0	0
5	10^9	11	0	0
~~6~~	12^9	13^{11}	0	0
7	14^{11}	15	0	0
8	16	17	0	0
9	18^{17}	19^{17}	0	0
~~10~~	20^{17}	24^{19}	0	0
11	22^{19}	23^{16}	0	0
~~12~~	24^{17}	25^{19}	0	0
~~13~~	26^{19}	27^{16}	0	0
~~14~~	28^{19}	29^{16}	0	0
15	30^{16}	31^{16}	0	0
16	1	1	0	0
17	1	1	0	1
~~18~~	1	1	0	1
19	1	1	1	0
~~20~~	1	1	0	1
~~21~~	1	1	1	0
~~22~~	1	1	1	0
~~23~~	1	1	0	0
~~24~~	1	1	0	1
~~25~~	1	1	1	0
~~26~~	1	1	1	0
~~27~~	1	1	0	0
~~28~~	1	1	1	0
~~29~~	1	1	0	0
~~30~~	1	1	0	0
~~31~~	1	1	0	0

Table S–40 Problem 5–5

Present states	Input x Next state		Outputs	
	0	1	0	1
1	2	3	0	0
2	4	5	0	0
3	5	7	0	0
4	8	9	0	0
5	9	11	0	0
7	11	15	0	0
8	16	17	0	0
9	17	19	0	0
11	19	16	0	0
15	16	16	0	0
16	1	1	0	0
17	1	1	0	1
19	1	1	1	0

5-6 The Mealy and Moore state-diagrams are shown in Fig. S–21.

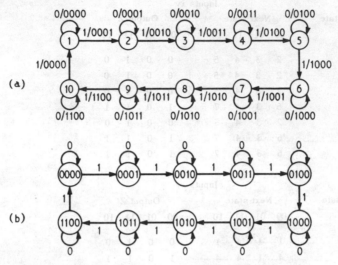

Fig. S–21 Problem 5–6

5-7 With a little thought, this circuit could easily be designed intuitively, nevertheless, applying the theory could produce the state-diagram shown in Fig. S–22(a), and the corresponding state-table in Table S–41(a). This may easily be reduced since it is obvious that states (1, 2, 3, 5) and (4, 6, 7) are identical, giving the reduced state-diagram and state-table shown in Fig. S–22(b) and Table S–41(b) respectively. The state-diagram is obviously that of a gated bistable circuit. Assigning the two

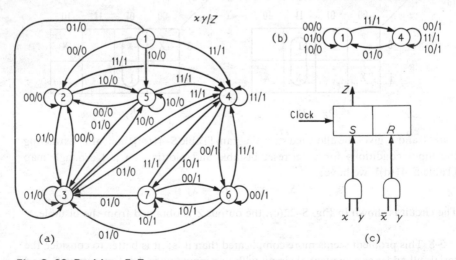

Fig. S–22 Problem 5–7

Table S–41 Problem 5–7

(a)

Present state	Next state				Output Z			
	00	01	11	10	00	01	11	10
1	2	3	4	5	0	0	1	0
2	2	3	4	5	0	0	1	0
3	2	3	4	5	0	0	1	0
4	6	3	4	7	1	0	1	1
5	2	3	4	5	0	0	1	0
6	6	3	4	7	1	0	1	1
7	6	3	4	7	1	0	1	1

Inputs xy

(b)

Present state	Next state				Output Z			
	00	01	11	10	00	01	11	10
1	1	1	4	1	0	0	1	0
4	4	1	4	4	1	0	1	1

Inputs xy

(c)

Present state	Next state				Output Z			
z	00	01	11	10	00	01	11	10
0	0	0	1	0	0	0	1	0
1	1	0	1	1	1	0	1	1

Inputs xy

(d)

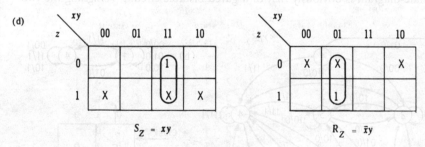

$$S_z = xy \qquad R_z = \bar{x}y$$

states 0 and 1, gives the allocated state-diagram [Table S–41(c)] then, after extracting the input conditions for a set-reset bistable and plotting on a Karnaugh map [Table S–41(d)], we have:

$$S_z = xy \qquad R_z = \bar{x}y$$

The circuit is shown in Fig. S–22(c), the output Z is obtained from the bistable.

5-8 This problem seems more complicated than it is; it is better to consider the serial full-adder as a sequential circuit with two inputs xy and a sum output S_0, and

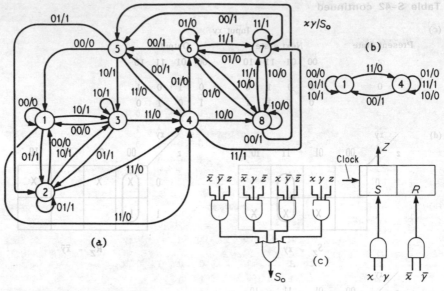

Fig. S–23 Problem 5–8

allow the carry to be indigenous to the circuit. The first attempt at a state-diagram
may look something like Fig. S–23(a), but this soon reduces to a two-state diagram;
the relevant state-tables are shown in Table S–42. The problem has been solved in

Table S–42 Problem 5–8

(a)

Present state	Next state				Output S			
	00	01	11	10	00	01	11	10
1	1	2	4	3	0	1	0	1
2	1	2	4	3	0	1	0	1
3	1	2	4	3	0	1	0	1
4	5	6	7	8	1	0	1	0
5	1	2	4	3	0	1	0	1
6	5	6	7	8	1	0	1	0
7	5	6	7	8	1	0	1	0
8	5	6	7	8	1	0	1	0

(b)

Present state	Next state				Output S			
	00	01	11	10	00	01	11	10
1	1	1	4	1	0	1	0	1
4	1	4	4	4	1	0	1	0

Table S–42 continued

(c)

Present state	Next state				Output S			
		Input xy						
z	00	01	11	10	00	01	11	10
0	0	0	1	0	0	1	0	1
1	0	1	1	1	1	0	1	0

(d)

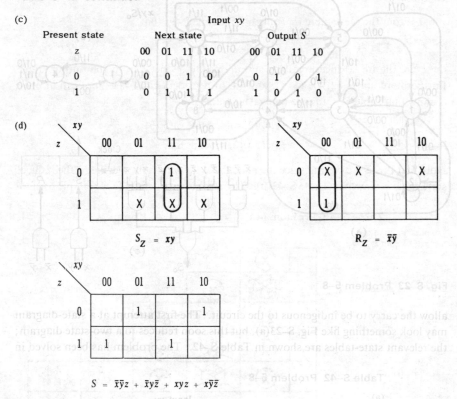

$$S_Z = xy$$

$$R_Z = \bar{x}\bar{y}$$

$$S = \bar{x}\bar{y}z + \bar{x}y\bar{z} + xyz + x\bar{y}\bar{z}$$

full, and it is interesting to note the familiar sum equations for the output, i.e.

$$S_0 = \bar{x}\bar{y}z + \bar{x}y\bar{z} + xyz + x\bar{y}\bar{z}$$

The carry logic is combined with the bistable circuit, this may easily be seen from the bistable equation, i.e.

$$z_+ = S + \bar{R}z = xy + (\overline{\bar{x}\bar{y}})z = xy + (x + y)z$$

Thus $\quad z_+ = xy + xz + yz$

Furthermore, note that this is an improvement on the conventional design which uses a combinational full-adder circuit, complete with carry logic, and a one-bit bistable store. In an actual design, the basic clock used for the serial system would be used to gate the bistable (or input gates) in the synchronous circuit.

Chapter 6

6-1 From the state-table in Table 6–25 we may say that

$$1 \not\equiv 2, \quad 1 \not\equiv 5, \quad 1 \not\equiv 6, \quad 2 \not\equiv 3, \quad 3 \not\equiv 5, \quad 3 \not\equiv 6$$

these are the initial incompatibles and are easily deduced from the output states. Furthermore states (2, 4), (4, 5), and (4, 6) are identical. The implication chart is shown in Table S–43(a) the equivalent states are

$$M = (1, 4)(2, 4)(4, 5)(4, 6)(5, 6)$$

thus

$$M = (3)(1, 4)(2, 4)(4, 5, 6)$$

Note that this is a covering since the machine is incompletely specified; the reduced state-table is shown in Table S–43(b). The state assignment is fairly simple for four

Table S–43 Problem 6–1

(a)

(b)

Present state	Next state				Output T			
	00	01	11	10	00	01	11	10
A (1,4)	C	C	D	A	1	1	0	1
B (3)	A	B	D	D	1	1	0	1
C (2,4)	C	D	D	B	0	1	1	1
D (4,5,6)	C	C	D	A	0	1	1	1

Inputs $x_1 x_2$

(c)

Next state	Present state
A	A,B,D
B	B,C
C	A,C,D
D	A,B,C,D

Table S–43 continued

(d)

Present state		Next state				Output T			
		Inputs x_1x_2							
y z		00	01	11	10	00	01	11	10
A 0 0		11	11	10	00	1	1	0	1
B 0 1		00	01	10	10	1	1	0	1
C 1 1		11	10	10	01	0	1	1	1
D 1 0		11	11	10	00	0	1	1	1

states since there are only three possible codes. Using the technique of examining the origin of the next states [Table S–43(c)] we find that, if possible, all states should be adjacent! However, applying rule 2, we see that (CD) and (AD) occur as the next states of A, B, and D, thus we would choose these to be adjacent. The partition approach gives one non-trivial partition with the substitution property:

$$P_1 = (AD)(C)(B)$$

Table S–44 Problem 6–1

(a)

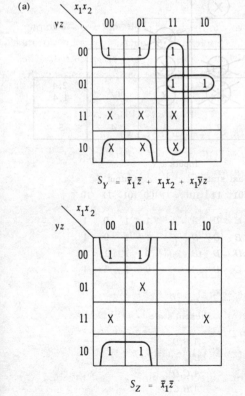

$$S_Y = \bar{x}_1\bar{z} + x_1x_2 + x_1\bar{y}z$$

$$S_Z = \bar{x}_1\bar{z}$$

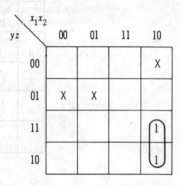

$$R_Y = x_1y\bar{x}_2$$

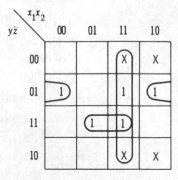

$$R_Z = x_1x_2 + x_2yz + \bar{x}_2\bar{y}z$$

Table S–44 continued

(b)

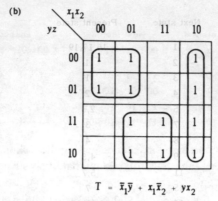

$$T = \bar{x}_1\bar{y} + x_1\bar{x}_2 + yx_2$$

This means using three bits (three bistables) for the allocation, i.e. two bits to distinguish the blocks and one bit for the elements. However, it is possible that the inclusion of an additional bistable could reduce the amount of combinational logic required and this approach should be investigated. The straightforward allocation of the four states using two bits is shown in Tables S–43(d) and S–44.

6-2 The state-table was reduced intuitively in the actual problem (No. 5, Chapter 5), this should be repeated using the implication chart. The next step is to allocate the internal states and, since there are thirteen states, four bits are required. The next state examination is shown in Table S–45. Using the partition approach the non-trivial partitions are:

$$P_1 = (1)(2, 3)(4, 5, 7)(8, 9, 11, 15)(16, 17, 19)$$
$$P_2 = (1)(2)(3)(4, 5)(7)(8, 9, 11)(15)(16, 17, 19)$$
$$P_3 = (1)(2)(3)(4, 7)(5)(8, 11)(9, 15)(16, 17, 19)$$
$$P_4 = (1)(2)(3)(4)(5, 7)(8)(9, 11, 15)(16, 17, 19)$$
$$P_5 = (1)(2)(3)(4)(5)(7)(8, 9)(16, 17, 19)(11)(15)$$
$$P_6 = (1)(2)(3)(4)(5)(7)(9)(8, 11)(16, 17, 19)(15)$$
$$P_7 = (1)(2)(3)(4)(5)(7)(8, 15)(9)(11)(16, 17)(19)$$
$$P_8 = (1)(2)(3)(4)(5)(7)(8)(9, 11)(15)(16, 17, 19)$$
$$P_9 = (1)(2)(3)(4)(5)(7)(8)(9, 15)(11)(16, 17, 19)$$
$$P_{10} = (1)(2)(3)(4)(5)(7)(8)(9)(11, 15)(16, 17, 19)$$
$$P_{11} = (1)(2)(3)(4)(5)(7)(8)(9)(11)(15)(16, 17)(19)$$
$$P_{12} = (1)(2)(3)(4)(5)(7)(8)(9)(11)(15)(16, 19)(17)$$
$$P_{13} = (1)(2)(3)(4)(5)(7)(8)(9)(11)(15)(16)(17, 19)$$

Since to implement any of these partitions directly requires at least five bits, we

Table S-45 Problem 6-2

Next state	Present state
1	16,17,19
2	1
3	1
4	2
5	2,3
7	3
8	4
9	4,5
11	5,7
15	7
16	8,11,15
17	8,9
19	9,11

Table S-46 Problem 6-2

Present state				Next state		Output T	
				Input x			
	A	B	C	D	0	1	0	1
1	1 1 0 0				0000	0100	0	0
2	0 0 0 0				0001	0101	0	0
3	0 1 0 0				0101	1101	0	0
4	0 0 0 1				0111	1111	0	0
5	0 1 0 1				1111	1011	0	0
7	1 1 0 1				1011	0011	0	0
8	0 1 1 1				0010	0110	0	0
9	1 1 1 1				0110	1110	0	0
11	1 0 1 1				1110	0010	0	0
15	0 0 1 1				0010	0010	0	0
16	0 0 1 0				1100	1100	0	0
17	0 1 1 0				1100	1100	0	1
19	1 1 1 0				1100	1100	1	0
Unused	1 0 0 0							
	1 0 0 1							
	1 0 1 0							

Table S–47 Problem 6–2

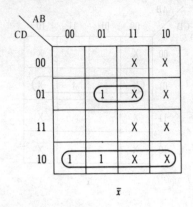

J_A

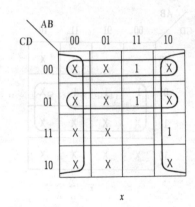

K_A

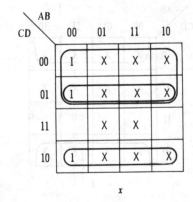

J_B

Table S–47 continued

K_B map ($\bar{x}$):

CD\AB	00	01	11	10
00	X		1	X
01	X		1	X
11	X	1		X
10	X			X

$\bar{x}$

K_B map (x):

CD\AB	00	01	11	10
00	X			X
01	X	1	1	X
11	X			X
10	X			X

x

K_B

J_C map ($\bar{x}$):

CD\AB	00	01	11	10
00				X
01	1	1	1	X
11	X	X	X	X
10	X	X	X	X

$\bar{x}$

J_C map (x):

CD\AB	00	01	11	10
00				X
01	1	1	1	X
11	X	X	X	X
10	X	X	X	X

x

J_C

K_C map ($\bar{x}$):

CD\AB	00	01	11	10
00	X	X	X	X
01	X	X	X	X
11				
10	1	1	1	X

$\bar{x}$

K_C map (x):

CD\AB	00	01	11	10
00	X	X	X	X
01	X	X	X	X
11				
10	1	1	1	X

x

K_C

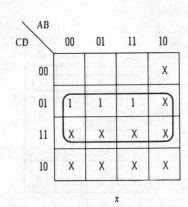
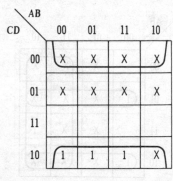

Table S–47 continued

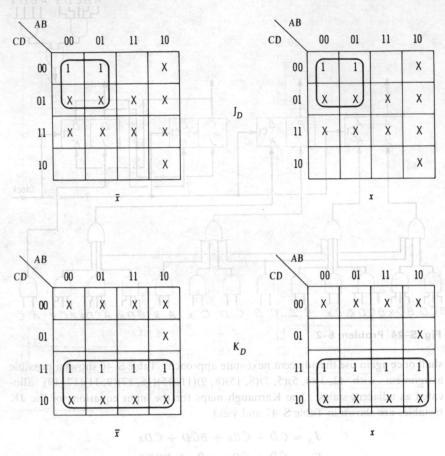

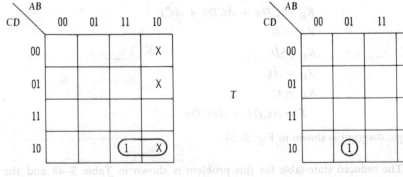

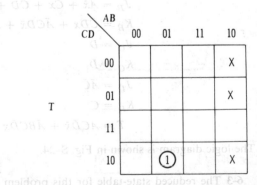

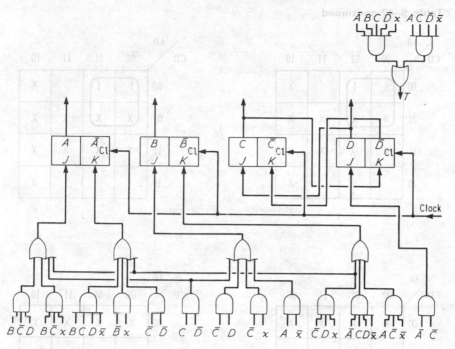

Fig. S–24 Problem 6–2

shall once again use the adjacent next state approach. Table S–46 shows a possible assignment with $(2, 3)(4, 5)(5, 7)(8, 15)(8, 9)(11, 15)(16, 17)(9, 11)(17, 19)$ allocated as adjacent states. The Karnaugh maps for the input equations of the JK bistables are shown in Table S–47 and yield

$$J_A = C\bar{D} + \bar{C}Bx + B\bar{C}D + \bar{C}Dx$$

$$K_A = \bar{C}\bar{D} + \bar{C}Dx + \bar{B}x + BCD\bar{x}$$

$$J_B = A\bar{x} + \bar{C}x + \bar{C}D + C\bar{D}$$

$$K_B = \bar{C}Dx + \bar{A}CD\bar{x} + A\bar{C}\bar{x}$$

$$J_C = D$$

$$K_C = \bar{D}$$

$$J_D = \bar{A}\bar{C}$$

$$K_D = C$$

$$T = AC\bar{D}\bar{x} + \bar{A}BC\bar{D}x$$

The logic diagram is shown in Fig. S–24.

6-3 The reduced state-table for this problem is shown in Table S–48 and the equivalent state-diagram in Fig. S–25. The state assignment is difficult to optimize

Table S–48 Problem 6–3

(a)

Present state	Next state, Inputs x_1x_2				Output			
	00	01	11	10	00	01	11	10
1	1	1	2	2	0	0	0	0
2	1	3	2	2	0	0	0	0
3	4	1	2	2	0	0	0	0
4	1	5	2	2	0	0	0	0
5	1	1	6	6	0	0	1	1
6	6	1	2	6	1	0	0	1

(b)

Next state	Present state
1	1,2,3,4,5,6
2	1,2,3,4,6
3	2
4	3
5	4
6	5,6

(c)

Present state	$y_1\ y_2\ y_3$	Next state, Inputs x_1x_2				Output T			
		00	01	11	10	00	01	11	10
1	0 0 0	000	000	010	010	0	0	0	0
2	0 1 0	000	110	010	010	0	0	0	0
3	1 1 0	100	000	010	010	0	0	0	0
4	1 0 0	000	011	010	010	0	0	0	0
5	0 1 1	000	000	001	001	0	0	1	1
6	0 0 1	001	000	010	001	1	0	0	1
Unused	1 0 1								
	1 1 1								

since there are no non-trivial partitions with the substitution property and the results of the next state examination are difficult to implement, thus a trial and error process is necessary to find the best assignment. A good starting point is to make (1, 2)(2, 3)(3, 4)(4, 1)(1, 6)(6, 5) adjacent, and this has been done in the assigned state-table, Table S–48(c). The Karnaugh maps for the JK bistable are shown in Table S–49 and give the following input and output equations:

$$Jy_1 = \bar{x}_1x_2y_2\bar{y}_3 \qquad Ky_1 = x_1 + \bar{y}_2 + x_2y_1$$

$$Jy_2 = x_1\bar{y}_3 + x_1x_2 + y_1x_2 \qquad Ky_2 = y_3 + \bar{x}_1\bar{x}_2 + \bar{x}_1y_1$$

$$Jy_3 = \bar{x}_1x_2y_1\bar{y}_2 \qquad Ky_3 = \bar{x}_1y_2 + x_2\bar{y}_2$$

$$T = x_1y_2y_3 + \bar{y}_2\bar{x}_2y_3$$

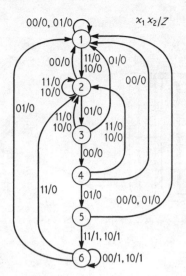

Fig. S–25 Problem 6–3

Table S–49 Problem 6–3

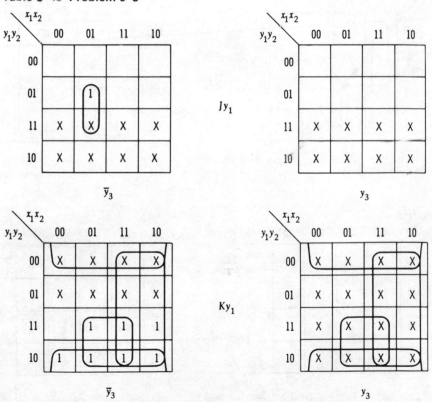

Table S–49 continued

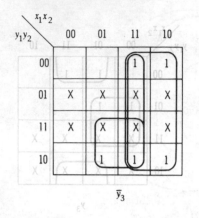

Jy_2

$\bar{y}_3$

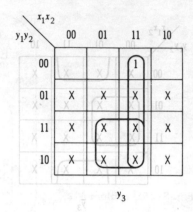

y_3

y_1y_2 \ x_1x_2	00	01	11	10
00	X	X	X	X
01	1			
11	1	1		
10	X	X	X	X

Ky_2

$\bar{y}_3$

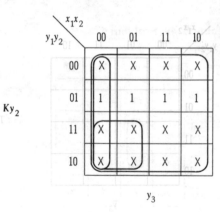

y_3

y_1y_2 \ x_1x_2	00	01	11	10
00				
01				
11				
10		①		

Jy_3

$\bar{y}_3$

y_1y_2 \ x_1x_2	00	01	11	10
00	X	X	X	X
01	X	X	X	X
11	X	X	X	X
10	X	Ⓧ	X	X

y_3

Table S–49 continued

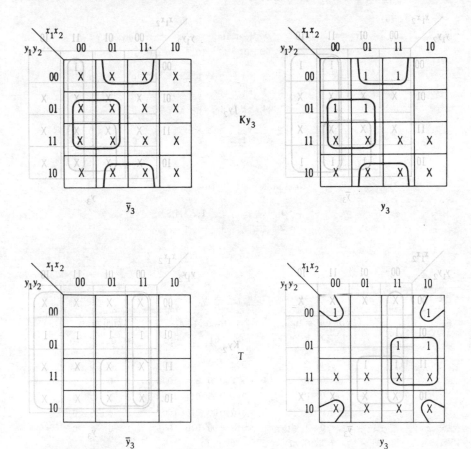

Ky_3

$\bar{y}_3$ y_3

T

$\bar{y}_3$ y_3

A similar result may be obtained using the Dolotta and McCluskey technique, which the reader is urged to try for himself.

6-4 The reduced state-table is shown in Table S–50, and the state-diagram in Fig. S–26; note that the circuit detects *all* sequences of five digits. There are three non-trivial partitions for this machine, i.e.

$$P_1 = (1)(2)(3)(4, 5)$$

$$P_2 = (1)(2)(3, 4, 5)$$

$$P_3 = (1)(2, 3, 4, 5)$$

Table S–50(c) shows the assigned state-table using partition P_3; the Karnaugh maps

Table S–50 Problem 6–4

(a)

Inputs $x_1 x_2$

Present state	Next state 00	01	11	10	Output T 00	01	11	10
1	2	1	2	1	0	0	0	0
2	3	1	3	1	0	0	0	0
3	4	1	4	1	0	0	0	0
4	5	1	5	1	0	0	0	0
5	5	1	5	1	1	0	1	0

(b)

Next state	Present state
1	1,2,3,4,5
2	1
3	2
4	3
5	4,5

(c)

Inputs $x_1 x_2$

Present state y_1 y_2 y_3	Next state 00	01	11	10	Output T 00	01	11	10
1 1 0 0	000	100	000	100	0	0	0	0
2 0 0 0	001	100	001	100	0	0	0	0
3 0 0 1	011	100	011	100	0	0	0	0
4 0 1 1	010	100	010	100	0	0	0	0
5 0 1 0	010	100	010	100	1	0	1	0
Unused { 1 0 1								
1 1 0								
1 1 1								

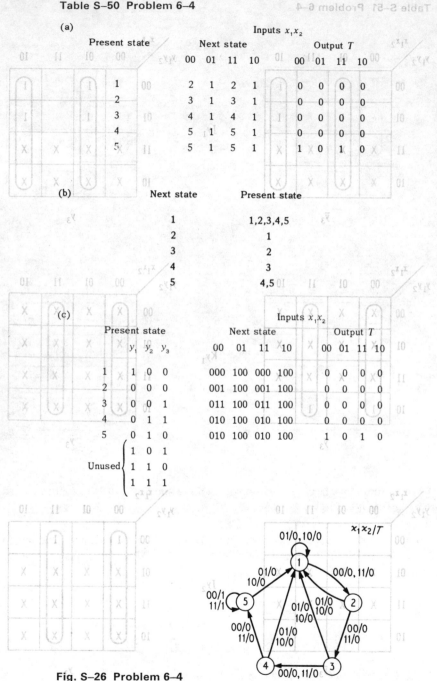

$x_1 x_2 / T$

Fig. S–26 Problem 6–4

Table S–51 Problem 6–4

K-map Jy_1

y_1y_2 \ x_1x_2	00	01	11	10
00	0	1	0	1
01	0	1	0	1
11	X	X	X	X
10	X	X	X	X

$\bar{y}_3$

K-map (top right)

y_1y_2 \ x_1x_2	00	01	11	10
00	1	1		1
01		1		1
11	X	X	X	X
10	X	X	X	X

y_3

K-map Ky_1

y_1y_2 \ x_1x_2	00	01	11	10
00	X	X	X	X
01	X	X	X	X
11	X	X	X	X
10	1	0	0	1

$\bar{y}_3$

K-map (middle right)

y_1y_2 \ x_1x_2	00	01	11	10
00	X	X	X	X
01	X	X	X	X
11	X	X	X	X
10	X	X	X	X

y_3

K-map Jy_2

y_1y_2 \ x_1x_2	00	01	11	10
00				
01	X	X	X	X
11	X	X	X	X
10				

$\bar{y}_3$

K-map (bottom right)

y_1y_2 \ x_1x_2	00	01	11	10
00	1		1	
01	X	X	X	X
11	X	X	X	X
10	X	X	X	X

y_3

Table S–51 continued

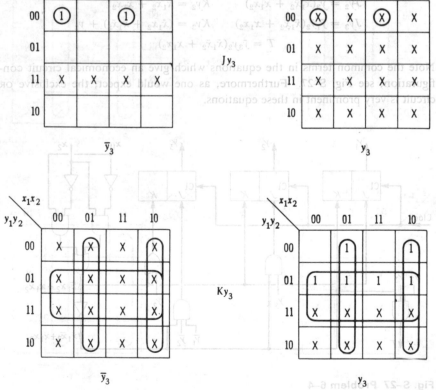

Ky_2

$\bar{y}_3$

y_3

Jy_3

$\bar{y}_3$

y_3

Ky_3

$\bar{y}_3$

y_3

Table S–51 continued

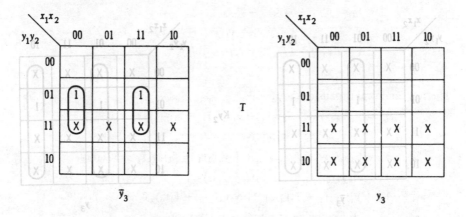

$$\bar{y}_3 \qquad\qquad\qquad y_3$$

for JK bistables are shown in Table S–51, yielding the input and output equations:

$$Jy_1 = \bar{x}_1 x_2 + x_1 \bar{x}_2 \qquad\qquad Ky_1 = \bar{x}_1 \bar{x}_2 + x_1 x_2$$
$$Jy_2 = y_3(\bar{x}_1 \bar{x}_2 + x_1 x_2) \qquad Ky_2 = \bar{x}_1 x_2 + x_1 \bar{x}_2$$
$$Jy_3 = \bar{y}_1 \bar{y}_2(\bar{x}_1 \bar{x}_2 + x_1 x_2) \qquad Ky_3 = (\bar{x}_1 x_2 + x_1 \bar{x}_2) + y_2$$
$$T = \bar{y}_3 y_2(\bar{x}_1 \bar{x}_2 + x_1 x_2)$$

Note the common terms in the equations which give an economical circuit configuration, see Fig. S–27. Furthermore, as one would expect, the exclusive OR circuit is very prominent in these equations.

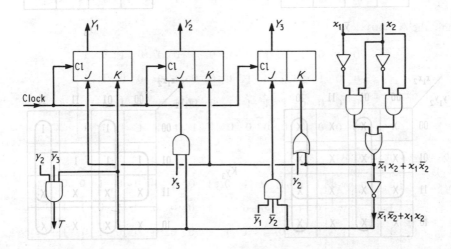

Fig. S–27 Problem 6–4

6-5 The circuit equations are:

$$Y_1 = \bar{y}_1\bar{y}_2 + \bar{y}_2\bar{y}_3y_4 + \bar{y}_1\bar{y}_4$$
$$Y_2 = y_1\bar{y}_2\bar{y}_4 + \bar{y}_1y_2\bar{y}_4 + y_1y_2y_4 + y_2y_3y_4 + y_1y_3y_4$$
$$Y_3 = y_3y_4 + \bar{y}_2y_3 + \bar{y}_1y_3 + y_1y_2\bar{y}_3\bar{y}_4$$
$$Y_4 = y_4$$

The full canonical expansions are:

$$Y_1 = \bar{y}_4\bar{y}_3\bar{y}_2\bar{y}_1 + \bar{y}_4\bar{y}_3y_2\bar{y}_1 + \bar{y}_4y_3\bar{y}_2\bar{y}_1 + \bar{y}_4y_3y_2\bar{y}_1 + y_4\bar{y}_3\bar{y}_2\bar{y}_1$$
$$+ y_4\bar{y}_3\bar{y}_2y_1 + y_4y_3\bar{y}_2\bar{y}_1$$
$$Y_2 = \bar{y}_4\bar{y}_3\bar{y}_2y_1 + \bar{y}_4\bar{y}_3y_2\bar{y}_1 + \bar{y}_4y_3y_2y_1 + \bar{y}_4y_3y_2\bar{y}_1 + y_4\bar{y}_3y_2y_1$$
$$+ y_4\bar{y}_3y_2\bar{y}_1 + y_4y_3y_2\bar{y}_1 + y_4y_3y_2y_1$$
$$Y_3 = \bar{y}_4\bar{y}_3y_2y_1 + \bar{y}_4y_3\bar{y}_2\bar{y}_1 + \bar{y}_4y_3\bar{y}_2y_1 + \bar{y}_4y_3y_2\bar{y}_1 + y_4\bar{y}_3\bar{y}_2\bar{y}_1$$
$$+ y_4y_3\bar{y}_2y_1 + y_4y_3y_2\bar{y}_1 + y_4y_3y_2y_1$$
$$Y_4 = y_4\bar{y}_3\bar{y}_2\bar{y}_1 + y_4\bar{y}_3\bar{y}_2y_1 + y_4\bar{y}_3y_2\bar{y}_1 + y_4\bar{y}_3y_2y_1 + y_4y_3\bar{y}_2\bar{y}_1$$
$$+ y_4y_3\bar{y}_2y_1 + y_4y_3y_2\bar{y}_1 + y_4y_3y_2y_1$$

Thus the **T** matrix is:

$y_4y_3y_2y_1 =$ 0 1 2 3 4 5 6 7 8 9 10 11 12 13 14 15

$$T = \begin{bmatrix} 1 & 0 & 1 & 0 & 1 & 0 & 1 & 0 & 1 & 1 & 0 & 0 & 1 & 0 & 0 & 0 \\ 0 & 1 & 1 & 0 & 0 & 1 & 1 & 0 & 0 & 0 & 0 & 1 & 0 & 1 & 1 & 1 \\ 0 & 0 & 0 & 1 & 1 & 1 & 1 & 0 & 0 & 0 & 0 & 0 & 1 & 1 & 1 & 1 \\ 0 & 0 & 0 & 0 & 0 & 0 & 0 & 0 & 1 & 1 & 1 & 1 & 1 & 1 & 1 & 1 \end{bmatrix}$$

and the **A** matrix:

$$A = \begin{bmatrix} 0 & 1 & 0 & 1 & 0 & 1 & 0 & 1 & 0 & 1 & 0 & 1 & 0 & 1 & 0 & 1 \\ 0 & 0 & 1 & 1 & 0 & 0 & 1 & 1 & 0 & 0 & 1 & 1 & 0 & 0 & 1 & 1 \\ 0 & 0 & 0 & 0 & 1 & 1 & 1 & 1 & 1 & 0 & 0 & 0 & 0 & 1 & 1 & 1 \\ 0 & 0 & 0 & 0 & 0 & 0 & 0 & 0 & 1 & 1 & 1 & 1 & 1 & 1 & 1 & 1 \end{bmatrix}$$

Now we can say that:

$$F = \begin{bmatrix} Y_1 \\ Y_2 \\ Y_3 \\ Y_4 \end{bmatrix} = \begin{bmatrix} y_1 \\ y_2 \\ y_3 \\ y_4 \end{bmatrix} \begin{bmatrix} 1 & 0 & 1 & 0 & 1 & 0 & 1 & 0 & 1 & 1 & 0 & 0 & 1 & 0 & 0 & 0 \\ 0 & 1 & 1 & 0 & 0 & 1 & 1 & 0 & 0 & 0 & 0 & 1 & 0 & 1 & 1 & 1 \\ 0 & 0 & 0 & 1 & 1 & 1 & 1 & 0 & 0 & 0 & 0 & 0 & 1 & 1 & 1 & 1 \\ 0 & 0 & 0 & 0 & 0 & 0 & 0 & 0 & 1 & 1 & 1 & 1 & 1 & 1 & 1 & 1 \end{bmatrix}$$

Thus $\mathbf{F} = \mathbf{BT}$.

Starting with

$$\begin{bmatrix} y_1 \\ y_2 \\ y_3 \\ y_4 \end{bmatrix} = \begin{bmatrix} 0 \\ 0 \\ 0 \\ 0 \end{bmatrix}$$

we have
$$\mathbf{F} = \begin{bmatrix} 0 & 1 & 0 & 1 & 0 & 1 & 0 & 1 & 0 & 1 \\ 0 & 0 & 1 & 1 & 0 & 0 & 1 & 1 & 0 & 0 \\ 0 & 0 & 0 & 0 & 1 & 1 & 1 & 1 & 0 & 0 \\ 0 & 0 & 0 & 0 & 0 & 0 & 0 & 0 & 0 & 0 \end{bmatrix} \cdots$$

Thus the machine will cycle 0–7 and repeat; the same operation will apply to any input from

$$\begin{bmatrix} 0 \\ 0 \\ 0 \\ 0 \end{bmatrix} \rightarrow \begin{bmatrix} 1 \\ 1 \\ 1 \\ 0 \end{bmatrix}$$

Since
$$\begin{bmatrix} 1 \\ 0 \\ 0 \\ 1 \end{bmatrix} \quad \text{and} \quad \begin{bmatrix} 0 \\ 1 \\ 1 \\ 1 \end{bmatrix}$$

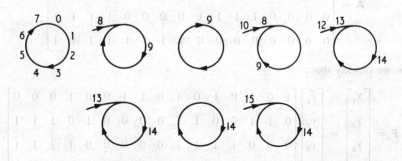

Fig. S–28 Problem 6–5

are characteristic vectors of **T**, whenever this input condition is reached the machine will go into a loop, i.e. starting with

$$\begin{bmatrix} y_1 \\ y_2 \\ y_3 \\ y_4 \end{bmatrix} = \begin{bmatrix} 0 \\ 0 \\ 0 \\ 1 \end{bmatrix}$$

we have
$$\mathbf{F} = \begin{bmatrix} 0 & 1 & 1 \\ 0 & 0 & 0 \\ 0 & 0 & 0 \\ 1 & 1 & 1 \end{bmatrix} \cdots$$

This action may be described diagramatically (see Fig. S–28); decimal notation is used for the vectors of **T**, i.e.

$$\begin{bmatrix} 0 \\ 0 \\ 0 \\ 1 \end{bmatrix} \equiv 8$$

To find the output after alternate clock pulses we must use the $\mathbf{T}^2$ matrix, i.e.

$$\mathbf{T}^2 = \begin{bmatrix} 0 & 1 & 0 & 1 & 0 & 1 & 0 & 1 & 1 & 1 & 1 & 0 & 0 & 0 & 0 & 0 \\ 1 & 1 & 0 & 0 & 1 & 1 & 0 & 0 & 0 & 0 & 0 & 0 & 1 & 1 & 1 & 1 \\ 0 & 0 & 1 & 1 & 1 & 1 & 0 & 0 & 0 & 0 & 0 & 0 & 1 & 1 & 1 & 1 \\ 0 & 0 & 0 & 0 & 0 & 0 & 0 & 1 & 1 & 1 & 1 & 1 & 1 & 1 & 1 & 1 \end{bmatrix}$$

This is obtained by looking up the columns of **T** in the **A** matrix and noting the corresponding column numbers, these are then used to select the columns of **T** which form the $\mathbf{T}^2$ matrix.

We may now use the $\mathbf{T}^2$ matrix to analyse the circuit, i.e.

If
$$\begin{bmatrix} y_1 \\ y_2 \\ y_3 \\ y_4 \end{bmatrix} = \begin{bmatrix} 0 \\ 0 \\ 0 \\ 0 \end{bmatrix} \quad \text{then} \quad \mathbf{F} = \begin{bmatrix} 0 & 0 & 0 & 0 & 0 & 0 \\ 0 & 1 & 0 & 1 & 0 & 1 \\ 0 & 0 & 1 & 1 & 0 & 0 \\ 0 & 0 & 0 & 0 & 0 & 0 \end{bmatrix} \cdots \text{ etc.}$$

Chapter 7

7-1 The state-diagram for this circuit is shown in Fig. S–29, with the primitive flow-table in Table S–52(a). The table cannot be reduced but rows (1, 2) and (4, 5, 6) can be merged, the merged table is shown in Table S–52(b). The merged flow-table contains only three rows, but since we require all three to be adjacent, it is necessary to use the spare secondary state d', Tables S–52(c) and (d). The derivation of the excitation and output maps is quite standard (note the elimination of the hazard in the Y_2 map, i.e. the x_1y_2 term) and gives the equations:

$$Y_1 = y_1\bar{y}_2 + x_1x_2\bar{y}_2$$
$$Y_2 = x_1\bar{x}_2 + y_1\bar{x}_1 + y_2x_2 + x_1y_2$$
$$Z = y_1$$

A NAND logic circuit is shown in Fig. S–30.

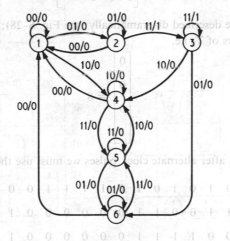

Fig. S–29 Problem 7–1

Table S–52 Problem 7–1

(a)	Inputs x_1x_2				Output
	00	01	11	10	Z
①	2	–	4		0
1	②	3	–		0
–	6	③	4		1
1	–	5	④		0
–	6	⑤	4		0
1	⑥	5	–		0

Table S–52 continued

(b)

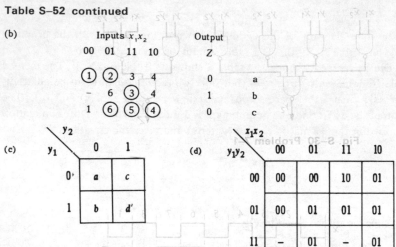

	Inputs $x_1 x_2$				Output	
	00	01	11	10	Z	
	①	②	3	4	0	a
	–	6	③	4	1	b
	1	⑥	⑤	④	0	c

(c)

y_1 \ y_2	0	1
0	a	c
1	b	d'

(d)

$y_1 y_2$ \ $x_1 x_2$	00	01	11	10	
00	00	00	10	01	a
01	00	01	01	01	c
11	–	01	–	01	d'
10	–	11	10	11	b

(e)

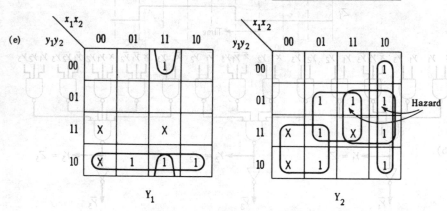

$y_1 y_2$ \ $x_1 x_2$	00	01	11	10
00			1	
01				
11	X		X	
10	X	1	1	1

Y_1

$y_1 y_2$ \ $x_1 x_2$	00	01	11	10
00				1
01		1	1	1
11	X	1	X	1
10	X	1		1

Hazard

Y_2

(f)

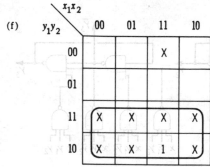

$y_1 y_2$ \ $x_1 x_2$	00	01	11	10
00			X	
01				
11	X	X	X	X
10	X	X	1	X

Z

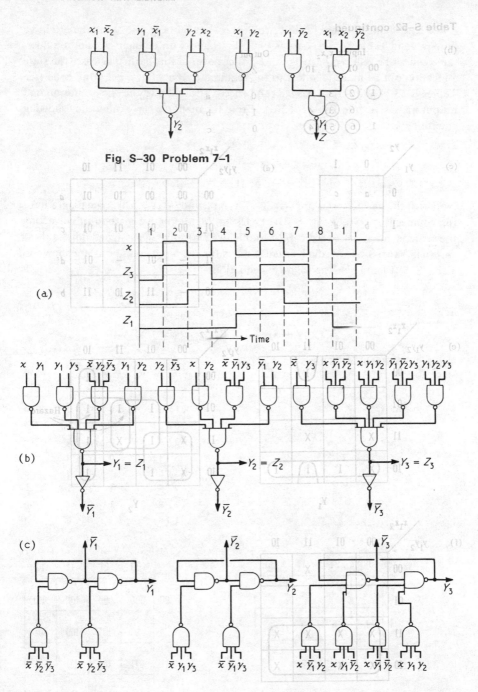

Fig. S–30 Problem 7–1

Fig. S–31 Problem 7–2

7-2 The timing diagram for this problem is shown in Fig. S–31, and the primitive flow-table in Table S–53(a). As is typically found with counter circuits the flow-table cannot be reduced or merged. Furthermore, in this particular case, the state allocation can be made identical to the required output states, i.e. Gray-code [see Tables S–53(b) and (c)]. Thus we can proceed straight away to the excitation and output maps shown in Table S–53(d). From the maps we can extract the following equations:

$$Y_1 = xy_1 + y_1 y_3 + \bar{x} y_2 \bar{y}_3 + y_1 y_2$$
$$Y_2 = y_2 \bar{y}_3 + x y_2 + \bar{x} \bar{y}_1 y_3 + \bar{y}_1 y_2$$
$$Y_3 = \bar{x} y_3 + x \bar{y}_1 \bar{y}_2 + x y_1 y_2 + \bar{y}_1 \bar{y}_2 y_3 + y_1 y_2 y_3$$

Note that the hazard terms are $y_1 y_2$, $\bar{y}_1 y_2$, $y_1 \bar{y}_2 y_3$, and $y_1 y_2 y_3$. The logic diagram for the counter is shown in Fig. S–31(b). Using the alternative method of extracting the set-reset equation for a d.c. SR bistable, we rearrange the assigned flow-table as shown in Table S–54(a); the Karnaugh maps for the input conditions are shown in Table S–54(b) and give the following equations:

$$Sy_1 = \bar{x} y_2 \bar{y}_3 \qquad\qquad Ry_1 = \bar{x} \bar{y}_2 \bar{y}_3$$
$$Sy_2 = \bar{x} \bar{y}_1 y_3 \qquad\qquad Ry_2 = \bar{x} y_1 y_3$$
$$Sy_3 = x \bar{y}_1 \bar{y}_2 + x y_1 y_2 \qquad Ry_3 = x y_1 \bar{y}_2 + x \bar{y}_1 y_2$$

Table S–53 Problem 7–2   (a)

	Input x		Output			
	0	1	Z_1	Z_2	Z_3	
	①	2	0	0	0	a
	3	②	0	0	1	b
	③	4	0	1	1	c
	5	④	0	1	0	d
	⑤	6	1	1	0	e
	7	⑥	1	1	1	f
	⑦	8	1	0	1	g
	1	⑧	1	0	0	h

(b)

y_3 \ $y_1 y_2$	00	01	11	10
0	a	d	e	h
1	b	b	f	g

(c)

$y_2 y_3$ \ xy_1	00	01	11	10
00	① 000	1 000	⑧ 100	2 001
01	3 011	⑦ 101	8 100	② 001
11	③ 011	7 101	⑥ 111	4 010
10	5 110	⑤ 110	6 111	④ 010

Table S–53 continued

(d)

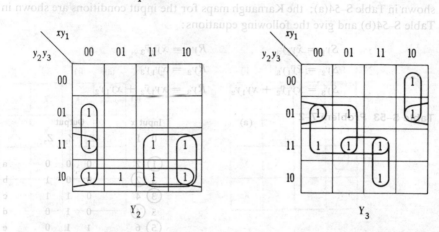

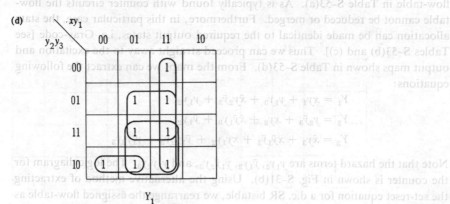

Table S–54 Problem 7–2

(a)

Present state			Input x	
			Next state	
y_1	y_2	y_3	0	1
0	0	0	000	001
0	0	1	011	001
0	1	1	011	010
0	1	0	110	010
1	1	0	110	111
1	1	1	101	111
1	0	1	101	100
1	0	0	000	100

Table S-54 continued

(b)

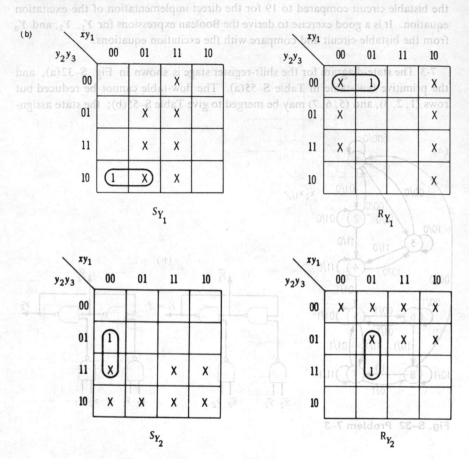

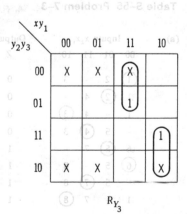

The logic diagram is shown in Fig. S–31(c). Note that 14 NANDS are required for the bistable circuit compared to 19 for the direct implementation of the excitation equation. It is a good exercise to derive the Boolean expressions for Y_1, Y_2, and Y_3 from the bistable circuit and compare with the excitation equations.

7-3 The state-diagram for the shift-register stage is shown in Fig. S–32(a), and the primitive flow-table in Table S–55(a). The flow-table cannot be reduced but rows (1, 2, 3), and (5, 6, 7) may be merged to give Table S–55(b); the state assign-

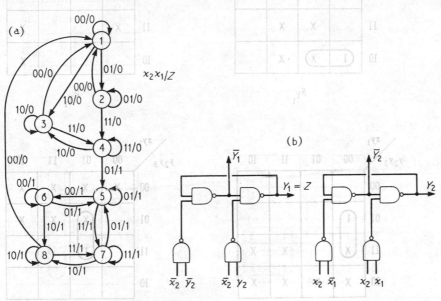

Fig. S–32 Problem 7–3

Table S–55 Problem 7–3

(a)

	Inputs $x_2 x_1$				Output
	00	01	11	10	Z
	①	2	–	3	0
	1	②	4	–	0
	1	–	4	③	0
	–	5	④	3	0
	6	⑤	7	–	1
	⑥	5	–	8	1
	–	5	⑦	8	1
	1	–	7	⑧	1

(b)

	Inputs $x_2 x_1$				Output	
	00	01	11	10	Z	
	①	②	4	③	0	a
	–	5	④	3	0	b
	⑥	⑤	⑦	8	1	c
	1	–	7	⑧	1	d

Table S–55 continued

(c)

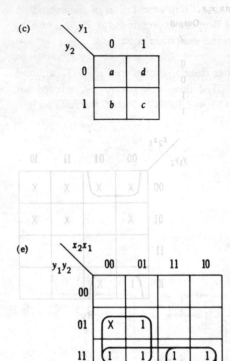

y_2＼y_1	0	1
0	a	d
1	b	c

(d)

y_1y_2＼x_2x_1	00	01	11	10
00	00	00	01	00
01	X	11	01	00
11	11	11	11	10
10	00	X	11	10

(e)

y_1y_2＼x_2x_1	00	01	11	10
00				
01	X	1		
11	1	1	1	1
10		X	1	1

Y_1

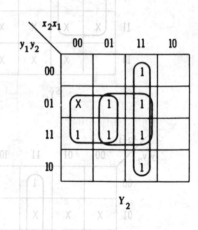

y_1y_2＼x_2x_1	00	01	11	10
00			1	
01	X	1	1	
11	1	1	1	
10			1	

Y_2

y_1y_2＼x_2x_1	00	01	11	10
00	0	0	0	0
01	X	X	0	0
11	1	1	1	1
10	X	X	1	1

Z

Table S–56 Problem 7–3

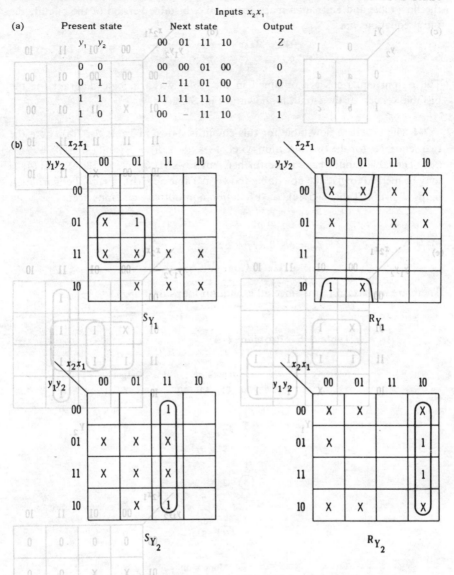

(a)

Inputs x_2x_1

Present state		Next state				Output
y_1	y_2	00	01	11	10	Z
0	0	00	00	01	00	0
0	1	–	11	01	00	0
1	1	11	11	11	10	1
1	0	00	–	11	10	1

ment is straightforward [see Table S–55(c) and (d)]. The excitation equations, obtained from the Karnaugh maps, see Table S–55(e), are:

$$Y_1 = \bar{x}_2 y_2 + x_2 y_1 + y_1 y_2$$
$$Y_2 = \bar{x}_2 y_2 + x_1 x_2 + x_1 y_2$$
$$z = y_1$$

Two hazard terms are required, i.e. $y_1 y_2$ for Y_1 and $x_1 y_2$ for Y_2. Table S–56 shows the flow-table and Karnaugh maps for the d.c. bistable version of the circuit, the input equations are

$$Sy_1 = \bar{x}_2 y_2 \qquad Ry_1 = \bar{x}_2 \bar{y}_2$$
$$Sy_2 = x_2 x_1 \qquad Ry_2 = x_2 \bar{x}_1$$

The output equations are obtained in the usual way; a logic diagram for the bistable version of the circuit is shown in Fig. S–32(b).

7-4 The primitive flow-table for this circuit is shown in Table S–57(a), note the two sequences for the two directions, i.e. ①→②→③→④ and ⑤→⑥→⑦→⑧. The table cannot be reduced further, but rows (1, 6), (2, 5), (3, 8), and (4, 7) may be merged to give the flow-table shown in Table S–57(b). From the Karnaugh maps shown in Table S–57(e), the excitation and output equations are:

$$Y_1 = ab + ay_1 + by_1$$
$$Y_2 = \bar{a}b + \bar{a}y_2 + by_2$$
$$Z = \bar{a}\bar{y}_1\bar{y}_2 + b\bar{y}_1 y_2 + ay_1 y_2 + \bar{b}y_1\bar{y}_2$$

There are no hazard terms since all excitation loops overlap.

Table S–57 Problem 7–4

(a)

		Inputs ab			Output
	00	01	11	10	Z
①	2	–	6		1
5	②	3	–		1
–	8	③	4		1
1	–	7	④		1
⑤	2	–	6		0
1	–	7	⑥		0
–	8	⑦	4		0
5	⑧	3	–		0

(b)

	Inputs ab			
00	01	11	10	
①	2	7	⑥	a
⑤	②	3	6	b
5	⑧	③	4	c
1	8	⑦	④	d

Table S–57 continued

(c)

y_1 \\ y_2	0	1
0	a	b
1	d	c

(d)

y_1y_2 \\ ab	00	01	11	10
00	00	01	10	00
01	01	01	11	00
11	01	11	11	10
10	00	11	11	00

(e)

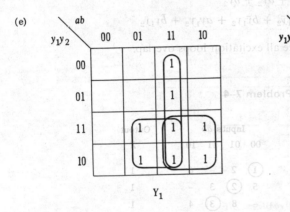

Y_1

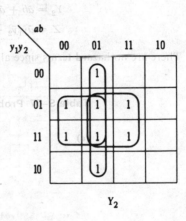

Y_2

7-5 It is easier to realize this circuit with a timing diagram (see Fig. S–33) rather than a state-diagram. In actual practice the duration of x_2 will be very much longer than x_1, so the difficulties arising from pressing the button twice in succession [Fig. S–33 (10) and (11)] will not occur. Note that the button needs to be pressed at clock frequencies to get this effect! The primitive flow-table is shown in Table S–58(a), note that no simplification is possible, but rows (1, 6), (2, 9), (4, 5), (7, 10),

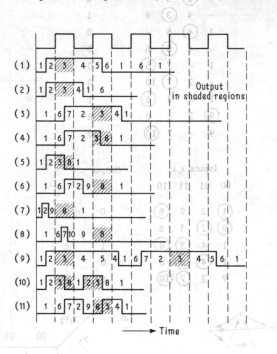

Fig. S–33 Problem 7–5

and (3, 8) may be merged to give Table S–58(b). The state-assignment requires the use of spare secondary states [see Table S–58(c) and (d)] and a possible assignment is shown in Table S–58(e). The Karnaugh maps for the excitation and output equations are shown in Table S–59; the equations are:

$$Y_1 = y_1 y_3 + x_1 y_1 + x_1 x_2 \bar{y}_2 \bar{y}_3 + \bar{x}_1 \bar{x}_2 y_2 y_3$$
$$Y_2 = y_2 \bar{y}_3 + \bar{x}_1 x_2 \bar{y}_3 + x_1 y_2 + y_1 x_2 + \bar{y}_1 y_2 \bar{x}_2$$
$$Y_3 = x_2 y_3 + y_2 y_3 + x_1 \bar{y}_1 y_2$$
$$Z = y_2 y_3$$

There are no hazard terms required and the equations may be implemented in the usual way.

Table S–58 Problem 7–5

(a)

	Inputs x_1x_2			Output
00	**01**	**11**	**10**	**Z**
①	2	–	6	0
9	②	3	–	0
–	4	③	8	1
1	④	5	–	0
–	4	⑤	6	0
1	–	7	⑥	0
–	2	⑦	10	0
1	3	⑧		1
⑨	2	–	8	0
9	–	7	⑩	0

(b)

	Inputs x_1x_2			Output	
00	**01**	**11**	**10**	**Z**	
①	2	7	⑥	0	a
⑨	②	3	8	0	b
1	4	③	⑧	1	c
1	④	⑤	6	0	d
9	2	⑦	⑩	0	e

(c)

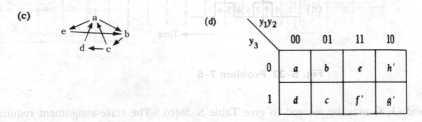

(d)

y_3	y_1y_2 00	01	11	10
0	a	b	e	h′
1	d	c	f′	g′

(e)

	y_1	y_2	y_3	Inputs x_1x_2 00	01	11	10	Output Z
a	0	0	0	000	010	100	000	0
d	0	0	1	000	001	001	000	0
c	0	1	1	111	001	011	011	1
b	0	1	0	010	010	011	011	0
e	1	1	0	010	010	110	110	0
f′	1	1	1	101	–	–	–	X
g′	1	0	1	100	–	–	–	X
h′	1	0	0	000	–	110	–	X

Table S–59 Problem 7–5

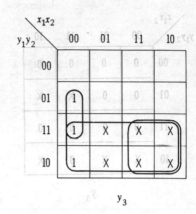

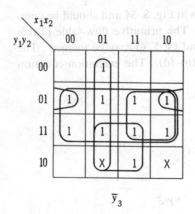

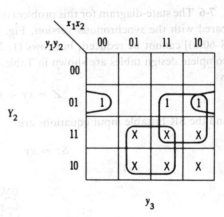

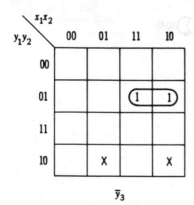

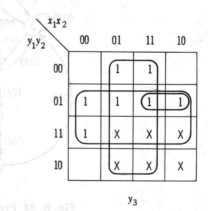

Table S–59 continued

y_1y_2 \ x_1x_2	00	01	11	10
00	0	0	0	0
01	0	0	X	X
11	0	0	0	0
10	X	X	0	X

$\bar{y}_3$

z

y_1y_2 \ x_1x_2	00	01	11	10
00	0	0	0	0
01	X	X	1	1
11	X	X	X	X
10	X	X	X	X

y_3

7-6 The state-diagram for this problem is shown in Fig. S 34 and should be compared with the synchronous version, Fig. S–22. The primitive flow-table [Table S–60(a)] cannot be reduced, but rows (1, 2, 3) and (4, 5, 6) may be merged. The complete design tables are shown in Tables S–60(b)–(d). The excitation equation is

$$Z = xy + \bar{y}z + xz$$

and the SR bistable input equations are

$$Sz = xy \qquad Rz = \bar{x}y$$

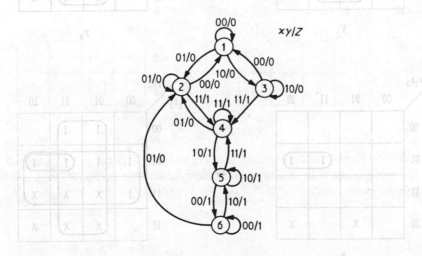

Fig. S–34 Problem 7–6

Table S–60 Problem 7–6

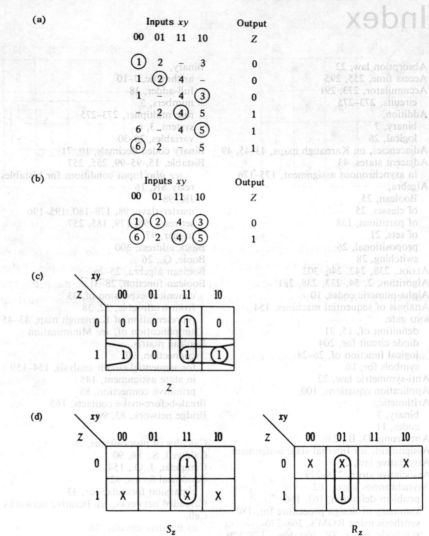

(a)

	Inputs xy				Output
	00	01	11	10	Z
	①	2	–	3	0
	1	②	4	–	0
	1	4	③		0
	2	④	5		1
	6	4	⑤		1
	⑥	2	–	5	1

(b)

	Inputs xy				Output
	00	01	11	10	Z
	①	②	4	③	0
	⑥	2	④	⑤	1

(c)

Note that the bistable implementation results in an identical circuit to that obtained for the synchronous case, this is possible since the bistable output, Z, is not fed back to the input gates.

Index